THE

RAY SOCIETY

INSTITUTED 1844

This volume (No. 138 of the series) is the issue to Members of the
RAY SOCIETY *for the year 1952, and is sold at a price of 27/6*

LONDON

1954

PLATE I.

Frontispiece

Capitula, from above. 1. Eradiata normalis. 2. Eradiata breviflora. 3. Radiata normalis. 4. Radiata longiflora. 5. Radiata breviflora. 6. Eradiata longiflora.

BRITISH KNAPWEEDS
A STUDY IN SYNTHETIC TAXONOMY

BY

E. M. MARSDEN-JONES, F.L.S., F.R.E.S.,

AND

W. B. TURRILL, D.Sc.(Lond.), F.L.S.,

Royal Botanic Gardens, Kew.

LONDON

PRINTED FOR THE RAY SOCIETY

SOLD BY

BERNARD QUARITCH, LTD.

11, GRAFTON STREET, NEW BOND STREET, LONDON, W.1

1954

Made and printed in Great Britain by
Adlard & Son, Ltd.,
Bartholomew Press, Dorking.

v

CONTENTS

FOREWORD

(By Sir EDWARD SALISBURY, C.B.E., D.Sc., LL.D., Sec. R.S., F.L.S., V.M.H., Director of the Royal Botanic Gardens, Kew.)

THE time has long passed since the mere study of herbarium specimens alone could contribute usefully to our knowledge of any but the most superficially investigated floras. To-day the need is for detailed acquaintance with the living plants, their breeding behaviour, and their reaction to environmental conditions at all stages of development.

This monographic study has a far wider interest than that of the particular group of plants with which it is concerned, for such intensive investigations as the authors have undertaken into the nature of these wild populations of closely related *Centaurea* species and their hybrid swarms, their diversity in space, their changes with time and the factors upon which these are dependent, cannot fail to be of significance for all students of plant life.

The knapweeds which were at one time collectively known as *Centaurea nigra* have long been recognized as a critical and difficult aggregate. Some who have studied these plants and attempted their segregation, supposed them to comprise several closely allied, if not easily defined, species with a considerable number of intraspecific aggregates within each. C. E. Britton, for instance, recognized four to eight or more of the former, and no less than seventeen of the latter. It was obvious that nothing less than a careful analysis of living material and well conceived breeding experiments could unravel a tangle that has been rendered more confusing by errors that have been perpetuated. Thus in the latest British flora two subspecies are presumed, of which one is stated to possess a pappus and the other to be devoid of such, but the authors of the present work have shown convincingly the artificiality of such a concept, since a pappus appears to be never absent in typical *Centaurea nigra* or *C. nemoralis* and its absence is evidence of hybridization with the continental species *C. jacea*. The way in which the presence of *C. jacea*, which occurs frequently in England as a casual, has left the mark of its presence in the descendants long after the parent has disappeared, is not the least interesting aspect of the authors' study. Dr. Turrill and Mr. Marsden-Jones have earned the gratitude of students of the British flora for bringing order out of chaos and giving us a clear concept of the three main components in this hybrid swarm, each relatively distinct and recognizable, but surrounded by a penumbra of the more complex products of this interfertile assemblage. We have here portrayed the phenotypic expression consequent upon the hybridization of two well defined species that find a permanent home in the wild habitats of this country and which can be regarded as natives, complicated by the presence of the casual which, though not usually itself permanent, has left the mark of its genetic complement upon the individuals of mixed origin that do in fact persist, thus emphasizing the important rôle which aliens and casuals, that are here to-day and gone to-morrow, may nevertheless play in changing the character of the living population of these islands, certainly in its flora perhaps in its fauna also.

The aspect just stressed serves as one example only of the wider import of such monographic treatment which far transcends the mere specialist appeal.

PREFACE

We record, in this work, an outline of our studies of British knapweeds. Most of our investigations have been concerned with *C. nigra*, *C. nemoralis*, and *C. jacea*, and we term these " knapweeds " without any qualification. Our treatment and our conclusions may well shock the orthodox whether he be taxonomist, ecologist, or geneticist. The methods we have employed can be summarized under four headings : A. Herbarium and library ; B. Field surveys and sampling ; C. Breeding ; D. Cultural testing. We are fully aware that much more remains to be done under every one of these headings. Comparison with continental material has been limited mainly to herbarium specimens of isolated origin and for nomenclatural purposes. We have no material from about 30 of the 112 vice-counties of Great Britain and from a still higher proportion of those of Ireland. From many vice-counties we have inadequate and often very poor samples numerically. Our study of ecological distribution, especially of soil relationships, has been superficial, and there is a wide field for investigation here. Our genetical experiments have been mainly concerned with about half-a-dozen characters but we know there are many others. Cultural tests could be extended almost indefinitely. In spite of our having analyzed, within our chosen limits, more than 13,000 wild knapweed plants and about 11,000 plants from controlled selfings and crossings, we realize how great are the gaps in the story we have attempted to tell. To wait for completion and perfection before publishing would, for a study of this kind, result in extended delay and possible loss of stimulus to some of our younger colleagues who are practically interested in synthetic taxonomy. The second World War greatly delayed the preparation of our work for publication and curtailed some of our plans for extended field studies   We dedicate what we have accomplished to all who are helping to rejuvenate plant taxonomy.

Our thanks are given to the many friends who have assisted us in diverse ways. The late Director of the Royal Botanic Gardens, Kew, Sir Arthur Hill, was keenly interested in the experiments at Kew and Potterne and gave every possible facility for carrying out the research. To the present Director, Sir Edward Salisbury, we are indebted for the facilities to complete our investigations and to prepare them for press and also for contributing a Foreword to this book. We pay tribute to the late C. E. Britton whose pioneer work on British knapweeds was partly responsible for our own interest in the group and who freely gave us his opinions on our original stock plants. That many of the conclusions we have reached differ from those of Mr. Britton in no way decreases our initial debt to him. To the many botanists who have sent us specimens of knapweeds we give our thanks, and especially to our colleagues at Kew who have helped us in practice and in theory. A special word of thanks is due to Mr. G. Atkinson, the gifted Kew artist and photographer. It is not easy adequately to illustrate those characters of knapweeds to which we have paid special attention. Mr. Atkinson's results with the material we have supplied speak for themselves. His skilful photographing of the phyllaries mounted on glass plates enables us to show the characters of these important organs accurately and more clearly than in any other published account we have seen of *Centaurea*. We made many joint experiments before devising the method finally used. We acknowledge our indebtedness to the Keeper and Staff of the Department of Entomology of the British Museum (Natural History) for the determination of the insects referred to by name in this work.

The experiments at Potterne were aided by a Royal Society's Government Grant and the preparation of the typescript by a grant from the Bentham-Moxon Trustees at Kew.

TERMS AND STANDARDS OF CAPITULUM AND FLORET CHARACTERS.

PERICLINE.—This is the sum total of the phyllaries (bracts) arising from the inflorescence receptacle and forming the lower part of the flowering capitulum. The general shape of the pericline at full anthesis (not in the fruiting condition) has been scored as follows :—

1. *Elongate-ovoid :* ratio of length to diameter approximately 3 : 2 or more.

2. *Ovoid :* ratio of length to diameter less than 3 : 2 but more than 1 : 1.

3. *Broadly ovoid :* ratio of length to diameter approximately 1 : 1.

4. *Obloid :* diameter greater than length.

PHYLLARIES, colour of disc at full anthesis.—The central portion, or disc, of the appendage or upper part of a phyllary, or bract, of the pericline is usually darker in colour than the margins whether these be entire, fimbriate, or pectinate. The colour ranges from black to a pale straw colour and is due, we are informed, to the presence of melanin, at least in the plants with dark phyllaries. The colours of the discs have been matched with the plates in Ridgway, ' Color Standards and Nomenclature,' Washington (1912). The lower central phyllaries, about the 2nd and 3rd turns of the spiral from the base, were used in matching. The following Ridgway terms are used and his plate numbers are given :—

Black, Plate LIII ; *Bone Brown*, Plate XL ; *Prout's Brown*, Plate XV ; *Russet*, Plate XV ; *Tawny Olive*, Plate XXIX ; *Light Ochraceous Buff*, Plate XV. These are here arranged essentially from deeper to lighter intensity of colour.

PHYLLARIES, margins of discs.—In scoring these it is essential to examine the 2nd and 3rd turns of the spiral (apparent rows) from the base. The following symbols and terms have been used :—

N = *None.*—In which the margin is divided into pectinations free from one another, *i.e.*, with no " fusing " of contiguous pectinations.

VL = *Very Little.*—In which a few of the pectinations are fused together from the base for a portion of their length.

L = *Little.*—In which more of the pectinations are fused together and some usually for most of their length.

S = *Some.*—In which the majority of the pectinations are fused at the base for some part of their length up to half this.

M = *Much.*—In which there is much fusion even beyond the half length of what would otherwise be pectinations. The margin is now for the most part irregularly fimbriate rather than pectinate.

VM = *Very Much.*—In which fusion is complete to well beyond the half-way mark outwards and much of the margin is no more than dentate though some is usually rather shallowly fimbriate.

C = *Complete.*—In which there are no pectinations or fimbriations and the margin is entire except for occasional irregular lacerations.

In actual scoring for phyllary margins constant comparison has been made to the standards carefully selected after extensive trials and then adhered to rigidly. These standards are dried capitula, mounted on cards, taken from plants of known origin from the wild or from plants bred from such, and all grown in the experimental ground of the Biological Station, Potterne, Wilts. The significance of the characters of phyllary margins is discussed below.

Hybrid Index.—For certain purposes a single figure value conveniently known as a hybrid index (H.I.) has been found useful. The H.I. gives at least a fair estimate of the degree of hybridity of the population, if the sample be a random and large one. It can be used for comparisons between populations or families, with due precautions. The hybrid index is obtained as follows : the percentage occurrence of the seven classes, N, VL, L, S, M, VM, and C is obtained, the figures are multiplied by 0, 1, 2 to 6 respectively, and the results summated. The H.I. will range between 0 (pure *C. nemoralis* or *C. nigra*) and 600 (pure *C. jacea*). So far as phyllaries are concerned the nearer the H.I. of a population is to 0 the nearer it is to *C. nemoralis* or *C. nigra* and the higher the value the more are shown the effects of *C. jacea* genes.

FLORETS, colour.—This has been matched with Ridgway, ' Color Standards and Nomenclature ' and the following Ridgway terms are used, the Ridgway plate number following the name : *Dull Dark Purple*, Plate XXVI ; *Rood's Violet*, Plate XI ; *Bishop's Purple*, Plate XXXVII ; *Argyle Purple*, Plate XXXVII ; *Purplish Lilac*, Plate XXXVII ; *Marguerite Yellow*, Plate XXX ; *White*, Plate LIII. The names are given here approximately in the sequence from deeper to lighter colour.

RAY FLORETS, presence or absence.

Radiata, with ray florets 2·5 cm. or more in length.
Semiradiata, with ray florets less than 2·5 cm. in length.
Eradiata, without ray florets.

DISC FLORETS, kind.

Normalis, with ordinary hermaphrodite structure.
Longiflora, with elongate disc florets, partly simulating ray florets.
If the corolla lobes be spread outwards and curled backwards the
condition is referred to as " *curly longiflora.*"
Breviflora, with small florets in which the stamens are not functional.
Rarely the anthers may produce a few pollen grains but typically the
florets are female only.
Quilled, with stiff florets in which the corolla lobes are poorly devel-
oped or do not separate properly.

PRELIMINARY KEY TO THE SPECIES OF CENTAUREA CONSIDERED IN THIS WORK.

Phyllary appendages not spiny

    Phyllary appendages not or scarcely decurrent

        Phyllary appendages adaxially strongly concave ; entire or very
        slightly fimbriate. Capitula radiate. Pappus absent. . *C. jacea.*

        Phyllary appendages flat or nearly so, finely pectinate. Capitula
        typically eradiate. Pappus typically present.

        Peduncles slender. Leaves usually narrow. Discs of phyllary
        appendages typically linear to lanceolate, appendages often not
        densely and completely overlapping . . . *C. nemoralis.*

        Peduncles stout. Leaves relatively broad. Discs of phyllary
        appendages ovate, appendages densely and completely over-
        lapping . . . . *C. nigra.*

    Phyllary appendages decurrent as dark margins . . *C. scabiosa.*

Phyllary appendages spiny . . . . *C. aspera.*

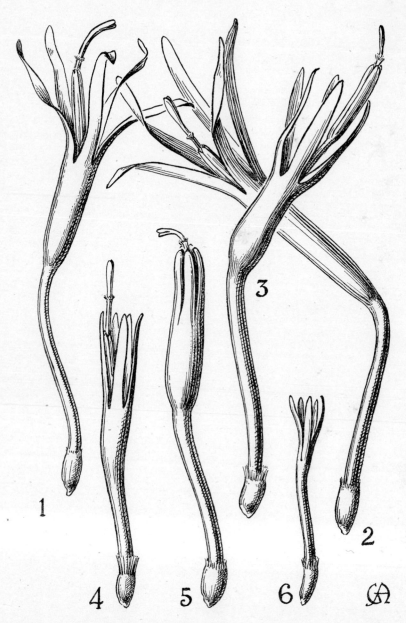

FIG. 1.—*Disc Florets*. 1. Longiflora curly. 2. Longiflora. 3. Normalis.
4. Breviflora. 5. Quilled. 6. Neuter.

CHAPTER I

GENERAL INTRODUCTION

TAXONOMY has often been derided, by those who know nothing of its methods, aims, and modern developments, as a dry static subject consisting solely of the description of dead herbarium specimens. The taxonomist is amused when, as so often happens, his detractors send him a polite letter requesting him " to name the enclosed specimens." Unfortunately, the correspondents are often so ignorant of taxonomy that they cannot even collect or properly pack adequate material for the naming without which they apparently cannot proceed with their researches. Think what would be the position of any worker with plant material if there had never been any attempt to classify plants and if no system of nomenclature, whether using Latin names or any other symbols, had ever been devised. The truth, however, is that while accurate description is basic to taxonomy, as it is to any branch of science, from physics, up or down, to cytology, and that the manufacture of " keys " and of a workable system of nomenclature give us, in the present state of knowledge, very useful tools for obtaining and distributing information, these are all preliminaries to the problems of taxonomy.

Careful investigation of the history of taxonomy shows that there has always been present in the minds of taxonomists wider viewpoints than the mere grouping into classes for practical convenience. Ray, Linnaeus, the de Candolles, J. D. Hooker,[*] and many other of the older taxonomists had always before them unsolved general problems over which they thought deeply. Not all those problems are yet solved. The modern taxonomist has so often a wider outlook than his critics ; so had the older taxonomists.

What are the problems that fascinate the taxonomist? They are " practical " and " theoretical." On the " practical " side he strives to obtain and to evaluate for purposes of classification as many data (" characters ") as possible. He studies both the structure and the behaviour of the organisms with which he is concerned. The study of structure, or morphology, is as wide as the study of "doing," or physiology. It includes gross morphology, histology, and cytology in so far as these are limited to shape, size, numbers, and arrangement of organs, cells and tissues, and cell contents respectively. Physiology for the plant taxonomist includes all that plants do throughout their life-histories. Germination of seeds or spores, establishment of seed-

---

[*] See, for example, Turrill, ' Pioneer Plant Geography,' and the quotations given there from the publications of Sir J. D. Hooker, on " species problems."

lings or sporelings, growth of organs, of tissues, of cells, multiplication, reproduction, and extension or restriction of range or distribution, these and other aspects of behaviour will yield " characters " of taxonomic value. The behaviour of plant communities, of taxon populations, of individuals, of organs, of cells, of chromosomes, any or all of these and other " doings " may give data to aid in obtaining the most widely useful classification. Obviously, no taxonomist can be a specialist in every branch even of botany. Taxonomists must rely for many data on the ecologist, the biochemist, the anatomist, the geneticist, the cytologist, and so on. One can only plead for more co-operation.

On the " theoretical " side, taxonomists have two main interests : the " how " of floras and the " how " of taxa, or phytogeography and evolution. Neither a flora nor a taxon is static. At a given time each has a describable composition, that is it is made up ultimately of individuals (including ramets) that have phenotypic and genotypic aspects. Individuals, however, come and go; they are born and in due time die. No two individuals are exactly alike both phenotypically and genotypically, hence there is variation from one season to another. Natural selection by environmental factors curtails or directs the effectiveness, the permanency, and the range of variation ; it does not stop it. The taxonomist has to consider variation of every kind. The degree of plasticity and the forms it takes may be his concern more than the causes, but he cannot fully understand and allow for the results in his classification without knowing the causes. Variations correlated with genotypic changes (" mutations " *sensu latissimo* and hybridization) are even more important taxonomically. Mutations may be quickly eliminated by natural selection but if observed and used for genetic experiments they may throw much light on the significance of the " normal " structure and behaviour. Some mutations may be favoured by the selective actions of the environment and, if they survive early accidents, may increase the variation of a taxon and in time radically change its constitution. Environments change, as well as taxa. There are environmental fluctuations, there are the seral changes basic to plant succession, there are drastic changes of a catastrophic kind, and there are long range changes, as of climate, occurring in periods of " geologic time."

The importance of hybridization in modifying floras and taxa and the chaos it sometimes presents to the taxonomist are not always realized. " Gene spread," " gene exchange," " hybrid swarm," and other phrases occur more frequently now than formerly in botanical literature. The occurrence of allopolyploidy following hybridization is accepted as one method of origin of new taxa, *Spartina townsendii* being often quoted as a classic example. The taxonomist recognizes that more or less sharply delimitable groups of organisms occur in nature. These he describes and names as taxa. Then he wants to know how they keep just so distinct. How is it that some taxa are very clear cut in the sum of their characters, while others are not?

What are the barriers to amalgamation of taxa and how constant and near to being absolute are they? How long, in the history of a taxon, have such barriers been as they are now? Barriers may be discontinuities in ranges, restrictions as reflected in ecological distribution, or incompatibilities of genetic systems. It is difficult to say if, in a state of non-interference by man, any one group is in general more important than either of the other two. Just at present man can alter ranges and distributions fairly easily. He is on the way to learning how to control genetic systems but for the time being genetic barriers seem usually to be less easily " got over " or " got around " than any other kind. Nevertheless, genetic barriers are sometimes only partial and may sometimes be changed. The taxonomist wishes to know all he can about them—what they occur between, how extreme they are, how long they have existed, and if they show any changes.

The taxonomy of plants and animals is one aspect of classification in general and has to conform to the general philosophical principles of classification. It might be closer to historic truth to say that taxonomy has had much to do with these general principles being recognized and elaborated (see John Stuart Mill, Jevons, and other philosophers and logicians). There are, however, certain peculiarities characteristic of taxonomy. It is doubtful if these peculiarities can be appreciated by the arm-chair philosopher manipulating words. First, the material to be classified consists of " living organisms ", not static particulars or particulars that can be regarded as relatively static. The herbarium botanist (or the museum zoologist) has to work with dead specimens but he regards, or should regard, these as more or less adequate samples or representatives of the organisms to be classified. The field worker has often a clearer picture of what has to be classified than has the herbarium or museum biologist. " Living " means changing at a rate and in ways characteristic of the organisms themselves. To the taxonomist changes are characters.

Secondly, the taxonomist has to deal with individuals (including ramets and apomicts) and with populations. This gives a twofold series of changes—ontogenetic and phylogenetic. In other words, the taxonomist has to take into consideration both the life-histories of individuals and the origin and development of " phyla " or " taxa." Since " phylum " is now often given a precise position in the hierarchy of biological classification it would be better to replace phylogeny (phylogenetic) by taxogeny (taxogenetic). A taxon is ultimately the sum total of individuals grouped together as any unit of classification. This was true of *Centaurea nigra* in 1925 and is true of *C. nigra* in 1953. Yet few, if any, of the individuals alive when we started our researches on the taxon are alive to-day. There has been continuity but also continuous change. The taxonomist has to study the changes in individuals from before birth to after death but he must, and this needs to be constantly restated, study populations, whole and partial.

Thirdly, the taxonomist has to classify organisms whose changes have a twofold basis of internal and external causes. At least, we accept that changes of genes and chromosomes give mutations, only some of which survive in a given selecting environment. Individual offspring and eventually taxa can diverge and the result is evolution from an original stock.

Fourthly, the converse of divergence can occur by hybridization of individuals, resulting in spread of alien genes through a population and even in amalgamation of taxa widely or locally.

We have stated some of the general interests that we had in view when we started our joint researches on the British knapweeds in 1925 or that have emerged in the course of our work. Why did we choose knapweeds as subjects for synthetic taxonomy? The following are some of the reasons for the choice. We each happen to have lived for most of our lives in " good " knapweed counties and knew that there was considerable variation within so-called species of the group. We knew that the British knapweeds grew well under the climatic and edaphic conditions of our experimental grounds at Kew and Potterne. It happened that we were engaged on experiments with spring and early summer flowering plants (*Ranunculus, Saxifraga, Silene*, etc.) and that the main flowering periods of the knapweeds (late June to September) did not clash with " rush periods " for our other joint work. In the early nineteen-twenties the late Mr. C. E. Britton published a series of papers on British knapweeds and we thought it desirable to test his proposed classifications by experiments and concentrated field studies. Though many of our conclusions differ radically from those of Mr. Britton we wish to state again that we received much help and every consideration from him in the preliminary stages of our investigations.

THE BRITISH KNAPWEEDS.

An Outline of the Story as We Tell It.

Three species, in the broad sense, have been long recognized as members of the British flora : *Centaurea scabiosa, C. nigra*, and *C. jacea*. Whether any or all of these can be considered native is arguable. If by " native " one means a species that fulfils the extreme conditions laid down by Dunn (' Alien Flora of Britain,' p. ix–x : 1905) and elaborated by Lloyd Praeger (The Botanist in Ireland, section 71 : 1934) none of the above species can be definitely classed as native. Dunn's statement runs " A species is only held to be a native in a natural locality to which it has spread by natural means from a natural source." There are very few, if any, entirely natural localities, in the sense of natural plant communities, suited to knapweeds, occurring in the British Isles. The habitats of maritime and aquatic communities, moorlands, most marshlands, closed woodlands, and high mountains are unsuited to species of *Centaurea*. The nearest approaches to " natural localities " frequented by knapweeds are cliffs and downs, more or less open heaths, and some not very marshy marshes, particularly in the south and south midlands of England. It is extremely significant that knapweeds tend as one proceeds farther north to be more and more definitely restricted in distribution to road verges, railway embankments, field paths, and in general to artificial or greatly disturbed or modified habitats. One sees this again and again in, for example, Yorkshire and Scotland. Plants of *Centaurea nigra* may abound in the grass at the roadsides but step from such into heath or moor and there is not a single plant of black knapweed. The spraying of road verges with modern week killers may greatly reduce the knapweed population of the British Isles.

The abundance of knapweeds on many chalk downs makes them important constituents of chalk communities. It is possible that they were present before man interfered with the natural vegetation by cutting, firing, and the grazing of his flocks and herds. This would depend largely on how far the downs were clothed with dense forest. It seems most probable that there was in pre-Roman times much more woodland than there is now on our chalk exposures and this is true also for the areas of oolitic limestone. Reference may be made to ' Salisbury, Downs and Dunes,' pp. 1–3 (1952). On the other hand, the herbaceous vegetation of the chalk is floristically relatively rich and decidedly characteristic, especially in forbs. Most of the constituents appear " natural " and are not such as would be likely to be introduced by man ; they are not escapes from agriculture or horticulture and are not weeds or ruderals, though there are exceptions to this statement.

The knapweeds with which we are concerned are plants of herbaceous communities. They are not tolerant of dense shade and none is a forest or woodland plant. They quickly succumb to smothering and even suffer from excess of their own top hamper. On chalk and oolitic limestone what we name *C. nemoralis* is the commonest knap-weed, though it is not infrequently contaminated by genes of *C. jacea*. To a certain extent there is ecotypic selection evident in the ecological distribution of *C. nemoralis* in Britain.

On heaths in the south and midlands of England the black knap-weed (*C. nigra*) is the common knapweed. There is more conclusive evidence than for the chalk downs that our heathlands were, and naturally should be, forest clad. In the south of England, clear-cut *C. nigra* can flourish under more acid conditions and withstand slightly more shade (though not much) and flowers earlier in the year (June to early July) than uncontaminated *C. nemoralis*.

Presumably many sea cliff areas cannot naturally maintain a forest vegetation. Knapweeds are common on many cliffs facing the sea from the south up to north Scotland. Another possible natural habitat is partially dried marshlands. True, these are generally seral stages and naturally would develop to climax forest. Nevertheless, marshes were formerly much more extensive in this country than they are now, and no doubt there were in the main river basins and in East Anglia always many at the right seral stage for knapweeds. We have, anyhow, been struck by the Centaurea populations in partially dried marshes in Oxfordshire and Somerset for example, as well as in some of the fens of Norfolk.

It must be noted that Godwin and Allison (' Phil. Trans. Roy. Soc.,' ser. B, **236**, 212 : 1952) record that, from " Late-Glacial Deposits at Nazeing in the Lea Valley, North London," " Pollen grains which could be referred with certainty to the genus Centaurea but not to a given species (the resemblance was close to C. scabiosa except for size), were found in M 4 (zone IV), M A (zones IV and VIa), and Y (zone III or earlier)." It is unfortunate that a specific determination of the pollen grains has not so far been possible, but it seems clear that at least one knapweed occurred in the London area from late glacial (III) to the boreal period (VI).

The completely native status of the species of Centaurea with which we are concerned remains questionable. One can only say with certainty that C. scabiosa, C. nigra, and C. nemoralis are now, in many parts of the British Isles, common members of the flora of various kinds of " grasslands," heaths, cliffs, and partially dried marshes. There is no doubt that their present range and ecological distribution in the British Isles owe much to the activities of man and that both have been, in this sense, artificially extended. The problems with regard to C. jacea are somewhat different. Possibly in a few places in the south of England, as in Sussex, it has as good a right to be termed " native " as have the other species, though we doubt even this. That it has been, and from time to time probably still is, introduced from the continent is the theory that satisfies most of the evidence. It occurs spasmodically in time and space. Its introduction is often by man with agricultural seeds, with chicken food (witness its occurrence in chicken runs), or with commercial products.

When C. jacea is introduced into populations of C. nigra and C. nemoralis, hybrids and, by segregation, backcrossing, and complicated intercrossing, hybrid swarms are produced. Sometimes, as on Epsom Downs, the original introduction of C. jacea is approximately known by dated herbarium specimens, but the species has been " swamped " by crossing leaving only dispersed genes and the phenotypic characters by which they can be recognized, as existing witnesses of its former occurrence. It is, however, of considerable value to have the corroborating evidence of earlier collectors and of preserved specimens. At Wellington College, Berks, we found, in 1926, existing plants of C. jacea in fair abundance together with many plants of hybrid origin. The introduction of C. jacea here was probably numerically a large one. In other localities, as in the Woodstock district of Oxfordshire and near Bradfield in Berkshire, we have traced C. jacea to the centre from the periphery of hybrid swarms. Near the periphery the indications of hybridity were weak—at least as based on the best criteria of phyllary shape. Plants with phyllaries scorable in our scheme as VL and L were found. Searching in all directions, plants with phyllaries S and M were found. This gave an approximate direction towards a centre and, several times, *C. jacea* plants were then discovered. Most often where hybrid swarms have been found, *C. jacea* had disappeared as such and there were no historical records of its past occurrence in the locality. The hybrid swarms were only determined as such by analogy with other populations and by comparison with bred families of known hybrid origin. The evidence, given in the body of this work, is, however, in our opinion, overwhelming. For some hybrid swarms of *C. jacea* and *C. nigra* or *C. nemoralis* there are two possibilities, either *C. jacea* was introduced into a population of *C. nigra* or *C. nemoralis* or a hybrid plant was introduced and itself segregated and crossed. Hybrids of *Centaurea* species of this group occur on the Continent, probably not infrequently. It has not, however, been possible to obtain conclusive evidence of the introduction of hybrids from the Continent. The occurrence of true *C. jacea* in some hybrid swarms has been proved.

We have concurrently carried out researches on *Centaurea* by three methods : analysis of field populations, herbarium and library studies, and controlled experiments. Preliminary field studies had, however, been carried out by each of us independently before our joint experiments and extended field investigations started. Our main aim has been to elucidate the taxonomy of the British knapweeds and our observations and experiments have been planned with this in view. For example, in our choice of stock plants for breeding and in our programme of selfing and crossing these, it was the elucidation of problems we first recognized in wild populations that was the main controlling factor. In other words our work as now published is to be regarded as an attempt to demonstrate the methods and some results of synthetic taxonomy, not primarily as either genetics or population analysis.

With these viewpoints in mind we return to hybrid swarms in *Centaurea*. The demonstration of the occurrence of these in various localities in the south and south midland vice-counties of England and proving that various so-called species are abstractions from such hybrid swarms have been amongst the results of our studies. What are the characters of interspecific hybridity in the knapweeds ? Without doubt the shape of the phyllaries gives the best evidence. We have found a scheme of scoring into seven classes, namely, N, VL, L, S, M, VM, and C, to work very satisfactorily both for wild populations and for bred families. Breeding work shows that the class sequence just given represents a series from *C. nigra* or *C. nemoralis* to *C. jacea*. Plants scored as N are *C. nigra* or *C. nemoralis* ; those scored as C are *C. jacea* ; those scored as L, S, or M are certainly hybrids ; those scored as VL or VM may be hybrids or may be *C. nigra* (or *C. nemoralis*) or *C. jacea* respectively. However, evidence has accumulated that there are other characters that " come in with *C. jacea*." They are certainly usually found in hybrid families bred under control as such and in wild populations considered to be hybrid swarms on characters of phyllary shape, remembering too that the putative parents are sometimes present. These characters are : diversity of leaf shape, range of flowering period, variation of phyllary colour and in particular the occurrence of phyllaries paler than Bone Brown, the occurrence of plants with shining, not matt, phyllaries, the presence of plants with floret colour paler than Dull Dark Purple and in particular such as are scored Bishop's Purple, the appearance of radiate capitula, the modification in an undue number of individuals of the normal hermaphrodite condition of the disc florets, and the very irregular development of the pappus on the cypselas. These characters have, of course, to be scored for individual plants, but in determining hybrid swarms it is their occurrence in the population as a whole that is important. None of them has the same diagnostic value as phyllary shape and it may be that a mutation for any one of them occurs occasionally in pure populations of *C. nigra* or *C. nemoralis*. The stated facts remain and have again and again proved useful in preliminary field surveys as indications of hybridity within populations— indications that have been confirmed by more detailed investigations.

THE CHARACTERS.

In taxonomy, a character is any describable structure or behaviour or range of such that can be used to define or differentiate taxa. There has to be a pragmatic choice of characters. Moreover, structure and behaviour are always complicated or compound and any character is both part of a larger whole and can itself be analyzed into component characters. One can, in this respect range from the cosmos to the proton and electron or whatever are, at present, the ultimate units of physics. Taxonomic characters do not always coincide with genetic characters, in the sense that one gene change may result in change in more than one taxonomic character. Alternatively, different gene combinations may give the same taxonomic character or characters. The genom is defined only by its gene content. The taxon is recognized by its phenotype but strictly should be defined by both its genotype and its phenotype or its genotypes and phenotypes. Taxonomists, in common with ecologists, recognize the importance of plasticity. They must allow for the influence of environment as well as of heredity.

In our *Centaurea* studies we had to select the characters to which we paid particular attention. Limitations of time and labour made such selection unavoidable. There are characters we studied in detail, others we studied superficially, and others that, with regret, we ignored. We paid more attention to characters, morphological and physiological, of reproduction than of vegetative growth. We concentrated on the structure of the inflorescence, florets, and infructescence and on the function of flowers and seed-setting. This is particularly true for our breeding experiments. Naturally our selfings and crossings had to be restricted to manageable numbers. Breeding experiments tend to increase in geometrical progression from season to season. From one F_1 family one may want to raise half-a-dozen or more F_2 families. Later there are F_3 and back-cross families to be raised and scored. In our field studies we took notice of a wider range of characters. This delimitation of our work was reasonable since, as already mentioned, our main aim was to understand the composition and history of our British knapweeds as they occur in the wild. Breeding experiments were to be a contribution to this understanding and not a separate aim in themselves.

We should like to emphasize here the value of herbarium methods. Since we can scarcely be accused of being merely herbarium botanists our remarks may have special validity. Again and again we have proved the importance of retaining, as we have done, samples of our stock plants and representative specimens of offspring families as herbarium specimens. These can be stored indefinitely in a relatively small space and used for frequent checking and comparison. Stock plants may die and unless a herbarium specimen has been kept no part of its structure can then be rechecked. We have also very often needed to compare wild plants with bred standards of known origin. It is impossible on grounds of space and labour alone to maintain all or even a sufficient number (for this purpose) of living plants from season to season. There is yet another practical value of preservation, even if only temporary preservation, of material by herbarium methods. Herbarium specimens can be studied and analyzed at any time. In particular, much work can be done on them in off-seasons, especially in the winter, when work in the breeding ground and the field does not occupy all the hours not needed for feeding and sleeping. It is surprising how many characters can be scored with full accuracy from well prepared dried specimens. There are, of course, limitations to the herbarium method as applied in synthetic taxonomy. Some characters, as floret colour or flowering period, have to be recorded from the living plants. There are also well-known special dangers, such as the risk of label mixing or damage by the drug store beetle.

It is of particular importance that the characters of phyllary shape can be studied as well in dried as in living material—one is, indeed, tempted to say that the preserved specimens may sometimes be the better, and this would be true if the living material were examined after heavy rain. We have proved the particular value of phyllary shape as giving characters of specific value and as criteria of hybridity. These characters can be readily determined by use of a good hand lens and we have only occasionally had difficulty in deciding into which of our seven classes a given plant should be scored. Difficulties must arise in what is practically " continuous " variation but they only affect a one point value in scoring. More important is the need to maintain the same level of scoring by frequent reference to standards. We place, then, for purposes of determining hybridity and the extent of parental gene influence, the highest value on phyllary shape for the double reason of the precision of our scoring and the high coincidence of the results so obtained from field studies and breeding experiments.

Our studies of phyllary colour have led to interesting general conclusions. Genes from *C. jacea* lead often to a high percentage of plants with phyllaries paler than Bone Brown. There is no doubt that we over-scored for phyllary colour, in that we made too many classes. This has not adversely influenced the published results since it is only a matter of adding to reduce the number of classes.

Pericline shape gave the least satisfactory results of all the selected characters. There is "something in it" and for some families in the breeding work and for some wild populations our scorings appear significant. We made a very large number of measurements of maximum length and maximum diameter, and attempted to score on the length/diameter ratio. Pericline shape has to be scored from living material. It cannot be accurately determined from pressed specimens and it is risky to use boiled up capitula and even material preserved in spirit. We were thus not able to "go back" and rescore on a different basis.

Floret colour also has to be scored "in the flesh." On the whole we regard our scoring as satisfactory. Shading and possibly other environmental factors may somewhat modify floret colour but we were usually able to recognize such fluctuations and allow for them. Marguerite Yellow is a relatively rare but recurrent mutation in the wild. Paler "purple" colours are usually associated with *C. jacea* and its hybrids while the brighter Rood's Violet is frequently characteristic of breviflora female plants. Occasionally in the wild we have found plants with white ray and coloured disc florets but none of our stock plants had this character fully developed. It is, however, of considerable interest that we have shown that the apparently minor character of mixed white and coloured flecked and flushed ray florets has a genetic basis. It must also be noted that we have never seen, in wild or bred material, plants with coloured ray and white or Marguerite Yellow disc florets in any of the knapweeds of the *C. nigra* and *C. jacea* series.

A very conspicuous difference between individuals, and sometimes populations, of knapweeds of the *C. nigra* and *C. jacea* series is the presence or absence of ray florets (radiata or eradiata). We have records of radiata plants from numerous vice-counties, but many of these are of casual occurrences. It is only in the central southern and south midland counties of England that, in our experience, radiata plants are abundant and often form a numerically dominant part of populations. From our studies we put forward the tentative hypothesis that the radiata character has been introduced into populations originally of *C. nigra* or *C. nemoralis* by hybridization with later arriving *C. jacea*. There is a good deal of circumstantial evidence in favour of this, but if it be true then *C. jacea* must have been a fairly old immigrant. We have no positive evidence that the radiata character or the gene combination (or combinations) responsible for it is extending its range in this country as a predominant character of populations. It has died out in some areas where it has been recorded as of casual occurrence, as on Epsom Downs. One might suppose that by enlarging the spread of florets in the capitulum at anthesis it would make the heads more conspicuous and more likely to attract insect visitors for pollination. We could find no evidence for this. In the wild and in the breeding ground, in fine weather, rayed and unrayed heads were visited again and again by pollinators—especially bees. Conspicuous heads might equally attract deleterious insects whose offspring produce galls or larvae feeding on the ovaries or cypselas. It has to be noted that there is a considerable range in the size and degree of neutrality of the ray florets. One could, indeed, from our wild and bred material arrange a series of specimens showing practically continuous variation, from normal eradiata (with the outermost florets actinomorphic male and female functional and no longer than the rest of the disc florets), through longer and longer and more zygomorphic rays (with correlated increasing failure of androecium to produce pollen and of stigmata to be receptive), to very long zygomorphic rays (with not even vestiges of stamens, style, and stigmata). We made an artificial separation into radiata and semiradiata at 2·5 cm. length of ray florets.

Disc florets show the variations of longiflora and breviflora. Longiflora occurs casually in many populations, probably throughout the country, as does also its much rarer variant curly longiflora. We have recorded it in *C. nigra*, *C. nemoralis*, *C. jacea*, and in hybrids. There can be little doubt that it is a recurrent mutation that does not widely establish itself. Probably it is selected against because of the longer florets making it difficult for potential pollinators to reach to the nectar at the base of the tube. This would more than counteract any possible advantage from increased conspicuousness. The breviflora character is frequently associated with brighter floret colour (Rood's Violet) and complete or partial male sterility. There is an increase in the occurrence of these frequently (but not invariably) associated characters in some hybrid families and populations.

Cypsela characters are difficult to score. We have scored them for selected bred families and wild populations. *C. jacea* has cypselas devoid of pappus (epappose) and pure *C. nigra* and pure *C. nemoralis* have, at least usually, cypselas with a pappus (pappose). Even the best developed pappus in our knapweeds of this group can have little or no use as a mechanism for fruit dispersal. The intermediate and irregular development of the pappus found in individuals and in populations is probably a sign of hybridization, at least often.

Such then in outline are some of the problems we found, the methods we adopted to solve them, and an indication of the solutions, sometimes fairly definite, sometimes tentative, we have reached. We would like to commend synthetic taxonomy to younger botanists as a branch of our science that has a great future before it. Our own methods can be greatly improved, extended, and, above all, varied. We have, however, found so much of deep interest at every stage of research and so many facts have come to light that can be incorporated in the taxonomy of the British knapweeds that we are convinced that our general principles have a sound basis and will appeal to an increasing number of students of plant life. Synthetic taxonomy, as we show for the knapweeds in the body of this book, unites herbarium and library studies, field work, laboratory research, and breeding ground experiments. What more can one want ?

CHAPTER II

TAXONOMIC HISTORY OF BRITISH KNAPWEEDS

It is convenient to commence with the 'Species Plantarum of Linnaeus,' 1753, in considering the taxonomic history and nomenclature of our British knapweeds. Linnaeus accepted, in 1753, fifty species in the genus *Centaurea*. Of these, we are in this work concerned mainly with *C. nigra* and *C. jacea*, and to a less degree with *C. scabiosa* and *C. aspera*.

C. nigra L. ' Sp. Pl.,' 911 (1753) is described as " Centaurea calycibus pinnatis : squamula ovata : ciliis capillaribus erectis." The " Habitat " is given as " In Anglia, Helvetia, Austria." Three synonyms are quoted and must be considered. The reference to Haller can be expanded to : Haller, ' Enum. Meth. Stirp. Helv.,' 691, pl. 23, fig. 1 (1742). There seems no reason why the figure should not be intended to represent *C. nigra* as we accept the species, though it is not an extremely good one. The synonym " Jacea nigra laciniata. Bauh. pin. 271 " calls for no further comment than to say it does not conflict with our present concept of *C. nigra*. The " Jacea austriaca Vl" refers to the figure published in Clusius, ' Rar. Plant. Hist. Liber Quartus,' p. vii (1601). This figure also may be taken to represent *C. nigra* as we accept the species. In the Linnean Herbarium at Burlington House there is a specimen which we can accept as the type of the species, since it agrees with the original description, so far as this gives specific characters, and with the synonyms so far as these can be interpreted. This Linnean specimen has fairly large capitula with dark phyllary appendages and has eradiata normalis floret characters.

C. jacea L. ' Sp. Pl.,' 914 (1753) has now to be considered. The description reads " Centaurea calycibus squamosis, foliis lanceolatis : radicalibus sinuato-dentatis, ramis angulatis." To this there are added four references and two synonyms and the " Habitat " is given as " in Europa septentrionali." To deal first with the synonyms. One is to Bauhin's Pinax and is of little or no use in interpreting the species. The other is " Jacea nigra Paul. dan. t. 256 " (1648), but this figure is a copy of Clusius, " Jacea austriaca VI " which Linnaeus quotes under his *C. nigra* ! The first reference is to ' Hort. Cliff.', 421 (published in 1737). Here we find the description as it was later copied for the ' Species Plantarum,' with a longer list of synonyms and the information " Crescit in pratis apricis lapides & agros, interque segetem frequens in Svecia, Dania, Germania, Hollandia, Anglia, Gallia." The references given to ' Fl. Suec.,' 709 (p. 254, 1745) to ' Roy. lugdb.,' 142 (1740), and ' Dalib. paris.,' 265 (1749), all trace

back to Hortus Cliffortianus and repeat the same description. Thus
far there is no apparent confusion and one can accept the description
in Hort. Cliff., repeated in ' Sp. Pl.,' ed. 1, as the basis for determining
the application of the name *C. jacea*, except that one has to exclude
the synonym " Jacea nigra Paul. dan. t. 256." There is, however,
trouble with regard to the specimen in the Hort. Cliff. Herbarium
at the British Museum (Natural History). In the description the
important word is " squamosis." This has to be interpreted in modern
terminology as referring to the phyllary appendages and as describing
them as entire or nearly so, or at least as not pectinate. The contrast
is with the phyllary appendages of *C. nigra* for which the description
is " calycibus pinnatis." In our symbol scoring and as we accept
the species, *C. nigra* has phyllaries N and *C. jacea* phyllaries C or
VM. The following notes have been made regarding the sheet in the
Hortus Cliffortianus Herbarium : One flowering stem with three
capitula and two basal or lower cauline leaves make up the specimen.
The leaves are coarsely lobed and almost pinnatifid, with four large
lobes and, on one leaf, the trace of a fifth small tooth. The capitula
are apparently eradiata normalis but it is difficult to be certain that
there were no ray florets since the material is not sufficiently well
preserved to show the details of structure of the outer florets. The
phyllaries are a rather high M, but scarcely VM. In Linnean terms,
the phyllaries are intermediate between " calycibus squamosis "
and " calycibus pinnatis " but rather nearer the former. One would
judge that the specimen represents what is usually considered as
C. jacea with some genes of a member of the *C. nigra* group.

In the Linnean Herbarium of the Linnean Society at Burlington
House there is a specimen of *C. jacea* from which the following notes
have been made : There are two flowering shoots with very narrow
leaves. The capitula are somewhat flattened by pressure and the
florets are worn by age and somewhat damaged by old insect attack.
The phyllaries are flattened with pale coloured appendages and VM
rather than C. There are present what are probably the remains of
ray florets on two capitula.

Thus the position is that the description of *C. jacea* L. is traced
back to Hortus Cliffortianus, but that the specimen now deposited
in the Hortus Cliffortianus does not agree with it while that in the
Linnean Herbarium of the Linnean Society does. We, therefore,
propose that the latter be accepted as the type specimen.

The next important taxonomic opinion we have to consider is that
of Jordan in ' Pugillus Plantarum Novarum praesertim Gallicarum,'
104 (1852). Here Jordan named and described *Centaurea nemoralis*.
The material used by him is stated as having the " Hab." " in sylvaticis
planitierum circa Lyon et in multis aliis, Galliae locis, haud infre-
quens." It is stated to differ from *C. nigra* L. by flowering nearly
two months later in the same place, by the smaller less globose and
less blackish pericline (involucre), by having the phyllary appendages
lanceolate not broadly ovate. narrower achenes, with a pappus a

third not a half part shorter than the achene, with the stem slenderer and more branched, with the branches longer more slender and more spreading. The plant has eradiate capitula. At a later date, in F. Schultz, ' Arch. Fl. Fr. et Allem.,' 320 (1842–55), Jordan proposed to do away with the name *C. nigra* L. and to replace it by *C. obscura* Jordan.

There are specimens from and collected by Jordan in the Kew Herbarium. Those collected in June and August, 1851, agree with Jordan's accounts and are therefore chosen as types of *C. obscura* and *C. nemoralis* respectively. There is no doubt that *C. obscura* Jord. is synonymous with *C. nigra* L. and there seems no valid reason for replacing the name *C. nigra* L. by *C. obscura* Jord. or by any other name. More critical is the status of *C. nemoralis* Jord. This is a plant with slender stems and branches, narrow upper cauline leaves (2–7 mm. broad), rather small capitula, with fairly small and fairly narrow discs to the phyllary appendages, without ray florets, and with normalis disc florets.

We have attempted to trace the botanist first responsible for applying the name *C. nemoralis* to British plants. The present limits of our search have led us to A. G. More in ' Journ. Bot.,' **9**, 144 (1871). The name, however, did not become popular for some years. It is used by Williams, ' Prodr. Fl. Brit.,' Part 2, p. 60 (1901) and by J. A. Wheldon in ' Rep. Bot. Exch. Club for 1912,' p. 261 (1913) and l.c. for 1914, p. 148 (1915). It is not used in Druce, ' British Plant List,' ed. 1 (1908) or in the ' London Catalogue,' ed. 10 (1908), but appears in Druce. ' British Plant List,' ed. 2, 1928, and in the ' London Catalogue,' ed. 11 (1925). Its wide general use for British plants is obviously due largely to C. E. Britton (see, for example, ' Rep. Bot. Exch. Club for 1921,' 412 : 1922). The name is accepted by Butcher and Strudwick, ' Further Illustrations of British Plants,' 217 (1946) and (as a subspecies of *C. nigra*) by Clapham, Tutin, and Warburg, ' Flora of the British Isles,' 1107 (1952).

As against the acceptance of the name *C. nemoralis* for British plants we have the statement by J. L. van Soest, in ' Nederl. Kruidk. Arch.,' Deel **54**, 87 (1947). He says that *C. nemoralis* Jordan is " Niet wild in Engeland en Scandinavie." Van Soest's paper deals with *Centaurea* sect. *Jacea* in the Netherlands and he was not primarily interested in the British knapweeds. It would appear that he considered the British plants that in recent years have been placed under *C. nemoralis* by various botanists are not that species but should be named *C. babingtonii* Lacaita. Before giving further consideration to *C. nemoralis* as a name applicable to British plants it is advisable to settle the status of *C. babingtonii*. The name was first used, in print, so far as we have traced, on labels issued with specimens by A. Hayek, ' Centaureae exsiccatae criticae,' Fasc. IV, 1924, 157, 158, and (as f. *pygmaea* Lacaita *in litt.*) 159. The label to 157 gives synonomy and we therefore choose the specimen of 157 in the Kew Herbarium as the standard specimen of what Lacaita intended for his *C.*

babingtonii. However, the matter is complicated nomenclaturally by the synonomy and by Lacaita's obvious intention, in using " *babingtonii* " as a specific epithet, to link up his species with Babington's var. *decipiens.* Even the history of this is confused when traced through the various editions of the 'Manual of British Botany.' Thus :

Ed. 1, 1843, p. 169, 2. *nigra* (L.) with β radiata and *C. nigrescens* Willd. not DC. " A radiant plant which is common near Bath."

Ed. 2, 1847, p. 181, 2. *nigra* (L.) with β radiata (" 1. linear or lanceolate ") and 3. *nigrescens* (" Willd." Koch) " 1. linear-lanceolate lower ones ovate sinuate-dentate or lyrate-sinuate." " Meadows and pastures in the West of England."

Ed. 3, 1851, p. 180. A similar account except that for *nigrescens* the description says " 1. lanceolate," " lower leaves ovate-lanceolate."

Ed. 4, 1856, p. 186. 2. *C. nigra* (" 1. lanceolate ") and 3. *C. nigrescens* " 1. green broader than in No. 2." Also the plants are said to be nearly always 1-headed and the heads smaller than in No. 2, globose.

Ed. 5, 1862, p. 188. α *C. nigra* (L.). β *C. decipiens* (Thuill.). " L. broader than those of α." " This, the *C. nigrescens* Bab., may be distinct."

Ed. 6, 1867, p. 197 ; ed. 7, 1874, p. 198 ; ed. 8, 1881, p. 204 ; ed. 9 (H. and J. Groves), 1904, p. 219 ; ed. 10. (A. J. Wilmott), 1922, p. 219, give similar accounts.

In ' Memorials Journals and Botanical Correspondence of Charles Cardale Babington,' 57 (1897), there is recorded the gathering of *Centaurea nigrescens* on 22 Aug. 1836. The locality was between Sea Mills and Stoke Bishop, V.-C. 34.

It has to be noted that Babington changed the name he applied to his west (or south) of England plant from *C. nigrescens* to *C. decipiens.* Also, presumably from the study of more material, he altered his description especially with regard to the breadth of the leaves. There are in herbaria various specimens, from near Bristol or Bath or from the Bath district, collected by Babington at various dates. In the Cambridge Herbarium there are several sheets and one of these has been selected as the standard relied on by Babington at least when he first recognized this radiate plant as worth a name. The interest is that this plant, agreeing with Babington's earliest descriptions, is not the same as the material distributed by Hayek, collected by Lacaita, " Insula Wight, *loco dicto,* ' East Afton ' secus vias," as *C. babingtonii,* but is in close agreement with other plants found in the west of England (as on King's Sedgemoore, Somerset) and in Oxfordshire (as near the Cherwell, Oxford ; Oxey Mead and Pixey Mead, near Oxford).

The name *nigrescens* (as *C. jacea* var. *nigrescens* Wild. et Dur. ' Prodr. fl. Belg.,' **3**, 790 : 1899) is used by Williams ,' Prodr. Fl. Brit.,' 58 (1901), quoting, on p. 59, *C. nigrescens* Willd. ' Sp. Pl.,' **3**, 2288 (1800) and *C. nigra* var. *decipiens* Bab. as synonyms. Unfortunately

Williams's account suggests he was accepting a hybrid swarm or a mixture of plants under this name. De Wildeman and Durand, it must also be noted, based their *C. jacea* var. *nigrescens* on " *C. nigrescens* Auct. [an Willd. ?]."

Van Soest (' Nederl. Kruidk. Arch.,' Deel **54**, 89 : 1947) retains the use of the name *C. babingtonii* Lacaita for British material adding as a synonym " *C.* nemoralis " radiate form " Butcher and Strudwick? " He also adds some comments, in Dutch, of which the translation is " Similar in structure of the heads to *C. nigra*, but is mostly (?) radiate ; appendages rather small, whereby some relationship to *C. debeauxii* is unmistakable. I see, however, no pappus in the material, which thus constitutes a critical point. The leaves are narrow especially the uppermost, which suggests the Angustifoliae."

So far as we have been able to ascertain after a very wide and long search, Lacaita never published a description, or indeed any account, of *C. babingtonii*, and van Soest has not published a latin description to validate the name from his date, though if he had it would have meant that his name was a later homonym of Lacaita's.

The name *C. babingtonii* thus appears to be in utter confusion. Lacaita by using, *ex* Hayek, the specific epithet *babingtonii* and quoting the reference to Babington's Manual obviously intended to apply the name to Babington's plant, but he determined and distributed actual specimens of another plant ! The names of the synonyms quoted by Lacaita trace back to *C. nigrescens* Willd. and *C. decipiens* Thuill. There has been much dispute as to what these plants were and the various interpretations of the meagre original accounts leave the names in confusion. We have not been able to see types and since the descriptions would apply to more than one taxon it seems impossible to be certain of the application of these names.

The earlier name is *C. decipiens* Thuillier, ' Fl. envir. Paris,' 445 (1799). The original description is extremely scrappy but can be translated into modern terminology as follows : basal leaves sinuate-dentate ; cauline leaves very narrow and dentate ; stems angular with several capitula of red florets ; periclines smaller than in *C. amara* ; phyllaries more scarious than those of *C. amara* and reddish, with the margins of the appendage pectinate with setaceous lanceolate pectinations. Flowers in July and August. Under *C. nigra*, in the same work, Thuillier notes " sans couronne," that is presumably with eradiate capitula. One might possibly assume that the other species, including *C. decipiens*, with which he deals were radiate. Nothing is said about presence or absence of pappus, but *C. decipiens* comes in the group " calycibus squamis aridis scariosis." There is nothing sufficiently definite in Thuillier's account to determine exactly what he intended by *C. decipiens*, but the " reddish " and " arid scarious " phyllaries suggest a *C. jacea* hybrid. It may be noted that Rouy (' Le Monde des Plantes,' **7**, No. 101, 111 : 1898), Briquet (' Monogr. des Centaurées des Alpes Maritimes,' 72 : 1902), and Gugler (' Anns. Mus. Nat. Hung.,' **6**, 62 : 1907) classify *C. decipiens* Thuill. under

C. jacea in the broad sense, though at the expense of some contradictions in descriptions.

We received on loan from the Conservatoire Botanique, Ville de Genève, a sheet written up as " Centaurea decipiens M. Thuillier 1803." If this was collected in 1803 it cannot be accepted as an original type, since the name was published in 1799. The specimen is of a single piece gathered from the base 8·7 dm. tall, with a dozen capitula on very slender branches. The upper cauline leaves are very narrow (linear), and the lower ones very narrowly pinnatifid. The periclines are ovoid and rather small (1·5 cm. long). The phyllaries are darkish brown (probably they were Prout's Brown in the living plant) and in outline shape are " low L " to " high VL." The capitula appear to be eradiate. Plants very similar to this have been collected in hybrid swarms of *C. jacea* × *C. nemoralis* in Wiltshire and in Oxfordshire. For example : V.-C.8, near Enford, 2.ix.1950 and V.-C.23, between Woodstock and Wootton, 31.viii.29 (with phyllaries ranging from N to M). The Dutch specimen collected by van Soest named *C. decipiens* Thuill., in the Kew Herbarium, is certainly a hybrid showing rather more *C. jacea* character in the phyllaries than in the Thuillier specimen referred to above. We can only conclude, tentatively, that *C. decipiens* Thuil. is a name more or less applicable to certain individuals with extremely narrow leaves from the hybrid swarm *C. jacea* × *C. nemoralis*.

We turn now to *C. nigrescens* Willd. ' Sp. Pl.,' **3**, 2288 (1804). This is said, in the original description, to have " corolla radiata," that is presumably to have ray florets and to have the " calyx," that is the phyllaries, " ciliate " not " plumose." It is extremely difficult to know exactly what is meant by these terms. The " key " distinction between *C. nigra* and *C. nigrescens* is given as " squamis setaceociliatis " for the former and " squamis ciliato serratis " for the latter. This suggests a structure of the appendages of the phyllaries of *C. nigrescens* intermediate between *C. nigra* and *C. jacea*. The " habitat " of *C. nigrescens* is given as " in Hungaria, Austria." No evidence has been found that Babington, Williams, Lacaita, or van Soest examined types of *C. decipiens* Thuill. or *C. nigrescens* Willd. Briquet refers to type material of the former as represented by " trois grands échantillons rameux, à feuilles étroites, les supérieures presque linéaires, ± tomenteuses, à calathides médiocres, dans lesquelles toutes les écailles, jusqu'aux ¾ de la hauteur des capitules, ont des appendices régulièrement pectinés." Hayek reports that in the Willdenow Herbarium there is a mixture of five sheets under the name *C. nigrescens* and from these he chooses two as agreeing with Willdenow's description and otherwise suitable to fill the type rôle. It seems clear from Hayek's account that *C. nigrescens* Willd. is equivalent to the material at Kew of the Flora Exsiccata Anstro-Hungarica 227, I., and this is a different plant from any British material seen and certainly from Babington's Bath specimens. (See Hayek, ' Die Centaurea-Arten Österreich-Ungarns ' in Denkschr.

Math.-Nat. Cl. K. Akad. Wiss. Wien, **70**, 725–6, 141–2 of separate : 1901.)

After this digression caused by the need to investigate the names *C. babingtonii, C. decipiens*, and *C. nigrescens*, we return to *C. nemoralis* Jord. to enquire further if this name can be applied to British plants. It can be stated clearly that exceedingly " good matches " are evident on careful comparison of Jordan's own collected and written up specimens and certain British plants from Oxfordshire, Wiltshire, Surrey, and other counties. As examples we quote : V.C.23, Woodstock, " Round the Firs ", No. 10/22.ix.28 and V.C.8, near East Coulston, B.7/20.viii.50. These are in the Kew Herbarium and many other specimens also there could be equally well quoted. Jordan's diagnosis is clear and the application of the name *C. nemoralis* is nomenclaturally unambiguous since we are not at the moment concerned with relative status. There are in the British Isles, and particularly in southern and southern midland vice-counties plants that agree with Jordan's description and specimens of his *C. nemoralis*. Moreover, as is definitely shown by our field work and breeding experiments, such plants are basic units of a taxon ecologically and genetically characterized and entering as an element into the constitution of hybrid swarms.

Two new names, with good descriptions in English, were published by C. E. Britton in ' Rep. Bot. Exch. Club, 1921,' 410 (1922), namely *Centaurea surrejana* and *C. drucei*. Unfortunately neither name is fixed by a holotype or, indeed, by quotation of any definite specimens. A type for each must, therefore, be made, by selection from specimens determined by C. E. Britton, as reasonably as possible. The characters particularly emphasized for *C. surrejana* are the erect flexuous stems, the large scattered spaced leaves, and the short subequal secondary branches, with the heads solitary or gemminate. We have selected *C. E. Britton* 2392, Epsom Downs, Surrey, 24 July, 1921, in Herb. Kew., as the type. It agrees well with the original description, was collected by C. E. Britton himself at about the time he described *C. surrejana*, and is so written up in his handwriting. This specimen has phyllaries N and capitula eradiate. Other specimens, so named by C. E. Britton, are different. Thus his No. 2617, also from Epsom Downs, has phyllaries L. Plants with short final branches and capitula, or some of them, gemminate occur in wild populations, especially when these are of hybrid origin, as at Wellington College. They also segregate occasionally from crosses. Thus in T.418 (an F_2 family from the cross S.P.35·1 × S.P.48) one plant in a family of 47 plants had the capitula close together.

For *C. drucei* we have selected C. E. Britton 2421A, near Tadworth, Surrey, 7 August, 1921, in Herb. Kew., as the type. This agrees with the original description, so far as this covers the characters, and is a specimen collected by and written up by C. E. Britton. It is, as are some other specimens so named by Britton and seen by us, a hybrid with a good many *C. jacea* genes in its genotype. The phyllaries are S and the capitula eradiata. Other specimens written up *C.*

3

drucei by Britton have phyllaries N or L, and he may well have included
plants with other phyllary values. Obviously, he gave the name to
individuals selected from hybrid swarms and themselves, at least very
often, heterozygotes.

The name *Centaurea pratensis* (dating from Thuillier, ' Flore des
environs de Paris,' 444 : 1799) has been applied, in herbaria and in
publications, to some British specimens. Two of our stock plants
(S.P.30 and S.P.47) were so named by C. E. Britton. These, though
both hybrids as our work has shown, were not of the same genotypic
or phenotypic constitution. It is quite evident that various British
botanists have selected plants from hybrid swarms, involving *C.
jacea, C. nemoralis,* and *C. nigra,* and have named them " *C. pratensis.*"
C. E. Britton at one time (' Rep. Bot. Exch. Club, 1921,' 415 : 1922)
put " *C. pratensis* Thuill." as a synonym of *C. nemoralis* Jord. var.
debeauxii (Gren. et Godr.) C. E. Britton. At a later date (in ' Rep.
Bot. Exch. Club, 1926,' 149–52 : 1927) he maintains it as a species
and quotes specimens from E. Sussex, W. Kent, Surrey, Berks, Bucks,
W. Gloucester, Chester, Perth, and Guernsey. Britton's account,
apart from the status he accords and the nomenclature he uses, fits
well into the conclusion we have reached and stated above that " *C.
pratensis* " of British authors is a name applied to various plants of
hybrid origin and structure. We have not seen in any British herbarium or been able to obtain on loan from abroad a type specimen of
C. pratensis Thuillier.

Other plants from the British Isles of hybrid origin have been
named *Centaurea jacea* subsp. *jungens* (see C. E. Britton, ' Rep. Bot.
Exch. Club, 1920,' 167 : 1921). Our stock plants 35·1, 35·2, and 49
were so named by C. E. Britton. *C. moncktonii* C. E. Britton (l.c.,
172) was acknowledged to be a hybrid and plants that have been
named *C. subjacea, C. nemophila,* and *C. viretorum* are, in part at least
and judging from phenotypic characters together with comparison
with bred plants of known hybrid origin, also selections from hybrid
swarms. We have shown that such hybrids segregate on selfing and
on crossing and we have made plants phenotypically similar by the
crossing of suitable stock plants. In other words we have proved
the hybrid origin of plants to which quite a number of specific names
have been given and our proof has been by analysis and by synthesis.
However, we have found in the wild and have made by breeding
experiments many plants that do not agree in their characters, or
combination of characters, with any named and described " species "
or other taxon. To name and describe these as " species," " subspecies," " varieties," or any other taxa would appear to serve no
useful purpose for they are innumerable, mostly ephemeral, and
generally individuals of hybrid swarms.

Something must now be said regarding variation within accepted
species. A considerable number of " subspecies," " varieties " and
" forms " have been given names. They, or most of them, appear to
fall into one or other of three groups :

1. Those diagnosed by a number of characters and possibly sometimes occurring as localized populations, as *C. jacea* subsp. *angustifolia* ;

2. those diagnosed by a single differential character, as *C. nemoralis* var. *diversifolia* formae *radiata* and *longiflora* ;

3. those, however diagnosed, that are certainly of interspecific hybrid origin, as *C, jacea* subsp. *jungens*.

The examples are all taken from the papers published by C. E. Britton and refer to his use of the names. Many other examples could be given. First, it must be stated that many of the characters used are correlated with different genotypes. They are not phenotypic fluctuations or modifications of one genotype. Secondly, authors have made little or no attempt to determine the correlation of characters in wild populations or to show by experiment whether the plants described are homozygotes or heterozygotes for this or that character. In group 2 above, it is " characters " not taxa that are named and described. Very often these characters can be variously combined in one individual. A plant can be radiata and longiflora, or eradiata and longiflora, or radiata and normalis, or eradiata and normalis. Add on other pairs of characters concerned with stem height, indumentum, leaf shape, phyllary shape, floret colour, and so on, and the number of possible combinations of phenotypic characters becomes very large indeed. To give them all names would serve no useful purpose. Names should only be given to paramorphs (intraspecific variants) when there is a strong reason to suppose that naming will aid further research or assist the application of knowledge. Thus, a " variety " may form a local population correlated with certain habitat factors and the ecologist may need a name for repeated use to designate the population ; or a variety, not perhaps in *Centaurea*, may have some peculiar economic value, say as a fodder plant, and the applied botanist requires a name by which he can refer to it. This is not the place to enter into a discussion of controversial questions regarding the naming of cultivated plants, hybrids, and variants in general. We wish, however, to explain that we have deliberately avoided inventing paramorphic names in this work and that our application of such words as " radiata " or " longiflora," or English phrases as " Dull Dark Purple " or " Bone Brown " is to characters not to taxa.

C. nemoralis var. *microptilon* (Gren.) C. E. Britton as interpreted in ' Bot. Exch. Club Report, 1921,' 414 (1922) deserves mention. The characters emphasized concern the appendages to the phyllaries. These are described as " not appressed, mostly subulate or linear-lanceolate, elongated, the upper part curved outwards, the lowest appendages spreading." We have found plants, with phyllaries answering to this description, in various hybrid swarms studied in the wild, as in the Woodstock district of Oxfordshire, and have also recorded them in various families in our breeding work. For example, plants with narrow, elongated and often recurved phyllary appendages occurred in T.98 (S.P.34·1 × S.P.15), in T.384 (T.98, plant 19 × T.98, plant 37), and in T.407 (T.98, plant 19 × T.98, plant 29). Our Stock Plant 7 came under this category and in T.53 we had a family of 13 plants that resulted from the selfing of this plant. An F_2 family of 17 plants (T.202) was raised by selfing T.53, plant 1. These two families showed no segregation for the characters scored, except that there was segregation for phyllary colour in T.202. That four plants had Prout's Brown phyllaries in T.202 is of some significance since paler phyllary colour is often associated with *C. jacea* crosses. The evidence from field observations and from our experiments suggests strongly that " var. *microptilon* " is a segregate of more or less " bottom recessive " status, especially so far as phyllary shape is concerned. All the F_1 and F_2 plants were scored as having phyllaries showing no fusion (that is, they were scored as N in our character classification scheme for phyllary shape).

We have discussed the taxonomic history of British knapweeds from the time of Linnaeus to the present day. There is one pre-Linnaean author in whose publications we have found some interesting records. Ray records (in ' Catal. Pl. Angl.,' 175 : 1670 and ed. 2, 169 : 1677) a rayed variant of " Jacea nigra " as occurring in the West of England (probably this should be read as " west of East Anglia " and not as the extreme west of England). Later (' Syn.,' 55 : 1690) he again refers to the rayed variant of the West of England and also to a variant " cum flore pleno " which is presumably the character variation termed longiflora by us.

Many pre-Linnean publications have been consulted but little has been found that is relevant to the problems interesting us in this work. It is often difficult to determine from imperfect descriptions and crude figures which of several species is intended and usually impossible to learn anything about the paramorphic characters or those suggesting hybridization. In other words, the early references to *Centaurea* in Britain throw little or no light on the history of the taxa here. One of the, if not the, earliest references to knapweeds in the British Isles is that in Gerard's Herbal, pp. 588 and 599 (1597). The figure for " Jacea nigra, Blacke Matfellon " (p. 588) may be accepted as representing *Centaurea nigra* s.l. and probably a radiata variant, though this is not quite certain. The flowering period is given as June-July and the English names as Matfellon, Bulweede, and Knapweed. In the 1633 and 1636 editions a different figure has been substituted and this is probably intended to represent an eradiate plant.

CHAPTER III

VEGETATIVE CHARACTERS

Seedlings.

No morphological differences have been observed between seedlings of *C. jacea*, *C. nemoralis*, and *C. nigra*. The shape and size of the cotyledons and the first three or four young foliage leaves show only a narrow range of variation and this range is very similar in all three species in seedlings of the same age grown under conditions as uniform as possible. Hybrids between these species sometimes show an increased rate of growth of seedlings. This is presumably a physiological character to be classified under " hybrid vigour."

Stem Heights.

The flowering stems, commencing to grow out in the spring, usually grow more or less erect. The stem habit is however, sometimes easily modified by environmental conditions. For example, ramets of Stock Plant 1, on five different soils, at Potterne, Wilts, had approximately erect flowering stems but ramets of the same clone grown in the Herbarium Experimental Ground at Kew had the flowering stems bending out from the base and then ascending, the plants thus developing hollow centres at an early stage of growth, that is a habit distinct from the " fairy ring " growth of older plants due to centrifugal spread and vegetative multiplication. This difference in habit between ramets at Potterne and Kew was maintained for the duration of the experiments (13 years).

There is a considerable range in stem heights from a few cm. up to 11 dm. in the wild and 14 dm. in cultivation (T.229). The following figures from measurements in cm. are for stock plants, collected directly from the wild but grown under conditions as uniform as possible at the Potterne Biological Station :

Number of plants.	Maximum stem height.	Minimum stem height.	Mean stem height.	Standard deviation.	Coefficient of variation.
C. nigra 4 . . .	85 .	62 .	75·5 .	11·45 .	15·2
C. nemoralis 17 .	92 .	50 .	67·8 .	10·96 .	16·2
C. nemoralis Warwickshire 16 . . .	105 .	60 .	86·9 .	13·98 .	16·1
C. jacea 10 . . .	120 .	52 .	91·9 .	18·84 .	20·5
C. jacea hybrids 18 .	85 .	45 .	71·1 .	11·33 .	18·9

None of these stocks was a " dwarf " plant when collected. Figures for dwarf chalk downland plants may be contrasted with the above figures. They belong to the taxon *C. nemoralis* and were collected on Walker's Hill, North Wilts, 170–228 m., 21.viii.1952.

Number of plants.	Maximum stem height.	Minimum stem height.	Mean stem height.	Standard deviation.	Coefficient of variation.
44	11	3	7·0	2·51	35·9

Dwarf Downland Plants under Cultivation.

A number of dwarf chalk downland plants of *Centaurea nemoralis* were collected on Clifford's Hill, near Devizes, North Wilts, 260 m., and transplanted to the Potterne Experimental Ground on Upper Greensand, 14 September, 1931. Maximum measurements (in cm.) were made of the original wild material and periodically, at full flowering period as far as possible, under cultivation up to 1939 or 1940.

D.2.

	Stem height.	Pericline length × diameter.	Ray florets length.	Disc florets length.
1931	10·4	1·3 × 0·5	2·5	1·6
1932	36·0	1·3 × 1·0	2·6	1·7
1933	47·0	1·4 × 0·9	—	—
1934	33·0	1·5 × 0·9	2·7	1·7
1935	48·0	1·4 × 0·8	2·7	1·8
1937	47·0	1·3 × 0·7	2·0	1·5
1939	—	—	—	—

D.3.

1931	13·0	1·2 × 0·6	2·8	1·6
1932	—	—	—	—
1933	64·0	1·4 × 0·9	2·6	1·8
1934	33·0	1·1 × 0·8	3·3	1·7
1935	57·0	1·2 × 0·7	2·8	1·7
1937	48·0	1·3 × 0·7	2·0	1·5
1939	45·0	1·2 × 0·9	2·1	1·5
1940	42·0	1·3 × 0·8	2·9	1·7

D.6.

1931	8·2	1·4 × 0·6	—	—
1932	30·0	1·5 × 0·9	2·9	1·8
1933	56·0	1·5 × 0·8	2·8	1·8
1934	41·0	1·4 × 0·9	3·3	1·8
1935	52·0	1·9 × 0·8	3·0	1·7
1937	51·0	1·3 × 0·7	2·4	1·6
1939	44·0	1·5 × 0·8	3·0	1·8
1940	44·0	1·5 × 1·1	2·5	1·8

D.9.

	Stem height.	Pericline length × diameter.	Ray florets length.	Disc florets length.
1931 .	8·4	1·0 × 0·5	1·9	1·2
1932 .	37·0	1·5 × 0·9	2·6	1·6
1933 .	46·0	1·2 × 0·7	—	—
1934 .	43·0	1·2 × 0·7	2·8	1·7
1935 .	47·0	1·2 × 0·7	2·5	1·6
1937 .	37·0	—	—	—
1939 .	—	—	—	—

D.10.

	Stem height.	Pericline length × diameter.	Ray florets length.	Disc florets length.
1931 .	13·0	1·4 × 0·6	2·5	1·6
1932 .	41·0	1·4 × 1·0	3·4	1·9
1933 .	50·0	1·4 × 0·8	2·8	1·8
1934 .	41·0	1·4 × 0·8	2·8	1·7
1935 .	31·0	1·2 × 0·7	2·9	1·6
1937 .	27·0	1·3 × 0·6	2·5	1·6
1939 .	—	—	—	—

D.12.

	Stem height.	Pericline length × diameter.	Ray florets length.	Disc florets length.
1931 .	9·0	1·4 × 0·6	—	—
1932 .	45·0	1·6 × 0·9	3·5	2·0
1933 .	58·0	1·5 × 0·7	2·8	2·0
1934 .	40·0	1·5 × 0·8	3·3	2·1
1935 .	44·0	1·5 × 0·7	3·0	1·9
1937 .	57·0	1·4 × 0·7	2·6	1·9
1939 .	—	—	—	—

D.13.

	Stem height.	Pericline length × diameter.	Ray florets length.	Disc florets length.
1931 .	13·0	1·2 × 0·6	2·4	1·5
1932 .	43·0	1·4 × 1·0	2·5	1·4
1933 .	61·0 .	1·4 × 1·0	3·0	1·8
1934 .	52·0	1·4 × 0·9	3·0	1·7
1935 .	48·0	1·3 × 0·7	2·9	1·6
1937 .	40·0	1·3 × 0·7	2·3	1·5
1939 ˙.	39·0	1·3 × 0·9	2·3	1·5
1940 .	39·0	1·3 × 0·9	2·5	1·6

Selfings and cross (scored 1940, 2 years old).

	Plant number.	Stem heights.	Pericline length × diameter.	Ray florets length.	Disc florets length.
T.602. D.6 selfed .	1 .	48·0 .	1·4 × 0·9 .	3·0 .	2·0
	2 .	44·0 .	1·4 × 0·9 .	2·6 .	1·7
	3 .	45·0 .	1·3 × 0·9 .	3·4 .	1·9
	4 .	46·0 .	1·3 × 0·9 .	2·5 .	1·8

	Plant number	Stem heights.	Pericline length × diameter.	Ray florets length.	Disc florets length.
T.603. D.3 selfed .	1	. 48·0	. 1·3 × 0·8	. 2·9	. 1·8
	2	. 42·0	. 1·4 × 0·8	. 2·8	. 1·8
	3	. 47·0	. 1·4 × 0·8	. 3·1	. 1·8
	4	. 43·0	. 1·2 × 0·8	. 3·0	. 1·8
	5	. 47·0	. 1·3 × 0·8	. 2·8	. 1·7
	6	. 48·0	. 1·4 × 0·8	. 3·4	. 1·9
	7	. 39·0	. 1·3 × 0·7	. 3·1	. 1·7
T.601. D.6×D.3 .	1	. 48·0	. 1·5 × 0·9	. 2·8	. 1·8

The plants investigated here would be named *C. nemoralis* Jord. var. *minima* C. E. Britton. Similar dwarf plants are common on many areas of chalk hill grassland, especially where there is heavy grazing by rabbits or other animals. The figures obtained by scoring our transplants suggest stem heights are, in the stocks used, correlated with genotypic differences from other taller growing stocks.

There are some striking regularities in the above tables. First, the year after transplanting there was always a great increase in height (if the plants flowered). This increase was still greater in the next year. The third year (1934) there was a decrease, in part at least due to unusual early summer drought that year. After this there was fluctuation due to external or individual causes. None of the plants attained stem heights recorded, at Potterne under similar conditions, for the great majority of the stock plants used in other experiments. An interesting contrast was a selfed family from S.P.1 growing in the next bed with flowering stems from 67 to 96 cm. On selfing and crossing two of the stock plants (D.3 and D.6) the stems of the offspring were relatively short and showed little variation.

It would thus appear that there are individuals of a distinct genetic constitution in *C. nemoralis* to which the varietal name *minima* can be applied. This does not preclude the occurrence of plants dwarfed by habitat conditions although they have genes for much taller stems. The " var. *minima* " with a genotypic basis may be regarded as an ecotype, but only experiments can separate it from plants phenotypically similar but genotypically different.

There were no striking regularities in changes of pericline size or floret lengths except for a tendency to increase in pericline size the first year of cultivation. It should be noted that in five of the seven plants there was fluctuation from the radiata to the semi-radiata condition and/or the reverse. The selfings and crossing gave radiata plants in the one year's scoring.

The effect of cutting and grazing on dwarfing knapweed plants is dealt with in the chapter on vegetative multiplication and reproduction.

Dwarf plants of knapweeds have been studied in the field in various vice-counties, especially N. and S. Wilts, Surrey, and Oxfordshire.

Probably they are widely scattered in exposed or dry situations, but only experiments can show whether they be ecads or ecotypes.

Turesson studied what he called *Centaurea jacea* f. *humilis* Schrank. He cultivated dwarf plants from salt meadows along the coast at Vellinga and Torekov, Sweden. A cross between a nearly erect and a spreading plant gave an F_1 intermediate and an F_2 of nearly erect 2 : intermediate 20 : spreading 4. He concluded the dwarf *C. jacea* f. *humilis* of the salt meadows " is made up of a heterogeneous assemblage of most diverse, genetically different types. They all react upon the extreme habitat conditions with dwarf growth, thus giving the impression of a homogeneous population . . . ." (' Hereditas,' **3**, 225–28 : 1922 and Fedde, ' Repert.' Beih., **41**, 20–21 : 1926).

Some evidence of the effects of soil conditions on the growth of *Centaurea nigra* S.P.1 was obtained from the Transplant Experiments at Potterne, 1928–40. The species proved a persistent perennial and did well on all the five soils (sand, calcareous sand, clay, chalky clay, Potterne soil) used, but did best on sand and a little less well on calcareous sand. It was the only species of those with which we experimented that flourished best on the sands. No morphological changes occurred on any of the soils at Potterne. The growth of basal and lower cauline leaves on clay and Potterne soil was relatively retarded so that spring shoots retained arachnoid indumentum for a longer period than on other soils. There was considerable vegetative multiplication of the " fairy ring " type. No effects to suggest soil exhaustion were observed to the end of the experiments.

INDUMENTUM OF STEMS.

There are more or less conspicuous differences between some plants in indumentum of the vegetative parts. For standardization the lower parts of the flowering stems were taken and scoring was on the basis of three classes : glabrous, asperulous, and hirsute. Stock Plants were scored as follows :

Glabrous : 17, 30, 34·1, 34·3, 45·1–45·8, 47, 48.

Asperulous : 1, 2, 5, 6, 7, 8·2, 10, 13·3, 16, 23, 25·2, 26·1, 27·3, 38·3, 49.

Hirsute : 13·6, 13·7, 21, 33, 34·2, 35·1, 36.

A few plants scored as glabrous were very slighty asperulous on some stems.

Families from selfings and crossings occasionally bred true but, more often segregated. Examples are :

		Glabrous.	Asperulous.	Hirsute.
T. 13	asperulous × asperulous	1	23	7
T. 56	asperulous × hirsute	15	55	4
T. 62	glabrous × glabrous	36	40	4
T. 64	glabrous × hirsute	5	19	11
T. 66	asperulous × hirsute	2	10	10
T. 67	glabrous × asperulous	9	8	13

		Glabrous.	Asperulous.	Hirsute.
T. 71 .	glabrous × glabrous	. 10	. 0	. 0
T. 72 .	asperulous selfed	. 0	. 73	. 8
T. 73 .	hirsute selfed	. 0	. 0	. 4
T. 74 .	asperulous × hirsute	. 3	. 48	. 3
T. 79 .	asperulous × glabrous	. 5	. 27	. 0
T. 82 .	glabrous × asperulous	. 6	. 12	. 0
T. 84 .	asperulous × hirsute	. 0	. 3	. 70
T.117 .	hirsute selfed	. 0	. 0	. 11

Basal Leaves.

All the plants considered here are half-rosette hemicryptophytes, *i.e.*, the flowering stems die down completely after fruiting and the over-wintering buds are approximately at ground level. The first sign of renewed growth is the appearance of basal leaves, in well formed plants often in large numbers (in *C. nigra* up to 103 per plant in May, in second year from germination of seed, in the experimental ground without competition). Many individuals are winter-green, in that new basal leaves appear in the late summer or autumn and survive the winter in the south of England. This is particularly true for early flowering *C. nigra*. The maximum of development of the basal leaves is, however, in the spring and early summer immediately before the stems that are to flower begin to elongate. Spring growth usually commences in March.

The basal leaves are mostly oblanceolate, acute, and very gradually taper to the petiole which is often as long as the blade. At least some basal leaves are entire or only slightly toothed and frequently all may be so described. In some plants, however, a majority may be toothed, lobed, or even pinnatifid. Environmental factors certainly have some influence on the number, size, and shape of basal leaves but genetical factors are also involved. We attempted to score the stock plants and many families for outline shape of basal leaves, using the descriptive terms entire, lobed, and pinnatifid. Leaves scored as entire were sometimes slightly toothed. There is no sharp line between the classes.

Stock Plants :

1. With entire (or slightly toothed) basal leaves : 1, 5, 6, 7, 8·2, 9, 13·1, 15, 16, 17, 18, 19, 23, 25·1, 25·2, 26·1, 26·2, 27·1, 27·2, 27·3. 27·4, 28, 29, 30, 31, 34·1, 35·1, 35·2, 36, 37, 38·1, 38·3, 40, 41, 44, 45·1, 45·2, 45·3, 45·4, 45·5, 45·6, 45·8, 47, 48, 49, 79·2.

2. With lobed basal leaves : 3, 4, 8·1, 10, 11, 12, 13·3, 13·7, 14, 21, 22·1, 24·2, 24·3, 24·4, 24·5, 26·3, 32, 33, 34·2, 38·2, 39, 42, 43, 46.

3. With pinnatifid basal leaves : 13·2, 13·4, 13·5, 13·6, 20, 22·2.

On selfing, the following stock plants bred true for shape of basal leaves : 1, 5, 27·3, 36 (entire) ; 3, 4 (lobed).

In some F_1 and F_2 families from crosses there was uniform true breeding, *e.g.*, T.69 (entire), T.76 (entire), and T.78 (entire).

On the other hand, there was frequent segregation both on selfing and on crossing.

Examples are :

T.62 : entire × entire, gave entire 37 : lobed 43.

T.66 : entire × lobed, gave entire 6 : lobed 17 : pinnatifid 10.

T.79 : entire × entire, gave entire 29 : lobed 3.

T.153 : F_2 from lobed × entire, gave entire 2 : lobed 44 : pinnatifid 13.

T.158 : F_2 from entire selfed, gave entire 7 : lobed 29 : pinnatifid 12.

T.169 : F_2 from entire selfed, gave entire 7 : lobed 19 : pinnatifid 8.

T.182 : F_2 from entire × entire, gave entire 19 : lobed 21 : pinnatifid 1.

T.198 : F_2 from lobed × lobed, gave entire 81 : lobed 10.

It is impossible to determine the exact genetical factors involved in the determination of basal leaf shape from our many scorings of which the above make a very small sample. On the whole the " entire " condition is most frequent in the wild. It may be that in some sense " entire " is dominant but in a heterozygote the basal leaves will develop the " lobed " condition if environmental characters retard the growth of flowering stems.

CHAPTER IV

VEGETATIVE MULTIPLICATION AND SEXUAL REPRODUCTION

All the plants dealt with in this work are naturally herbaceous perennials. Under suitable environmental conditions they can be long lived. The material (our Stock Plant 1) used for the Transplant Experiments of the British Ecological Society at Potterne was collected in the wild in 1922 as one plant. Ramets of this were maintained at Potterne on five distinct soils and at Kew, without artificial re-cloning or treatments, except for removal of " top hamper " on several occasions, from April, 1928, to December, 1940, and were still flourishing when the experiments were concluded. Our experience leads us to conclude that a stock can be kept growing and healthy for an indefinite number of years by re-cloning and re-planting at intervals of three to five years. In the wild, however, knapweed plants do not " live for ever." The average length of life is possibly not more than three or four flowering seasons. Two factors, apart from " accidents," were shown, by experiment and by observation in the wild to be important in limiting life span of established plants : the complex factor of competition with other vegetation and smother by own top hamper. Close competition with dense vegetation quickly reduces the number of flowering stems produced and eventually kills a plant, apparently mainly by over shading. If own top hamper be considerable in amount it reduces very greatly the number of " tillers " produced in the autumn and next season. It is slow to decay and persistent in position and we have had many examples of it killing individual plants, both those raised directly from seed and those grown as ramets.

Only two methods of multiplication have been found by us to occur in the British knapweeds of the species dealt with in this work : vegetative spread and sexual reproduction by one-seeded cypselas. We have no evidence of the occurrence of apomitic seeds such as are common in *Hieracium, Taraxacum, Crepis,* and other genera of the *Compositae.* The results of numerous selfings under protection from out-crossing show that if seeds be formed apomictically this must be a very rare happening. Florets are too small for deanthering but plants left protected but untouched, except for thorough brushing off of pollen at anthesis of the capitula, set no seed. Examples of such experiments are : T.47, plant 1, protected and left. No seed set from 44 capitula. T.42, plant 3, protected and left. No seed set from 3 capitula.

VEGETATIVE MULTIPLICATION.

Artificial cloning is very easy with many plants of the *Centaurea nigra* and *C. jacea* groups. Thus, from one plant, itself a ramet, of Stock Plant 1 we obtained at one re-cloning 156 ramets that were all established as physiologically independent "individuals." Natural propagation in these knapweeds is of the close colony kind. For Stock Plant 1, which in this respect can be taken as a general standard, we have previously (*Journ. Ecol.*, **25**, 193 : 1937) described the process of natural cloning, on different soils under the conditions of transplant experiments, as follows : " There is very considerable and increasing natural cloning on all the soils. The flowering stems die back in autumn to near soil level. At soil level for about an inch the stem is from 0·5 to 1·2 cm. in diameter, compared with the flowering stem diameter of 0·3 to 0·4 cm. From the thickened portion from 1 to 11 lateral shoots arise and grow horizontally, mostly turned away from the centre, for an average distance of 2·5 cm., ending in a rosette of basal leaves surrounding a growing point. Many of these rosette shoots flower the year after their production. Detachment from the parent stock occurs 1–2 years after flowering by the rotting of the short horizontal stem growth (short rhizome). Such vegetative multiplication has frequently been observed in the wild and is best studied in the late autumn. In the experimental plots centrifugal growth is strongly marked and it is becoming more and more difficult to distinguish the offspring ramets of the original ramets. The side rows have " moved " laterally towards the outside of the plots and now form more or less half-circles, while the inner halves of the circles have been killed off by the shading effects of the contiguous rows. Side plants have " moved " as much as 12 in., *i.e.*, to the maximum possible extent, and are now close against the boards." It may be noted that the rate of " movement " in one direction would average just over 2·5 cm. a year. In these experiments there was no competition with other vegetation, *i.e.*, apart from the shading and other effects of contiguous rows of ramets of the same clone. Natural cloning continued to increase, to the end of the experiments five years later, on all soils. The greatest amount of cloning occurred on sand, least on Potterne (Upper Greensand) soil, and intermediate degrees on clay, calcareous sand, and chalky clay. The " fairy ring " type of spread was often very obvious.

SEXUAL REPRODUCTION.

Reproduction, ecological distribution other than extremely local, and geographical range involve the production of seeds by fertilization. The seeds are dispersed in one-seeded indehiscent fruits formed from inferior ovaries and technically termed cypselas. These cypselas may have a small, presumably vestigial rather than rudimentary, pappus of short bristles, though these are often absent. Even when developed to the maximum extent observed in the plants dealt with in this work, they can have little or no effect in increasing dispersal efficiency. It may, indeed, be said that the knapweeds of the *C. nigra* and *C. jacea* series have no obvious special mechanism for fruit or seed dispersal. The ripe cypselas are shaken or jerked out of the mature capitula for a few decimeters from the parent plant, by high winds or passing animals. Dispersal, in Britain, is, and presumably for long has been, mainly by human agency. High winds or chance attachment to animals, including birds, may on relatively rare occasions lead to wider dispersal.

REPRODUCTIVE CAPACITY.

The reproductive capacity of the knapweeds varies enormously owing to the number of variables involved and the wide ranges of several of them. These variables include : 1. length of life of the individual, or more precisely for the present purpose, the number of reproductive seasons it has ; 2. the number of capitula a plant produces per season, depending on the number of flowering stems and the branching of these ; 3. the number of potentially fertile florets, *i.e.*, with developed sex organs, per capitulum ; 4. the effectiveness of pollination resulting in fertilization, *i.e.*, for most stocks, of cross pollination ; 5. the number of cypselas produced ; 6. the survival of these cypselas from the attacks of enemies ; 7. the percentage germination of the seeds ; 8. the establishment of the seedlings.

We have little evidence of length of life of individual knapweed plants in the wild but under cultivation they remain alive and reproducing from one to at least twenty years and, no doubt, by suitable treatment, ramets, that is physiologically independent individuals of one genetical individual, could be kept alive and reproducing indefinitely. The figures we now present are, therefore, concerned with *annual reproductive capacity*.

NUMBER PER PLANT OF CAPITULA THAT FLOWERED.

C. nigra.—Grass field near Lavington Station, South Wilts, 19.vii.52. Capitula radiata normalis. 20 plants.

Range 1 to 52. Mean 8·2. S.D.11·12. Coefficient of variation 135·6.

C. nemoralis and *C. jacea* hybrids.—Chalk down, Rams Cliff, South Wilts, 22.vii.52. Capitula radiata normalis. 12 plants.

Range 1 to 215. Mean 50·0. S.D.61·30. Coefficent of variation 122·6.

C. nigra.—Cultivated (8.x.52) in the Herbarium Experimental Ground, Kew, from cypselas collected at High Force, Teesdale, 3.ix.49. Capitula eradiata normalis.

Capitula per plant 465, 245, 266, 343, 38, 314, giving a mean of 278·5. The plant with only 38 capitula did not grow quickly in the early stages and became largely smothered by lush growing neighbouring plants, thus providing an example of competition effect. The high figures for five of the plants are associated with favourable conditions of cultivation.

It must be noted that early flowering stocks, particularly of *C. nigra* s.s. in the south of England, may have a period of secondary flowering. Usually, early flowering varieties flower in June or early July. If the flowering stems be destroyed, as by cutting in hay fields, secondary flowering stems may grow out and produce capitula in September or October. These may set seed. Dates on herbarium sheets may refer to such secondary flowering stems and collectors should score for this. Without such scoring, dates on labels may be, and often are, misleading.

Number of Florets per Capitulum.

C. nigra radiata normalis, grass field near Lavington Station, South Wilts, 19.vii.52. 10 capitula from 10 plants.

Ray florets : range 14 to 19, mean 16·5, S.D.2·07, coefficient of variation 12·5.

Disc florets : range 36 to 75, mean 54·3, S.D.12·34, coefficient of variation 22·7.

Correlation of ray to disc florets, $r = -0.28$.

C. nemoralis eradiata normalis, chalk grassland between Mickleham and Headley, Surrey, 31.vii.52. 20 capitula from 20 plants.

Disc florets : range 43 to 98, mean 76·65, S.D.14·31, coefficient of variation 18·7.

C. nemoralis radiata normalis and *C. jacea* hybrids, chalk downland, Rams Cliff, South Wilts, 22.vii.52. 15 capitula from 15 plants.

Ray florets : range 15 to 25, mean 18·26, S.D.2·74, coefficient of variation 15·0.

Disc florets : range 41 to 102, mean 62·87, S.D.16·07, coefficient of variation 25·6.

Correlation of ray to disc florets, $r = 0.70$.

C. nemoralis radiata normalis, dwarf plants with a single stem with a single capitulum, chalk downland, Walker's Hill, North Wilts, 210 m., 25.viii.52. 12 plants.

Stem heights in cm. : range 4 to 12, mean 8·42, S.D.2·23, coefficient of variation 26·5.

Total florets : range 40 to 59, mean 50·25, S.D.6·19. Coefficient of variation 12·3.

Correlation between stem height and total number of florets, $r = 0.35$.

Ray florets : range 11 to 17, mean 13·4, S.D.1·99. Coefficient of variation 14·8.

Disc florets : range 28 to 46, mean 36·83, S.D.5·67. Coefficient of variation 15·4.

Correlation between ray and disc florets, $r = 0.096$.

C. nemoralis radiata normalis, chalk grassland, Avebury, North Wilts, 29.viii.52.   16 capitula from 16 plants.

Ray florets : range 12 to 19, mean 15·25, S.D.2·02.   Coefficient of variation 13·2.

Disc florets : range 28 to 72, mean 46·4, S.D.11·40.   Coefficient of variation 24·6.

Correlation between ray and disc florets, r = 0·42.

C. nigra eradiata normalis, grown in the Herbarium Experimental Ground, Kew, 17.vii.52, from cypselas collected High Force, Teesdale, 3.ix.49.   10 capitula.

Disc florets : range 96 to 115, mean 106·10, S.D.6·99, coefficient of variation 6·6.

AVERAGES AND RANGES OF APPARENTLY " GOOD " CYPSELAS PER CAPITULUM.

Number of capitula examined.	Cypselas in undamaged capitula.	Cypselas in capitula damaged by larvae.	Cypselas in capitula damaged by gall flies.	Cypselas in capitula damaged by larvae and gall flies.
A. 27	40·1 (0 to 82) 17 capitula	2·7 (0 to 10) 4 capitula	5·8 (0 to 29) 5 capitula	37 (37) 1 capitulum
B. 155	39·6 (5 to 73) 97 capitula	33·6 (7 to 73) 39 capitula	19·5 (0 to 48) 11 capitula	24·2 (3 to 41) 8 capitula
C. 52	25·1 (0 to 59) 31 capitula	16·3 (0 to 36) 14 capitula	19·1 (9 to 28) 6 capitula	21 (21) 1 capitulum
D. 22	41·3 (24 to 60) 3 capitula	14·4 (1 to 61) 8 capitula	17·0 (0 to 27) 5 capitula	8·3 (0 to 20) 6 capitula
E. 61	38·5 (0 to 60) 33 capitula	21·1 (0 to 35) 28 capitula	0	0
F. 40	18·0 (0 to 50) 10 capitula	13·7 (0 to 40) 19 capitula	10·4 (0 to 26) 7 capitula	5·2 (1 to 15) 4 capitula
G. 64	35·1 (13 to 58) 35 capitula	22·6 (1 to 45) 18 capitula	8·2 (5 to 13) 5 capitula	10·3 (2 to 15) 6 capitula
H. 54	21·6 (0 to 56) 22 capitula	12·6 (0 to 38) 18 capitula	17·8 (6 to 47) 6 capitula	8·9 (0 to 18) 8 capitula

A. *C. nemoralis*, Kingsdown, near Box, North Wilts, October, 1951.   In capitula attacked by larvae an average of 19·7 damaged cypselas was found and in those attacked by larvae and gall flies an average of 21 damaged cypselas was found per capitulum.   These are additional to the good cypselas recorded in the table.

B. *C. jacea* × *C. nemoralis* hybrid swarm, Rams Cliff, South Wilts, October, 1951.   In capitula attacked by larvae an average of 9·8 damaged cypselas and in those attacked by larvae and gall flies 9·2.

C. *C. nemoralis*, Walker's Hill, North Wilts, September, 1951. In capitula attacked by larvae an average of 11·7 damaged cypselas and in those attacked by larvae and gall flies 3.

D. *C. nemoralis*, Barrow, North Down, Devizes, North Wilts, September, 1951. In capitula attacked by larvae an average of 8·1 damaged cypselas and in those attacked by larvae and gall flies 6·8.

E. *C. nemoralis*, Devizes, roadsides near Golf Links, North Wilts, September, 1951. In capitula attacked by larvae an average of 11·6 damaged cypselas.

F. *C. nemoralis*, Smithen Down, South Wilts, chalk grassland, September, 1951. In capitula attacked by larvae an average of 8·7 damaged cypselas and in those attacked by larvae and gall flies 4·2.

G. *C. nemoralis*, Chitterne Down, South Wilts, September, 1951. In capitula attacked by larvae an average of 9·0 damaged cypselas and in those attacked by larvae and gall flies 4·7.

H. *C. nemoralis* and *C. nemoralis* × *C. jacea*, Rushall, South Wilts, chalk grassland, September, 1951. In capitula attacked by larvae an average of 9·5 damaged cypselas in those attacked by larvae and gall flies 7·0.

In the eight samples (A to H) scored there was a total of 475 capitula. Of these 248 or 52·2 per cent. were undamaged and had an average of 34·6 " good " cypselas per capitulum ; 148 or 31·2 per cent. were damaged by larvae and had an average of 21·3 " good " cypselas ; 45 or 9·5 per cent. were damaged by gall flies (*Urophora jaceana*) and had an average of 14·8 " good " cypselas ; 34 or 7·2 per cent. were damaged by larvae and gall flies and had an average of 13·4 " good " cypselas. Thus, from random sampling of these Wiltshire populations of *C. nemoralis* and *C. nemoralis* × *C. jacea* hybrids 47·7 per cent. of otherwise potentially " good " cypselas were destroyed by the combined action of larvae and gall flies in the capitula attacked. Taking all the samples together (damaged and undamaged capitula) the average number of " good " cypselas per capitulum was 27·1 and this represents a loss of 21·7 per cent. of cypselas for the populations by the attacks of larvae and gall flies.

G. C. Varley has published a full account (in *Journ. Animal Ecology*, **16**, 139–87 : 1947) of " The natural control of population balance in the knapweed gall-fly (*Urophora jaceana*)." The following Hymenoptera parasitic on *Urophora jaceana* or its parasites occurred in some of our material : *Apanteles sicarius*, *Bracon* sp., *Eurytoma curta*, *Habrocytus dentifer*, *Isocolus rogenhoferi*, *Tetrastichus* sp., *Torymus cyanimus*. Of the three moths listed by Varley and whose larvae attack the capitula of knapweeds, *Metzneria metzneriella* emerged from our stocks.

Cypselas in 10 capitula from plants grown at Kew, 29.viii.52, from seed collected High Force, Teesdale, 3.ix.49, *C. nigra* eradiata normalis : range 24 to 61 mean 42·3, S.D.12·08, coefficient of variation 28·6.

4

Black fly attacks on flowering stems of *C. nigra* have been observed in the Experimental Ground and in the wild. Rarely the attacks are sufficiently intense and prolonged to reduce reproductive capacity.

Pests (other than Insects) and Diseases.

Reproductive capacity can be reduced by grazing, by slugs, and by birds. Knapweeds are not particularly palatable but are not known to be poisonous or harmful to grazing animals, whether wild or domesdicated. They are certainly sometimes eaten by sheep and more rarely cattle in the field and are not infrequently a constituent of hay. The effect of cutting and grazing was well seen in a grass field, about 1 mile from Fritwell, Oxfordshire (V.-C.23), 28.viii.29 : 17 plants, dwarfed by earlier cutting for hay followed by cattle grazing, ranged from 2 to 16 cm. in height, with a mean of 6·1 cm., S.D.3·33. Of the 17 plants, 14 had single capitula, 2 had 2 each, and 1 had 3.

Long, ' Common Weeds of the Farm and Garden,' p. 40 (1910), says that sheep will eat *Centaurea nigra* but that it is rejected by cattle. On p. 175, however, he refers to it as " a useless plant in grassland, with tough, hard stems which are avoided by stock, although the young leaves are readily eaten by cattle and sheep." He also notes that black knapweed was one of the species of weeds prominent at Rothamsted in the unmanured grass plots that had been mown for hay every year since 1856 but had not been grazed since 1874. In the plots receiving mineral manures only, black knapweed proportionately increased in that from which potash was omitted.

Slugs occasionally climb up the flowering stems and bite off the top parts of the corollas in open capitula. If ray florets be bitten off capitula may be wrongly scored as eradiata unless the " accident " be recognized. Slugs also damage basal leaves.

More serious is the damage done by birds to ripe or nearly ripe capitula. Goldfinches are extremely fond of knapweed seeds (and of those of other *Compositae*). They settle on the inflorescences or near the tops of fruiting branches and peck out the cypselas which they split open longitudinally, extract the kernel (the seed proper), and reject the pericarp, all with what appears to be one jerk of the head. Once a flock of goldfinches finds a group of fruiting *Centaurea* plants the birds " will not leave them alone " till they have extracted practically every " good cypsela " and destroyed it. Their precision in opening the cypselas is remarkable, as seen at Kew on 16.vii.52. House sparrows may also " get a taste " for *Centaurea* seeds and may then be responsible for a great deal of seed destruction. Goldfinches and sparrows seem usually to wait till a few capitula on a plant or a group of plants have ripe cypselas, located loosely in an open mature " cup " of phyllaries. They are attracted by these and then, becoming impatient, they start " ragging " younger capitula not yet mature, tearing away the phyllaries to reach the immature cypselas. The above observations have been made in the experimental ground and no figures are available regarding bird damage to knapweeds in the wild.

We have not found any fungus, bacterial, or virus diseases that kill knapweed plants or reduce their reproductive capacity. Such may occur but we have not made a special search for them.

It is of interest to record that *Orobanche elatior* Sutton established itself on a clump of *C. nigra* × *C. jacea* in the Experimental Ground at Potterne Biological Station. It had been grown for some years on *C. scabiosa* quite near and had spontaneously parasitized the *C. nigra* hybrid.

SEEDS PER CAPITULUM IN CONTROLLED SELFINGS AND CROSSINGS OF PLANTS IN CULTIVATION.

(See Chapter VI for further details of families.)

Family.	Origin.	Number of capitula examined.	Maximum number of cypselas.	Minimum number of cypselas.	Mean number of cypselas.	Standard deviation.	Coefficient of variation.
T. 22	S.P.10 selfed	19	24	1	10·70	7·40	69·1
T. 65	S.P.1 × S.P.36	9	34	8	25·00	9·59	38·4
T.225	T.73·3 selfed	23	58	0	13·09	18·73	143·1
T.230	T.73·1 × T.73·3	9	52	2	33·44	16·54	49·5
T.232	T.85·11 selfed	23	17	0	6·61	5·83	88·2
T.255	T.13·27 selfed	36	31	0	7·75	9·27	119·6
T.261	T.13·8 selfed	44	39	0	19·18	10·62	55·4
T.276	T.78·17 selfed	27	54	11	33·30	13·28	39·9
T.294	T.84·34 selfed	35	20	0	10·54	7·07	67·1
T.355	T.66·19 selfed	30	44	7	25·63	9·01	35·1
T.537	T.317·25 selfed	44	38	0	12·82	12·18	95·0

Taking together all the controlled selfings and crossing made in our experimental work the following figures were obtained :

Selfings.—235 made. 4666 capitula used. 12,324 apparently " good " cypselas obtained, *i.e.*, an average of 2·64 per capitulum.

Crossings.—312 made. 1575 capitula used. 31,482 apparently " good " cypselas obtained, *i.e.*, an average of 19·35 per capitulum.

The highest single number per capitulum occurred in T.222 with 94. This was a cross of two sibs of an F_1 from two stock plants. Other high numbers occurred in :

T.3 with 75 ; T.74 with 78 ; T.76 with 84 and 92 ; T.103 with 88 and 89 ; T.311 with 78 ; T.312 with 79 ; and T.597 with 71 and 73. All of these were crosses.

Regularly very high numbers occurred in T.222 (with 88, 94, 88, 84 80, 93, and 74) and T.324 (with 73, 74, 88, 73, 60, 76, 78, 86, 74). Both of these were crosses.

Entire sterility of 15 or more heads occurred in T.9, T.83, T.268, T.417, T.460, T.487, T.511, and T.530, all of which were selfings.

Extreme ranges from 0 per capitulum were shown by T.225 (0 to 58), T.261 (0 to 44), T.317 (0 to 50), T.384 (0 to 36), and T.537 (0 to 41). Of these T.317 and T.384 were crosses and the others selfings.

Generally speaking, percentage germination of the cypselas counted in connection with the experiments here considered was near to the average. There were, however, exceptions in certain crossings and selfings. The following table gives some examples of failure to raise families as large as was expected from the number of apparently well-formed cypselas sown. A large number of these cypselas either failed to germinate or the seedlings failed to establish themselves and to survive to the flowering stage.

Cross or selfing.	Origin.	Number of capitula used.	Number of cypselas.	Number of plants raised.
T. 90	T.2·2 selfed	19	12	0
T.185	T.56·2 × T.56·4	3	48	14
T.202	T.53·1 selfed	25	130	17
T.204	T.56·2 selfed	16	13	3
T.325	T.146·7 selfed	14	63	1
T.330	T.146·4 × T.146·3	8	426	14
T.338	T.74·15 selfed	17	44	0
T.357	T.66·19 × T.66·1	7	366	17
T.374	T.77·22 × T.77·1	6	135	14
T.413	T.117·10 selfed	21	16	3
T.469	T.224·67 selfed	14	70	0
T.525	T.229·64 × T.229·7	3	19	1
T.526	T.229·7 selfed	16	14	0
T.535	T.214·37 selfed	20	16	1
T.544	T.214·63 selfed	16	68	4

(See Chapter VI for further details of families.)

ABORTED CAPITULA.

Capitula that do not " open " and whose florets cannot be pollinated are fairly common late in the season on late-flowering plants. In some bred plants, however, definitely aborted capitula occur, in varying proportions, at the full flowering season. Many of these remain small, about 5 mm. long, and do not develop further. A few are partially aborted, with some attempt at growth and even partial expansion. Examples are :

T.110 (S.P.34·2 × S.P.2).   1 plant out of 13.
T.108 (S.P.2 × S.P.34·2).   4 plants out of 33.
T.483 (T.224·58 × S.P.1).   3 plants out of 59.
T.539 (S.P.1 × T.224·67).   1 plant out of 20.
T.326 (T.14·39 selfed).   13 plants out of 81.
T.528 (T.326·64 selfed).   2 plants out of 9.
T.538 (T.326·16 × T.326·64).   8 plants out of 8.
T.543 (T.326·11 selfed).   1 plant out of 1.

In T.538 there was partial abortion of the capitula with incomplete expansion of some of them. In the other families the plants with aborted capitula showed most or all of the capitula aborted.

GERMINATION.

On the soils of the Transplant Experiments at Potterne the best germination of cypselas of *C. nigra* occurred on sands and not on clays and in the spring and in some years also in the autumn.

The cypselas are slightly compressed and at germination a longitudinal split appears in the pericarp, developing from below upwards. This split occurs at one margin in the plane of compression. Occasionally a split, usually shorter and delayed, appears at the opposite margin. The radicle grows through the split pericarp at the base of the cypsela, however this be orientated. In its earliest stage it is short and stumpy and there is a dense tuft of fine root hairs. At a slightly later stage the hypocotyl elongates considerably and rapidly. At its apex are the two cotyledons bent parallel to the hypocotyledonary axis (nodding) and carrying the pericarp husk still enshrouding the unexpanded cotyledons. These are unequal, the one nearer the hypocotyl being the longer. Finally the pericarp husk falls off and the cotyledons expand. In the incubator the whole process takes about a week at 25° C. in late February and early March. Under the artificial conditions of the incubator the hypocotyl is 2–3 cm. long, the larger cotyledon (immediately before expansion) 6 mm. long, and the smaller cotyledon 5 mm. long.

GERMINATION UNDER ARTIFICIAL CONDITIONS.

Eleven samples of 100 apparently " good " cypselas were plated in Petri dishes on damp filter paper and the dishes placed in an incubator kept at 25° C. in the Jodrell Laboratory, Kew. They were plated on 23.ii.1953 and were scored at 2 or 3 or 4 day intervals until the ungerminated cypselas began to go mouldy. The following samples were used :

G.1. N. Ireland, Co. Antrim, Selsham, 7.ix.52.

G.2 and G.3. S. Wiltshire, Rams Cliff, 10.ix.52.

G.4. S. Wiltshire, Rushall, 10.ix.52.

G.5. S. Wiltshire, Winterbourne Stoke Down, 10.ix.52.

G.6 to G.11. K.3263, cultivated in the Herbarium Experimental Ground, Kew, 2.x.52, from cypselas originally collected in Teesdale, 3.ix.49.

Samples G.2, G.3, and G.6 to G.11, were from single plants, G.1, G.4, and G.5 were from a number of plants.

	25·2.	27·2.	2·3.	4·3.	6·3.	9·3.	11·3.	14·3.	18·3.
G. 1	26	81	84	85	87	87	87	89	89
G. 2	88	97	97	99	99	99	99	99	99
G. 3	85	94	94	94	94	94	94	95	95
G. 4	14	56	60	83	83	84	84	84	84
G. 5	47	83	83	83	83	83	83	83	83
G. 6	9	46	55	63	70	72	72	72	72
G. 7	2	31	43	48	53	55	57	57	57
G. 8	35	79	85	87	88	88	89	89	89
G. 9	15	36	57	62	65	66	66	67	67
G.10	53	82	83	84	89	89	89	89	89
G.11	11	49	67	71	72	73	73	73	73

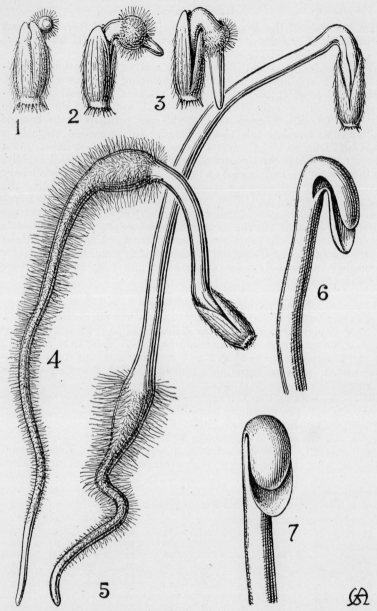

Fig. 2.—*Germination.* 1–3. Early stages of germination. 4–5. Later stages of germination. 6–7. Cotyledons before expansion and upper part of hypocotyl.

The figures in the above table are both actual and percentage germinations that had occurred up to the given dates. The lowest germination was for G.7 (57 per cent.) and the highest for G.2 (99 per cent.). The mean was 81·55 and the S.D. of the mean 12·8.

There are several features of interest. Up to 88 per cent. of germination occurred within 48 hours of plating. Generally, lower germination after two days was correlated closely with lower final percentage germination. There was, as a whole, higher germination under the artificial conditions of this experiment than has been found with cypselas sown in soil. The last cypsela to germinate did so 17 to 19 days after plating.

GERMINATION (IN SOIL) OF SEEDS FROM CONTROLLED SELFINGS AND CROSSINGS (SAMPLES).

From 68 selfings : sown 306, germinated 239, percentage germination 78·10.

From 65 crossings : sown 288, germinated 129, percentage germination 44·76.

Total sown 594, total germinated 368, total percentage germination 61·96.

ANNUAL REPRODUCTIVE CAPACITY.

One of the most striking features of the various figures given above is the great range shown for most populations for most of the factors involved in sexual reproduction. This is indicated, in part, by the frequently high standard deviations. Attention should also be called to the often considerable differences in the figures for plants in the wild and under cultivation. In particular, environmental conditions modify the number of capitula produced by a single plant. Numerous individuals in some dwarf chalk downland populations of *C. nemoralis* have only a single capitulum. The highest number so far recorded was 465 for a plant of *C. nigra* grown at Kew. The number of florets per capitulum can also be increased by the improved conditions of cultivation, at least by a quarter to a half. Since most plants of the knapweeds investigated show self-incompatibility (with correlated cross-compatibility or cross-incompatibility), " open " pollination may be expected to yield the maximum number of " seeds " (*i.e.*, " good cypselas ") when other environmental factors are as similar as possible. The wide ranges in the numbers of " good cypselas " obtained from controlled selfings and crossings is mainly explained by genetical incompatibility or compatibility. Pollination mechanism in the wild generally results in successful fertilization except perhaps occasionally in very small populations.

Annual reproductive capacity varies, in round figures, in different populations from 16 (in wild dwarf downland plants) to 7068 (in cultivated plants). Taking reasonable averages of 20 capitula per plant, 27 cypselas per capitulum and 60 per cent. germination, the annual reproductive capacity is 324.

FLOWERING PERIODS.

Observations in the field in many parts of the British Isles and detailed records of plants in the experimental ground have shown that there are significant differences in flowering periods between different stocks and different populations. Owing to the frequent occurrence, especially in early flowering plants, of secondary flowering, dates given on labels of herbarium sheets may be, and sometimes certainly are, unreliable as indications of primary flowering periods. As might be expected, there are complications due to the interaction of environmental and genetical factors. For general scoring purposes we have made three groups : " early," primary flowering June to early July ; " medium," primary flowering July ; " late," late July to September. These dates have to be slightly modified from season to season according to the general weather conditions of the year and sometimes for local conditions.

In the south of England it is frequently obvious that *C. nigra* is early and *C. nemoralis* late or medium, as we have defined our classes. On the other hand, plants determined as *C. nigra* flower later as latitude increases from south to north in Great Britain.

The following is the scoring for our Stock Plants :

Early (E) : 1, 13·5, 23, 25·2, 27·2, 27·3, 27·4, 29, 30, 31, 33 35·1, 35·2, 36, 45·1, 45·2, 45·4, 45·6, 45·8, 47, 48, 49.

Medium (M) : 9, 10, 11, 13·1, 13·2, 13·6, 13·7, 14, 19, 20, 22·1, 22·2, 24·3, 25·1, 26·1, 26·3, 28, 32, 38·1, 38·2, 38·3, 39, 44, 45·3, 45·5, 46.

Late (L) : 2, 5, 6, 7, 8·1, 8·2, 12, 13·3, 16, 17, 34·1, 34·2, 37, 41, 42.

Crossings and selfings gave the following results :

E × E giving E only : T.13, T.14, T.62, T.64, T.65, T.66, T.67, T.68, T.69, T.74, T.76, T.78, T.79, T.81, T.82, T.84.

E selfed giving E only : T.60, T.72, T.73.

L × L giving L only : T.93, T.96, T.101, T.102, T.103, T.108, T.110, T.113.

L selfed giving L only : T.88, T.92, T.95, T.115.

E × L giving M only : T.80, T.85, T.97.

L × E giving M only : T.100, T.111.

L × E giving E only : T.107.

E × E giving M only : T.71, T.75, T. 77.

E × L giving L only : T.87.

These results are interesting. They show that plants from the wild generally breed true to period of flowering and that early × late or late × early give a family of plants with medium flowering period. Only 5 families (T.71, T.75, T.77, T.87, and T.107) are exceptions to this regular behaviour out of a total of 41 families. Every one of these five is of interspecific origin involving *C. nigra* or *C. nemoralis* and *C. jacea*.

The samples of families given above were all scored the same year and fairly represent the general behaviour. They point to a genetic basis for flowering period with the F_1 between extreme early and late intermediate (medium) in reciprocal crosses. There is complicated segregation in some F_2 families for this character.

Our Stock Plant 1, from near Christchurch, South Hants, is one of the earliest flowering stocks we have studied intensively. It was used in the Transplant Experiments of the British Ecological Society at Potterne from 1927 to 1940 continuously. With regard to primary flowering throughout this period the first date of flowering of a ramet on any one of the soils ranged from 6 June to 23 June and the last day of first flowering of any ramet from 15 June to 9 July. On the whole a lag in flowering was shown by ramets on Potterne soil (Upper Greensand). Otherwise there was no regular correlation between primary flowering and soils (sand, calcareous sand, clay, chalky clay, and Potterne soil). On the other hand the weather of any one season often resulted in significant differences in flowering periods. As examples, in contiguous years, may be quoted : 1934, 16 to 26 June, and 1935, 23 June to 5 July ; 1938, 21 June to 9 July ; 1939, 13 June to 4 July, and 1940, 6 to 15 June. The days are the first and last date for first flowering of any one ramet on any of the soils. On the whole, 1940 was the " earliest " and 1938 the " latest " of the seasons from 1927 to 1940 inclusive.

POLLINATION.

The common type of capitulum in the *Compositae*, and capitula of the knapweeds come into this category, is sometimes compared functionally with a flower, such as that of a buttercup. The comparison holds to a certain extent, but in addition to the well known morphological differences there are several important physiological ones. The pericline of phyllaries (bracts) in its function of protection of the developing florets up to anthesis corresponds to some calyces. The ray florets in adding to the conspicuousness of the capitulum so far function as do some petals. The reproductive parts (the androecium and gynoecium of the disc florets) are in the central part of the capitulum as they are in the central part of a flower. The cypselas are the disseminules corresponding to the achenes of a buttercup which physiologically correspond to the seeds of a pea or bean. The knapweeds are insect-pollinated (entomophilous) and are visited by many species of insect for pollen and/or nectar and the capitula at anthesis have colour and give out an odour which, to humans, is not very strong. The disc florets containing the functional gynoecium and androecium are actinomorphic and gamopetalous. An insect visiting a capitulum during anthesis will apply its head and push down its proboscis successively into several or many florets with open corollas. Every floret has to be dealt with separately, whether for pollen or nectar collecting, and in this the capitulum does not resemble a single gamopetalous flower. An insect can, however, pollinate many florets without more than turning or crawling a very short distance, that is without flying. Every floret has only one ovule requiring only one viable and compatible pollen grain to bring about fertilization, but the movements of an insect may pollinate stigmata of florets additional to the one being probed at any moment of the visit.

The pollen presentation mechanism in *Centaurea* has been described by several authors (see Müller, ' The Fertilization of Flowers,' 346–49 : 1883, and Small, ' The Origin and Development of the Compositae,' New Phytologist Reprint, No. **11** : 1919, chapter 3, pp. 61, etc.). When a floret first opens, the anther tube closely surrounds the style and the two adpressed stigmatic lobes. The anthers open inwards and shed the pollen into the androecial tube where it is retained in the upper part by a compact ring of hairs on the style. The filaments become sensitive, so that if touched, as by an insect's proboscis, they contract and a considerable quantity of pollen is pushed out at the top of the anther tube by the adpressed stigmatic lobes that together are cylindrical. This is the male or pollen presentation phase. The style then gradually elongates and grows up beyond the anther tube. The margins of the style branches or stigmatic lobes bend outwards and the lobes more or less, but usually only slightly, separate and expose the stigmatic papillae to pollination. Self-pollination by re-curving of stylar arms or stigmatic lobes does not occur, but it is, of course, possible that " own " pollen grains get moved on to stigmatic surfaces as a result of insect visits since the florets in a capitulum develop acropetally over a period of one to two weeks. Relatively inner florets are at a male stage while relatively outer ones are at a female stage during much of the period of anthesis of a capitulum. Also genetically " own " pollen can be transferred by insect visitors from the florets of one capitulum to those of another of the same plant. The structural and behaviour devices connected with entomo-phily are not accident proof to prevent " own " pollen reaching recep-tive stigmata. They do, however, greatly favour cross-pollination and superimposed on their mechanism is the phenomenon of incompatibility which is dealt with in some detail in a later chapter.

Pollination is normally brought about, by nectar seeking insects, when they insert their proboscis into the floret tube. The following are average measurements for corollas of disc florets of *Centaurea nigra* eradiata grown at Kew, 12.viii.52 :

normalis : lower narrow white portion 9 mm., coloured portion 5 mm. and this is widest just below the middle, lobes 5 mm. long ; diameter of lower (white) portion of tube 0·5 mm., of upper (coloured) portion at widest part 1·5 mm.

longiflora : lower narrow white portion 10 mm., coloured portion 6 mm., and this is slightly widened upwards, lobes 11 mm. long ; diameter of lower (white) portion of tube 0·5 mm., of upper (coloured) portion 1·0 mm. widening to 1·5 mm. at throat.

breviflora : lower narrow white portion 6 mm., coloured portion 3 mm., and this is slightly widened upwards, lobes 4·5 mm. long ; diameter of lower (white) portion of tube 0·75 mm., of upper (coloured) portion 1·5 mm. at widest part.

We have several times observed bees on capitula of *C. nigra* s.l. and its hybrids, intoxicated, on warm days apparently by fermented nectar. The conditions approximated to those described for *C. scabiosa* and *C. nigra* by J. Lloyd Williams in *Journ. Bot.*, **35**, 8–11 (1897).

Many species of insects visit *Centaurea* heads, sometimes in large numbers especially in warm, fine, sunny weather. Collections were made in localities as follows with the times given as " Summer Times."

1. Monmouth, Monmouth School Playing Field, 2.vii.52, 10.15 a.m.–12 noon ; 3.vii.52, 11 a.m.–12 noon ; and 4.vii.52, 11.15 a.m.–12.15 p.m.

2. Monmouth, Wyesham, railway bank, 4.vii.52, 2.50–3.50 p.m., 5.vii.52, 10.15–11.30 a.m.

3. S. Wilts, Littleton Panell, 7.vii.52, 11.10 a.m.–12.10 p.m. ; 8.vii.52, 11.40 a.m.–12.20 p.m. ; 10.vii.52, 3.30 p.m.–4.30 p.m. ; and 21.vii.52, 5.45 p.m.–6.45 p.m.

4. S. Wilts, Rams Cliff, 12.vii.52, 2.45 p.m.–3.45 p.m. ; 22.vii.52, 11.15 a.m.–12.15 p.m. ; and 17.viii.52, 11 am.–11.30 a.m.

5. Surrey, Kew, Herbarium Experimental Ground, 14–18.vii.52 and 28.vii–1.viii.52, various times from early morning to sunset.

6. Oxford, near Burford, 6.viii.52, 11.30 a.m.

7. S. Wilts, Dauntsey's School, 13.viii.52, 11.35 a.m.–12.35 p.m. ; 1.ix.52, 3.30 p.m.–4.20 p.m. ; 5.ix.52, 3.35 p.m.–4.20 p.m. ; and 13.ix.52, 12.15 p.m.–12.45 p.m.

8. S. Wilts, below Fore Hill, 17.viii.52, 4.20 p.m.–5.5 p.m. ; 19.viii.52, 3.25 p.m.–4.15 p.m. ; and 21.viii.52, 11.35 a.m.–12.35 p.m.

9. N. Wilts, Walker's Hill, 21.viii.52, 3.5 p.m.–3.25 p.m. ; 23.viii.52, 2.25 p.m.–4.10 p.m. ; 25.viii.52, 1.25 p.m.–3.50 p.m. ; and 27.viii.52, 2.45 p.m.–3.15 p.m.

10. N. Wilts, near Devizes, earthwork on North Down, 22.viii.52, 2.25 p.m.–4.5 p.m. ; and 29.viii.52, 12 noon–12.30 p.m.

11. N. Wilts, Avebury, 29.viii.52, 1.35 p.m.–4.5 p.m.

12. S. Wilts, Winterbourne Stoke Down, Salisbury Plain, 2.ix.52, 3.30 p.m.–4.5 p.m.

A. Insects captured on capitula taking pollen, nectar, or both were :

COLEOPTERA.

Crepidodera transversa (Marsham) (8 ♂).
Rhagonycha fulva Scop. (1 ♂, 2 ♂, 4 ♀).

LEPIDOPTERA suborder RHOPALOCERA.

Aglais urticae L. (3 ♀ and ♂, 7 ♀, 9 ♀, 11 ♀ and ♂, 12 ♀).
Aphantopus hyperanthus L. (2).
Coenonympha pamphilus L. (9 ♀).
Colias croceus Fourc. (11 ♂).

Lycaena phlaeas L. (9, 10, 11 ♀).
Lysandra coridon Pod. (9 ♀, 11).
Maniola jurtina L. (1 ♂, 2 ♂, 3 ♀ and ♂).
Melanargia galathea L. (4 ♀ and ♂).
Ochlodes venata Br. et Grey (2 ♀).
Pararge megera L. (7 ♀, 11).
Pieris brassicae L. (7).
Pieris rapae L. (3 ♀, 4 ♀ and ♂, 7 ♀).
Polyommatus icarus Rott. (9 ♀ and ♂, 1 ♂, 11 ♀).
Thymellicus sylvestris Pod. (2 ♂, 4 ♀, 5 ♀).
Vanessa atalanta L. (7).
Vanessa cardui L. (2, 3 ♂, 10, 11).

LEPIDOPTERA suborder HETEROCERA.

Amathes sexstrigata Haw. (10 ♂).
Plusia gamma L. (10).
Pyrausta lutealis Hükn. (8 ♀, 10 ♂).
Zygaena lonicerae Esp. (2 ♀ and ♂, 3 ♀).

HYMENOPTERA.

Anthophora bimaculata Panz. (5 ♀).
Apis mellifera L. (1 ☿, 3 ☿, 4 ☿, 5 ☿, 7 ☿, 9 ☿).
Bombus agrorum Fabr. (3 ☿, 4 ♀ and ♂, 5 ☿, 7 ♂, 10 ♂).
Bombus humilis Illiger (1 ☿, 3 ☿, 12 ☿).
Bombus lapidarius L. (4 ♀, 5 ♂ and ☿, 7 ☿, 10 ♂ and ☿, 11 ☿, 12 ♂).
Bombus lucorum L. (5 ♂).
Bombus ruderarius Müll. (1 ♂ and ☿).
Bombus soröensis Fabr. (7 ☿, 9 ☿).
Bombus subterraneus L. (3 ♀).
Bombus sylvarum L. (1 ☿, 8 ♂).
Bombus terrestris L. (5 ♂, 7 ♂, 11 ♂).
Glypta longicauda Htg. (6 ♀, 7 ♀).
Halictus albipes Kirby (8 ♀, 9 ♂).
Halictus calceatus Scop. (8 ♂, 9 ♂, 11 ♂).
Halictus leucozonius Schrank (5 ♂, 7 ♀ and ♂, 8 ♀ and ♂, 9 ♂).
Halictus morio Labr. (5 ♀).
Halictus rubicundus Christ (7 ♂, 8 ♀, 11 ♀).
Halictus smeathmanellus Kirby (7 ♀).
Halictus tumulorum L. (9 ♂).
Halictus xanthopus Kirby (8 ♀, 9 ♂).
Megachile centuncularis L. (1 ♀).
Megachile ligniseca Kirby (4 ♀, 5 ♀).
Melitta leporina Panz. (8 ♂).
Nomada flavopicta Kirby (11 ♀).
Osmia spinulosa Kirby (4 ♀, 9 ♀).
Psithyrus campestris Panz. (3 ♀ and ♂, 7 ♂, 8 ♂, 12 ♂).
Psithyrus rupestris Fabr. (3 ♀).
Psithyrus vestalis Fourc. (5 ♂).

DIPTERA.

Bucentes geniculata Deg. (7 ♀ and ♂, 8 ♀ and ♂).
Calliphora erythroecephala Meig. (12 ♀).
Chrysogaster metallina Fabr. (1 ♂, 2 ♀).
Cnemodon vitripennis Meig. (5 ♀ and ♂).
Cryptolucilia cornicina Fabr. (11 ♂).
Dilophus febrilis L. (8 ♂, 9 ♂).
Empis albinervis Meig. (1 ♀).
Empis livida (1 ♀ and ♂).
Eristalis abusivus Collin (10 ♀).
Eristalis arbustorum L. (1 ♀, 8 ♀, 10 ♀ and ♂, 11 ♀, 12 ♂).
Eristalis horticola Dig. (2 ♀, 5 ♀, 8 ♀).
Eristalis intricarius L. (10 ♀).
Eristalis nemorum L. (3 ♀ and ♂, 9 ♀, 10 ♀, 11 ♀).
Eristalis pertinax Scop. (7 ♀).
Eristalis tenax L. (1 ♀, 4 ♀, 7 ♀ and ♂, 8 ♂, 9 ♀ and ♂, 10 ♀ and ♂, 11 ♀, 12 ♀).
Helophilus pendulus L. (7 ♀).
Melanostoma mellinum L. (10 ♀).
Melinda anthracina Meig. (11 ♂).
Myiatropa florea L. (5 ♀).
Onesia agilis Meig. (1 ♂, 8 ♀, 9 ♂).
Phaonia incana Wied. (3 ♀).
Physocephala rufipes Fabr. (8 ♀).
Platychirus albimanus Fabr. (5 ♀ and ♂, 7 ♀, 10 ♀).
Platychirus manicatus Meig. (7 ♀, 8 ♀ and ♂).
Pollenia vespillo Fabr. (1 ♂, 8 ♀).
Rhingia campestris Meig. (7 ♂, 9 ♀, 10 ♀ and ♂).
Sarcophaga sp. (7 ♀).
Scaeva pyrastri L. (2 ♀).
Sicus ferrugineus L. (8 ♀).
Sphaerophoria scripta L. (5 ♀).
Syritta pipiens L. (5 ♀).
Syrphus balteatus Deg. (4 ♂, 5 ♂, 7 ♀ and ♂).
Syrphus ribesii L. (3 ♀, 5 ♀, 7 ♀, 8 ♀).
Volucella bombylans L. (1 ♀, 3 ♀).

B. Insects captured on capitula but not observed taking pollen or nectar were :

HEMIPTERA.

Calocoris norvegicus Gmel. (1, 3, 5, 8).
Plagiognathus arbustorum Fabr. (1).

COLEOPTERA.

Brachypterus glaber Steph. (3).
Meligethes aeneus Fabr. (5, 7).

Miarus plantarum Germ. (7, 8, 9).
Oedemera lurida (Marsham) (4 ♂).
Oedemera nobilis (Scop.) (2 ♀).

LEPIDOPTERA suborder HETEROCERA.

Nemotois scabiosella Sc. (4 ♂).
Simaethis fabriciana L. (7).

DIPTERA.

Urophora jaceana (Hering) (5 ♀).

In the above list the figures in brackets refer to the localities where specimens were caught. The sex is indicated by the usual symbols after the figure referring to the locality.

Open Pollination.

Open pollination in the wild and seeds grown at Potterne Biological Station scored 24.viii.28.

A. Harbury, Warwick. *C. nemoralis* semiradiata longiflora phyllaries VL, gave : 1 semiradiata longiflora : 7 eradiata longiflora : 29 eradiata normalis.

B. Harbury, Warwick. *C. nemoralis* eradiata normalis phyllaries L, gave : eradiata normalis 38.

D. Harbury, Warwick. *C. nemoralis* eradiata normalis phyllaries VL, gave : eradiata normalis 34.

E. Harbury, Warwick. *C. nemoralis* eradiata normalis phyllaries L, gave : eradiata normalis 17.

J. Burford Road, 3 miles from Chipping Norton, Oxford. *C. nemoralis* radiata longiflora phyllaries N, gave : radiata longiflora 2 : semiradiata longiflora 6 : eradiata longiflora 1 : semiradiata normalis 2 : eradiata normalis 22.

M. Burford Road, 10 miles from Chipping Norton, Oxford. *C. nemoralis* eradiata normalis phyllaries N, gave : eradiata normalis 18 : eradiata longiflora 1 : semiradiata longiflora 1.

The wild population at Harbury consisted mainly of eradiata normalis with scattered eradiata longiflora and at least one or two radiata longiflora plants. Near Chipping Norton only one radiata normalis was found in association with hundreds of eradiata normalis. The Harbury population showed some contamination with *C. jacea*.

CYTOLOGY.

B. Roy examined a selection of our stock plants and hybrids cytologically. He published an account of his researches in *Journ. Genetics*, **35**, 89–95 (1937). The following is a summary of his results in so far as they concern the work dealt with in this book.

In the subgenus *Cyanus* the basic chromosome number is 10 and *C.*

scabiosa with $2n = 20$ is a diploid while *C. collina* with $2n = 60$ is a hexaploid of this series. Subgenus *Jacea* contrasts in that the basic number is 11 and the species with which we are concerned, *C. nigra*, *C. nemoralis*, and *C. jacea*, are all tetraploids, $2n = 44$, judging from the British material examined. There is thus very clear correlation between the cytological findings and our experimental results. Crosses between species with $x = 10$ and $x = 11$, respectively, failed. Those between species with $2n = 44$ ($x = 11$) were often fertile and frequently highly fertile. Sterility due to incompatibility is, of course, quite a different story, though the tetraploidy of the species of subgenus *Jacea* with which we are concerned has to be remembered in attempting to explain details of empirical results.

Within the subgenus *Jacea*, Roy obtained $2n = 44$ or $n = 22$, for the chromosome numbers which were counted, from the metaphase plates of root tips and divisions of pollen mother cells, from the following plants supplied by us :

C. jacea S.P.34·2, S.P.45·3, S.P.48.
C. nemoralis S.P.17, T.24·6, T.24·7, T.37·5.
C. nigra S.P.113.
C. jacea × *C. nemoralis* S.P.47.

CHAPTER V

WILD POPULATIONS AND INDIVIDUALS

OUR field work has been both extensive and intensive. We have scored wild populations in the field in England, Wales, Scotland, Ireland, and the Channel Islands, in a total of 44 vice-counties. In addition, we have received useful series of specimens from many correspondents, to whom we express our thanks. Obviously our field work could not be equally intensive in all parts of the British Isles. It has been most concentrated in our " home " vice-counties of North Wilts (V.-C.7), South Wilts (V.-C.8), Surrey (V.-C.17), and Oxford (V.-C.23). Apart from reasons of personal convenience there was the advantage that these vice-counties are amongst those with the most numerous and most varied populations of *Centaurea*. Less, but still considerable, sampling has been done in other vice-counties, such as West Cornwall (V.-C.1), North Devon (V.-C.4), West Kent (V.-C.16), Berkshire (V.-C.22), West Norfolk (V.-C.28), Monmouth (V.-C.35), Warwick (V.-C.38), Cardigan (V.-C.46), and Jersey. As will be seen below, population samples mostly, but not all, of our own collecting have been analyzed for many other vice-counties but the samples have not always been large or repeated.

In the report we now submit we also include herbarium material, collected as such and not as part of population samples. It is certain that such material, if well collected, has considerable value but it is not to be regarded as forming random samples of populations. Collectors tend to preserve the unusual, abnormal, and rare. Thus, from an area where 99 per cent. of the *Centaurea nigra* s.l. plants are eradiata and 1 per cent. radiata there may be collected for the herbarium the same number of each variant, the collected material but not the population being 50 per cent. radiata and 50 per cent. eradiata. Nevertheless, we cannot ignore localized and often dated preserved specimens since they give evidence of the occurrence of variants within populations. A careful selection of specimens illustrating our own field work has been added to the Herbarium of the Royal Botanic Gardens, Kew. We have fully examined the many other collectings now at Kew and in addition have seen the British *Centaurea* material in the herbaria of the British Museum (Natural History), the Royal Botanic Garden, Edinburgh, the Druce Herbarium at Oxford University, the Cambridge University Herbarium, and the Herbarium of University College, Leicester. We thank those in charge of these collections for the facilities granted to us to examine the specimens.

We now give the results of our studies of wild material or of plants grown directly from wild stock of known origin. The sequence followed is that of vice-counties as set out in Druce, ' The Comital Flora of the British Isles ' (1932). In spite of various errors, some of which are bound to occur in a compilation of this kind, and of the fact that it was published over twenty years ago and now needs bringing up to date, this is still a useful work of reference. The task of replacing it appears to be more difficult than some of its critics have admitted. However, for *Centaurea* we base our remarks on specimens we have seen, and most of which are at Kew or are represented at Kew by adequate voucher samples. Only incidentally and for special purposes do we refer in this chapter to published records. This is because so many records in county floras, local lists, and papers in journals are insufficiently critical or detailed for our purposes. We prefer to acknowledge gaps rather than to accept statements we cannot both check and interpret, as far as is possible at present, with actual specimens.

In the following account the word " knapweeds " is used in the limited sense of species and hybrids of the *C. nigra*, *C. nemoralis*, and *C. jacea* series as occurring in the vice-counties numbered and named.

V.-C.1 : *West Cornwall.*—The knapweeds in West Cornwall are, with few exceptions, *C. nigra* eradiata. Most often the capitula are relatively large and the leaves generally fairly broad and range from entire or slightly toothed to pinnatifid. A survey of the Land's End district (19–30.vii.32) showed that the many plants examined were clear of contamination with *C. jacea* except on Sennen Green where one plant had narrower leaves, phyllaries VL, and was radiata, and in the same local population one other plant had phyllaries VL and one phyllaries L, while 137 had phyllaries N. It is of particular interest that the only radiata plant seen amongst thousands in the Land's End district was in a small population showing some phyllary characters associated with *C. jacea* hybrids. Three longiflora plants were found. *C. nigra* eradiata normalis plants have been seen from Lambourne Hill area, near Trevose Head, near Perranporth, St. Keverne, Merryn, and Lambriggan. From near Trevose Head one plant had phyllaries VL and two others phyllaries N. A plant with eradiata longiflora characters came from near Perranzabule Church. In Herbarium Watson at Kew there is a small specimen, radiata normalis, N, Kynance Cove, vi.1872, that may be *C. nemoralis* and was probably a casual introduction. At Lambourne Hill, St. Ives, and Lambriggan there were a few plants intermediate between *C. nemoralis* and *C. nigra*.

V.-C.2 : *East Cornwall.*—The majority of the plants in this vice-county are again *C. nigra* eradiata normalis, though radiata plants may be slightly commoner than in V.-C.1. Population samples include those from Trebarwith, 14.ix.29, all with phyllaries N, normalis 10 : longiflora 1, eradiata 4 : radiata 7 ; Polzeath, 15.ix.29, all eradiata normalis, phyllaries N 18 : VL 2 ; and near Callington, 8–ix.23, all eradiata normalis, phyllaries N 20 : VL 2. The samples suggest populations of *C. nigra* that have been sometimes contaminated with *C. nemoralis*. Other specimens of *C. nemoralis–nigra*, normalis, N, have been seen

5

from Mawgan (radiata), Polperro (radiata), Veryan (eradiata), Launceston (eradiata), and Par Harbour. St. Blazey, rough grassland, 10.viii.53 : *C. nigra*, eradiata normalis, N 15 ; *C. nigra*, with probably some infiltration of *C. nemoralis* genes, eradiata normalis, N 8 ; *C. nigra*, with probably some infiltration of *C. nemoralis* genes, eradiata longiflora, N 2. Edge of Bodmin Moor, 4.viii.53, *C. nigra*, eradiata normalis, N 37. Mevagissey Bay, cliffs, roadsides, etc., 7.viii.53, a mixed population of *C. nemoralis*, *C. nigra*, and intermediates, all eradiata : *C. nigra*, normalis, N 35 ; *C. nigra*, normalis, VL 1 ; *C. nigra*, longiflora, N 1 ; *C. nemoralis*, normalis, N 18 ; *C. nemoralis-nigra*, normalis N 41 ; *C. nemoralis-nigra*, normalis, VL 2 ; *C. nemoralis-nigra*, breviflora, N 1. Between Callington and Liskeard, 10.viii.53, *C. nigra*, eradiata normalis, N 8 ; *C. nemoralis-nigra*, eradiata normalis, N 13.

V.-C.3 : South Devon.—In South Devon there is considerably more evidence both of *C. nemoralis* and, locally, of introgression of *C. jacea* in the southern part of the vice-county than in Cornwall or North Devon. Samples have been scored as follows : Lea Mount, 11.viii.28, *C. nemoralis* with a few genes of *C. jacea*, radiata normalis, N 2 : VL 1 ; Oaklands Farm, Dawlish, 17.ix.28 and 13.vii.29, a hybrid swarm with *C. nigra*, *C. nemoralis*, and hybrids with *C. jacea*, N 16 : VL 9 : L 8 : S 9 : M 5 : C 1, radiata normalis 26 : radiata longiflora 1 : eradiata normalis 14, the leaves vary considerably ; Tiverton, viii.29 and viii.30, *C. nigra*, N 9, radiata normalis 5 : eradiata normalis 4. Specimens have also been seen as follows : *C. nigra* radiata normalis, all N, viii.38, from Kingsteignton, Hennock, Drewsteignton, Wolborough Milber, Abbotskerswell (also eradiata normalis), Kerswells, Cornworthy, Dean Prior, West Buckfastleigh ; *C. nemoralis* radiata normalis, Berry Head, viii.39 ; *C. nigra* eradiata normalis, Beetor Cross, Dartmoor, 20.ix.29, N, Merrivale Bridge, Dartmoor, 20.ix.29, N, and Newton Abbot, 29.vii.31 and 22.vii.33, N 2 : VL 2 ; *C. nigra* radiata normalis N 2, Plymouth and Lympstone, 24.viii.36, N 2. *C. nemoralis* "albiflora," between Dunstone and Holberton, 20.ix.1875. *C. nemoralis* radiata normalis, Brixham Cliffs (N), Beer (VL), Watcombe (N and VL), Oddicombe cliffs near Torquay (N, one very dwarf plant, 3·5 cm. tall with one captiulum). Exmouth, cliffs east of Golf Course, *C. jacea* × ? *C. nigra*, phyllaries S. Near Tavistock, edge of Dartmoor, on low stone wall, 10.viii.53, *C. nigra*, eradiata normalis, N 2. Near Two Bridges, rough grass verge, 10.viii.53, *C. nigra*, eradiata normalis, N 5. Six miles west of Exeter, road verge, 10.viii.53, *C. nemoralis* with genes of *C. jacea*, all radiata normalis, N 5 : VL 2 : L 1. Near Morton Hampstead, 10.viii.53, *C. nigra*, eradiata normalis, N 5.

V.-C.4 : North Devon.—Populations and specimens studied for North Devon have been accepted as *C. nigra* and *C. nemoralis* and intermediates with little certain trace of *C. jacea*. The following illustrate this : Bishop's Tawton, Barnstaple, 28.viii.29, *C. nemoralis* and intermediates, radiata normalis 4 : eradiata normalis 15 : eradiata longiflora 4, N 20 : VL 3 ; Combe Martin district, 4.viii.36 and

22.vi.47 (*C. nigra*), eradiata normalis 4 : eradiata longiflora 1, N 5 ; Braunton district, vii.39, eradiata normalis 86 : eradiata longiflora 2, N 72 : VL 12 : L 2 (a slight trace of *C. jacea* contamination probable). Also specimens of *C. nigra* eradiata normalis N from Westward Ho (14.vii.39), Horsey Island (17.vii.39), Lydford (17.viii.36), Clawton (22.vii.36), and Ilfracombe (1833) and of *C. nigra* radiata normalis, near Barnstaple (1833), Oakhampton (1831), and Ilfracombe, 17.viii.24. *C. nemoralis* (?) radiata normalis, Okehampton, 8.ix.37.

V.-.C.5 : *South Somerset.*—Blue Anchor, on sea cliffs, 13.viii.36, radiata normalis 18, N 14 : VL 4. It is interesting that the whole sample has radiata capitula mostly of large size as in typical *C. nigra*. Some of the specimens have long slender branches similar to those of *C. nemoralis* and the cauline leaves are also narrow. The knapweeds of South Somerset require more investigation and the Blue Anchor sample can at present only be tentatively determined as *C. nemoralis* and *C. nemoralis* × *C. nigra*.

V.-C.6 : *North Somerset.*—Most of the material seen from North Somerset is accepted as *C. nemoralis–nigra* and *C. nigra* normalis. Typical examples are : Street district, vii.28, radiata 21, N 19 : VL 2 ; Walton Hill, Poldens, vii.27–28. radiata 8, N 8 ; and Burrington, Mendips, 7.ix.30, eradiata 4, N 4. Single specimens of *C. nigra* normalis N have been seen from near Bath, 9.vii.36 (radiata) ; Chard, 3.vii.36 (radiata) ; Bath, Combe Down, 10.ix.1836 (eradiata) ; Bath, vi.1844 (radiata). Specimens somewhat tentatively determined as *C. nemoralis* were from wood on Worle Hill, 30.viii.1850 (radiata normalis N) ; Bath, 17.vii.1844 (radiata normalis VL) ; Stapleton, near Bristol (radiata normalis N). Two specimens that were probably *C. nigra* × *C. nemoralis*, were from North Stoke, 29.vii.1853, and were radiata normalis N. Samples from near Bath, ix.1836, vii,.1844 16.ix.1844, probably represent a hybrid swarm involving *C. jacea* ; the specimens seen were radiata normalis N 1 : L 2. Of particular interest were plants on King's Sedgemoor, 21.vi.37. These are placed under *C. nigra* with a slight trace of contamination with *C. jacea* as judged by phyllary shapes, with the scoring radiata normalis 106, N 102 : VL 3 : L 1. The King's Sedgemoor population with its rayed capitula and mostly brightly coloured florets (Rood's Violet) is very similar to populations found in marshy or periodically flooded areas in Oxfordshire (see below). Near Bathford, grassy bank, 29.vii.1953. A very mixed population of *C. nigra* in part with genes of *C. nemoralis* and a few genes of *C. jacea* : *C. nigra*, radiata normalis, N 9 ; *C. nigra*, radiata longiflora, N 2 ; *C. nigra*, eradiata normalis, N 7 ; *C. nigra*, eradiata normalis, VL 1 ; *C. nigra*, radiata normalis, VL 2 ; *C. nemoralis–nigra*, radiata normalis, N 7 ; *C. nemoralis–nigra*, eradiata normalis, N 7 ; *C. nemoralis–nigra*, eradiata normalis, VL 2 ; *C. nemoralis–nigra*, eradiata normalis, L 1 ; *C. nemoralis–nigra*, radiata longiflora, N 2 ; *C. nemoralis–nigra*, semiradiata longiflora, N 1. Near Sparkford, rough grassland on slope, 10.viii.53, *C. nemoralis*, radiata normalis with some genes of *C. jacea*, N 53 : VL 5 : L 2. One plant, with phyllaries N, had florets Pale Laelia Pink.

*V.-C.*7 : *North Wilts.*—Wiltshire, with its wide range of soils and considerable area of calcareous substrata is an excellent county for the study of knapweed populations. Both *C. nemoralis* (especially on the chalk) and *C. nigra* occur and there is fairly frequent evidence of the past presence of *C. jacea*. For North Wilts the following samples illustrate the composition of knapweed populations. Near Sandy Lane, 5.ix.26, five plants normalis N, radiata 3 : eradiata 2, *C. nemoralis* × *C. nigra*. Clifford's Hill, chalk, 14.ix.31, *C. nemoralis* radiata normalis, with trace of *C. jacea*, N 21 : VL 3 : L 1 : S 1 ; many plants on this downland were dwarf. Near Golf Links, Devizes, 28.viii.50, 20 plants, *C. nemoralis*, radiata normalis. Avebury, on chalk, 23–28.viii.50, sample of 122 plants of *C. nemoralis* radiata normalis with trace of hybridization with *C. jacea*, N 115 : VL 2 : L 2 : S 3 ; we did not find *C. jacea* at Avebury, but Druce recorded it from the area (' Rep. Bot. Exch. Club, 1930,' 358 : 1931, as *C. augustifolia*). Near Box, Kingsdown, 1951, sample of 28 plants of *C. nemoralis* with some *C. jacea* characters, both *radiata* and *eradiata* plants present, N 21 : VL 2 : L 2 : S 3. Near Atworth, 30.viii.50, sample of 17 plants of *C. nemoralis*, radiata, eradiata, normalis, and longiflora variants occurred. Just west of Atworth, road verge, 29.vii.53 : *C. nigra*, radiata normalis, N 3 ; *C. nemoralis–nigra*, radiata normalis, N 3 : eradiata normalis, N 1. Walker's Hill, chalk, viii–ix.50, sample of 130 plants of *C. nemoralis* radiata normalis with some *C. jacea* characters in a few plants, N 128 : L 2 ; a number of dwarf plants occurred on the open downland between 570 and 760 feet (170 and 228 m.). North Down, near Devizes, chalk, 23.viii.50, *C. nemoralis*, radiata normalis, 24 : longiflora 1. In addition, one *C. jacea* × *C. nemoralis*, radiata normalis, phyllaries S.

*V.-C.*8 : *South Wilts.*—On the chalk or near it the populations of knapweeds are generally *C. nemoralis* radiata normalis. The following samples illustrate this :

Near Enford, 2.ix.50, 8 plants.

Downs south of Bratton, 19.viii.51, 54 plants.

Westbury Hill, 29.viii.50, 12 plants.

Yarnbury Castle, 3.ix.50, 7 plants.

Smithen Down, 11.ix.50, 36 plants.

Horse Down Tilshead, 16.viii.50, 9 plants.

Near Shrewton, 19.viii.50, 8 plants eradiata normalis.

South of West Amesbury, 4.ix.53, 19 plants, eradiata normalis.

Occasionally there are symptoms of hybridization of *C. nemoralis* with *C. jacea* as these samples illustrate :

Near East Coulston, 20.viii.50, 15 plants of *C. nemoralis* of which radiata normalis 7 : radiata longiflora 2, eradiata normalis 5, and eradiata normalis hybrid with S phyllaries 1.

Below Fore Hill, 13.viii.50, 31 plants, of which radiata 22 (including longiflora 4 and breviflora 1) and eradiata 6 (including breviflora 2) and these 28 *C. nemoralis* ; in addition 3 possible hybrids (radiata 2, eradiata 1) with phyllaries VL. From the same locality on 19.viii.52, a sample gave N 10 : VL 3 : L 3 : S 1. Winterbourne Stoke Down, Salisbury Plain, 19.viii.50 and 7.ix.52, radiata normalis N 56 : radiata longiflora N 1 : eradiata normalis N 9 : radiata normalis VL 8 : eradiata longiflora VL 2 : radiata normalis L 4 : radiata normalis S 3.

Chitterne Down, August, 1950, 59 plants, scored as follows :

C. nemoralis radiata normalis 48.
C. nemoralis radiata longiflora 3.
C. nemoralis eradiata normalis 3.
C. nemoralis eradiata longiflora 1.
Hybrid radiata normalis, rays white tinged pink, L phyllaries 1.
Hybrid radiata normalis, VL phyllaries 1.
Hybrid radiata longiflora, L phyllaries 1.
Hybrid eradiata normalis, Marguerite Yellow florets, VL phyllaries 1.

Over much of Wilts *C. nigra* is rarer than *C. nemoralis*. Between Stonehenge and Amesbury, 18.viii.50, three plants only of *C. nigra* eradiata normalis occurred as a pocket in *C. nemoralis* populations. Between Potterne and Urchfont, 17.viii.27 a population of *C. nigra* had both radiata and eradiata plants.

In a field near Lavington Station, 11.vii.52, a sample of 156 plants were *C. nigra* radiata normalis and with these were putative hybrids with *C. jacea* showing phyllaries VL 9 : L 7. In this sample also three plants had Marguerite Yellow florets and five had white rays tinged or flushed with colour. In the Manor Drive, Littleton Panell, there is juxtaposition of *C. nigra* and *C. nemoralis*. Plants of the former, scored 27.vii.53, were radiata normalis, N 23 : VL 1 : L 1.

In Potterne Field, in a clover and grass ley, 16.vi.30, a sample of a *C. nigra* population contaminated with *C. jacea* was scored. All were radiata normalis and phyllaries gave N 4 : VL 4 : L 2 : S 2 : M 1. Twenty years later (16.viii.50) the *C. nigra* plants had disappeared but in another portion of the field on a sloping bank there was a sample population of 20 plants of *C. nemoralis* with traces of hybridization with *C. jacea*. The plants were all radiata normalis except for one breviflora and the phyllaries were scored as N 16 : VL 1 : L 3. On 20.ix.52, five plants gave N 2 : VL 1 : L 1 : S 1.

At Rams Cliff, West Lavington, on chalk a sample of 430 plants was analyzed between 28.vii.51 and 4.viii.51. Floret characters were : radiata normalis 417 : radiata longiflora 1 : radiata breviflora 7 : eradiata normalis 5. Phyllaries showed : N 109 : VL 86 : L 96 : S 116 : M 23. The hybrid index for gene expression of *C. jacea* is 167·00. Neighbouring fields are arable and have been under various crops for at least the past fourteen years. In 1938 and in 1946 one field was cropped with sainfoin. Another field in 1940 was sown with vetches. *C. jacea* or a hybrid may have been introduced with such leguminous seeds from abroad. The vegetative and inflorescence characters indicated that the three species, *C. nigra*, *C. nemoralis*, and *C. jacea*

were involved in the origin of this population. Broad-leaved and
narrow-leaved plants occurred and in some the phyllaries were black.

Plants were raised from natural seed of individual plants from Rams
Cliff, August, 1951, and grown at Dauntsey's School, West Lavington,
1952. The population was a hybrid swarm of *C. jacea*, *C. nemoralis*, and
C. nigra. The maternal parent and offspring from natural seed were
scored for phyllaries as follows :

		Parent.		Offspring (all radiata normalis).
Plant	1	.	M	.	N 1 : L 1 : S 7 : M 9
Plant	2	.	M	.	N 1 : VL 1 : L 4 : S 9 : M 5
Plant	3	.	M	.	VL 1 : L 1 : S 5 : M 5
Plant	4	.	M	.	N 1 : S 2
Plant	5	.	M	.	S 2 : M 2
Plant	6	.	M	.	N 1 : VL 5 : L 1 : S 10 : M 2
Plant	7	.	M	.	L 1 : S 7 : M 6
Plant	8	.	M	.	N 2 : VL 1 : L 4 : S 7
Plant	9	.	S	.	VL 1 : L 2 : S 6 : M 7
Plant	10	.	S	.	S 3

V.-C.9 : *Dorset*.—Portland Isle, *C. nemoralis* radiata normalis, N, 4
dwarf plants. Burton Bradstock, viii.28 (dwarf plants) and vii.35,
C. nemoralis and *C. nigra* radiata normalis 116, N 103 : VL 13. Abbots-
bury, vii.35, cut hay field, secondary flowering, *C. nigra*, radiata
normalis 4, N 3 : VL 1 ; *C. nigra*, radiata normalis, vii.35, grassy bank,
radiata normalis, N 1.   Corfe district, vii.36, *C. nigra*, radiata normalis
4 : radiata longiflora 1 : eradiata normalis 1, N 5 : VL 1. Swanage,
vii.36, *C. nemoralis* and *C. nigra*, radiata normalis 41, N 40 : VL 1.
Arne, vii.36, radiata normalis 1 : eradiata normalis 1, N 2. Swyre,
vii.35, *C. nemoralis*, radiata normalis, N 1 : eradiata normalis, N 1.
Lyme Regis, ix.25, *C. nigra*, radiata normalis 4 : eradiata normalis 2,
N 5 : VL 1. Burton Common, near Bridport, 16.viii.35, *C. nemoralis*
(including dwarf plants), radiata normalis 9, N 8 : VL 1. Cranborne,
6.vii.36, *C. nigra*, radiata normalis, N 1. Steepleton, 28.viii.1894,
radiata normalis, N 1.   Ridgeway Hill, Dorchester, 28.viii.1894,
eradiata normalis, N 1. Poundbury, Dorchester, 15.viii.1833, *C. nemoralis*, radiata normalis, N, dwarf plants. Gillingham, viii.1865, *C.
nemoralis*, radiata normalis, N 1. West Bay, Bridport, near sea,
18.ix.38, *C. nemoralis* radiata normalis, N 14.

A field survey from Osmington Mills to Kimmeridge, 20–23.vii.28,
showed the knapweeds almost at their maximum flowering. Thousands
of plants of *C. nemoralis* were seen and all were rayed. No trace of
C. jacea or of hybridization with this was observed. *C. scabiosa* was
common and often grew near to *C. nemoralis* but no plants suggesting
putative hybrids were found.

V.-C.10 : *Isle of Wight*.—Staplers, 20.viii.1869, *C. nemoralis*,
eradiata normalis, N 1. Afton Down, near Freshwater, *C. nemoralis*
with some contamination with *C. jacea*, radiata normalis 9, N 6 : VL
2 : L 1. *C. nemoralis*, radiata normalis, from Carisbrook, ix.29, N 6 ;

Bowcombe Down, 8.viii.06, N 1 ; above St. Lawrence, W. of Ventnor, 14.viii.50, N 1. *C. nemoralis*, Forelands, ix.29, eradiata normalis, N 1 ; 2½ miles E. of Yarmouth, viii.29, radiata normalis, N 1. Dwarf downland plants are common in the Isle of Wight and have been known at least since 1858 from near Ventnor (Herb. Cantab.), *C. nemoralis*, radiata normalis, N 1. Near Newport, 1846, *C. nemoralis*, radiata normalis, N 1.

*V.-C.*11 : *South Hants.*—Millbrook, 1840, *C. nemoralis*, radiata normalis, N 1. Near Burley, 24.vii.28, only *C. nemoralis* eradiata with very narrow leaves was seen. Deep in the New Forest away from cultivated ground, knapweeds were absent. Hurst Castle shingle beach, on stabilized shingle, 4.vii.33 and 26.vii.50, *C. nemoralis-nigra*, radiata normalis, N 2. Near Milford-on-Sea, grassy hedge bank, 19.vii.37, *C. nigra*, radiata normalis, N 1. Hinton Admiral, 26.viii.34, *C. nemoralis-nigra*, radiata normalis, N 1. Near Winchester, in grassy field, 2.vii.28, *C. nigra* eradiata normalis, N 1. N. of Winchester, grassland, 4.vii.34, *C. jacea* × *nigra*, radiata normalis, L 1. 1¼ miles S. of Lymington, 7.viii.37, *C. nemoralis*, radiata normalis, N 1. Southborne, 5.viii.36 and 16.vii.37, *C. nigra*, radiata normalis, N 1 : eradiata normalis, N 7. Porchester, 26.vii.29, *C. nigra*, eradiata normalis, N 1.

*V.-C.*12 : *North Hants.*—North Warnborough district, 14.viii.27, *C. nemoralis*, radiata normalis 17 : eradiata normalis 7 ; N 20 : VL 4. Hook Common, 13.viii.27 and 18.vii.31, *C. nemoralis-nigra*, N 7, radiata normalis 4 : eradiata normalis 2 : eradiata longiflora 1. N. of Whitchurch, vii.29, radiata normalis, N 1 ; radiata normalis 2, VL 1 : M 1 ; the first plant *C. nigra*, the other two hybrids. Lyss (Liss), viii.01, *C. nigra*, eradiata normalis, N. Andover, 28.vii.1900, *C. nigra* (?), radiata normalis, N 1. Greywall, 14.viii.27, *C. jacea* × *C. nigra*, radiata normalis, L 1. 5 miles N. of Basingstoke, 1.vii.30, *C. nigra*, radiata normalis, N 1.

*V.-C.*13 : *West Sussex.*—Selsey, 24.viii.36, *C. nemoralis* eradiata normalis, N 1. Horsham, 10.viii.36, *C. nigra*, eradiata normalis, N 1. Southwick, vii.29, hybrid with *C. jacea* as one parent, radiata normalis, Amberley, 28.viii.1849, *C. nemoralis*, radiata normalis, N 2 : VL 1 (Herb. Cantab.). Near Amberley, 19.viii.28, *C. nemoralis*, radiata normalis, N 1. Near Littlehampton, *C. nemoralis* dwarf, radiata normalis, N 2. Angmering, chalk downs, 31.viii.29, *C. nemoralis* dwarf, eradiata normalis, N 3. Rackham Hill, 25.ix.20, *C. nemoralis-nigra*, radiata normalis, N 2. Downs between Kithwest Hill and Wepham Down, 25.ix.20, *C. nemoralis-nigra*, radiata normalis, N 1. Paddock near Hassocks, viii.02, *C. jacea*, radiata normalis, C 1. Henfield, *C. jacea*, radiata normalis, VM 1.

*V.-C.*14 : *East Sussex.*—Crowborough, hay field, 1.x.50, *C. nigra* eradiata, 231 plants, normalis 134 : breviflora 75 : partially breviflora 16 : longiflora 6. This population has been under intermittent observation since 1932 and throughout the period has been remarkable for the high percentage of breviflora (female) plants. Wadhurst, 6.viii.36,

C. nigra, eradiata normalis, N 1. Near Lewes, 11.viii.31, *C. nigra*, eradiata normalis, N 1. Eastbourne, 20.viii.20, *C. nigra*, eradiata normalis, N 1. Rottingdean, chalk cliffs, 21.ix.1884, *C. nemoralis*, eradiata normalis, N 7. Downs between Cuckmere Haven and Birling Gap, 1.ix.23, *C. nemoralis*, normalis, N 4. Denton, 26.viii.21, *C. jacea*, VM 1. Near Hastings, *C. jacea* radiata normalis, C 2. Hornbridge, by road to Hellingly, 1834, *C. nigra-nemoralis*, N 1. Near Westdean, 2.viii.1825, *C. nemoralis* with narrow leaves, N 1. Seaford, 4.viii.14, hybrids, radiata normalis 3, S 2 : M 1.

*V.-C.*15 : *East Kent.*—Lenham, 17.vii.36, grassy roadsides, *C. nigra* with possibly some contamination with *C. jacea*, eradiata normalis, VL 1 ; 28.vii.37, *C. nigra*, eradiata normalis, N 1. Faversham, 1.ix.1894, *C. nigra*, eradiata normalis, N 1. Between St. Margarets and Kingsdown, viii.1865, *C. nemoralis*, eradiata longiflora, N 1.

*V.-C.*16 : *West Kent.*—Between Keston and " The Salt Box," open grassy place, 10.viii.30, *C. nemoralis-nigra*, with some hybridity with *C. jacea*, N normalis 262 : N breviflora 15 : N longiflora 1 : VL normalis 58 : VL breviflora 4 : L normalis 31 : L breviflora 1 : S normalis 6. Hybrid index 38·11. Near Keston, 29.viii.25, *C. nigra* (?) dwarfs, eradiata normalis, N 4. Between Downe and Orpington, 10.viii.30, in grass field, *C. nemoralis-nigra*, eradiata normalis, N 3. Luddesdown, 31.vii.21, *C. nemoralis-nigra*, eradiata normalis, N 1. Edenbridge, ix.26, *C. nigra*, eradiata normalis, N 1. Upper Halling, 19.viii.1894, *C. jacea* × *C. nigra*, hybrid, radiata normalis, L 1. Near Belvedere, 2.ix.11, hybrids involving *C. jacea*, radiata normalis, VL 1 : S 1 : M 1. Ifield, 31.vii.21, hybrid, eradiata normalis, S 1. Downe, field near Darwin's House, 30.viii.31, *C. nemoralis-nigra*, eradiata normalis, N 1. Biggin Hill, in grass of old hay field, 26.vii.51, *C. nigra*, eradiata normalis, N 2. Slopes over Upper Halling, A. H. Wolley-Dod, *C. jacea* × *C. nigra* (?), hybrid S 1 (N.H.M.). Field near Crossness (Erith Marshes), A. H. Wolley-Dod, ix.1893, *C. jacea* × *C. nigra* (?), hybrid S 1 (N.H.M.).

*V.-C.*17 : *Surrey.*—A great deal of collecting and scoring has been done in Surrey and it seems advisable to arrange the more important records alphabetically according to localities.

Albury Downs, various dates, *C. nemoralis*, N, radiata normalis 9 : eradiata normalis 4 : eradiata longiflora 2. Ashtead, various dates, *C. nemoralis*, with possibly some contamination with *C. nigra*, all eradiata normalis, N 21. Bagshot, 28.vi.31, *C. nigra*, eradiata normalis, VL 1. Banstead Downs, various dates, *C. nemoralis*, eradiata normalis, N 3 ; *C. nemoralis* × *C. nigra*, eradiata normalis, 20.vii.36. Brookwood, 8.vii.29, *C. nemoralis* × *C. nigra*, eradiata normalis. Box Hill, various dates, *C. nemoralis*, eradiata normalis, N 20 ; 7.ix.26, *C. nigra*, eradiata normalis N ; 7.ix.26, *C. nigra* × *C. nemoralis*, eradiata normalis N 2. Byfleet Golf Course, 16.ix.32, *C. jacea* × *C. nigra*, radiata 5 : eradiata 9, N 3 : VL 2 : L 1 : S 8 : M 5. Byfleet to Wisley, near the Canal, 16.ix.32, *C. nigra*, eradiata normalis, N 12 : VL 1. Byfleet to Wisley, near R. Wey, 21.vi.27 and 16.ix.32, *C. jacea*

× *C. nigra* and *C. nigra*, eradiata normalis, N 6 : VL 4 : L 2.   Between Byfleet and Wisley, roadsides, etc., various dates, *C. jacea* × *C. nigra* and *C. nigra*, eradiata normalis, N 3 : VL 2 : L 2.   Chertsey, 21.ix.29, *C. nigra*, slightly contaminated with *C. jacea*, eradiata normalis, N 13 : VL 2 : L 1.   Claygate, ix.1844, *C. nigra*, eradiata normalis, N 1, " var. *alba* " ;   1845, *C. nemoralis*, eradiata longiflora, N 1 ;   vi.1844, *C. nigra-nemoralis*, radiata normalis, N 1 ;   1836, *C. nemoralis*, eradiata longiflora, N 1 ;   viii.1843, *C. nemoralis*, eradiata longiflora, N 1 ; among sown clover, 1875, *C. nigra* × *C. jacea*, radiata normalis, S 1 ; 1849 ; *C. nigra* (?), eradiata normalis N 1, " var. *alba* ; "   ix.1865, *C. nigra*, eradiata normalis, N 1 ;   1840, *C. nigra-nemoralis*, eradiata normalis N 1 ;   19.viii.28, *C. nemoralis*, eradiata normalis, N 1 ;   9.viii.31, *C. jacea* hybrids, eradiata normalis, S 2 : M 1.   Between Chilworth and Shelford Stations, 29.ix.1866, *C. nigra*, eradiata longiflora, N 1. Coulsdon, 14.ix.30, *C. nemoralis*, eradiata normalis, N 3.   Chiddingfold, 7.vii.36, *C. nigra*, eradiata normalis, N 1.   Clandon Downs, 10.viii.30 and vii.1887, *C. nemoralis*, radiata normalis, N 3 : eradiata normalis, N 1.   Croydon district, 12.ix.23, *C. nemoralis*, eradiata, normalis, N 1.   Esher, 4.vii.26, *C. nigra*, eradiata normalis, N 2. Near Cutmill Pond, 2.vii.29, *C. nigra*, eradiata normalis, N 1 : VL 2 ; *C. nemoralis-nigra*, eradiata normalis, VL 1.   Farden Downs, 19.ix.31, *C. jacea* × *C. nemoralis*, S 1.   East Horsley, 31.viii.30, *C. nigra*, eradiata normalis, N 116 : VL 11 (6 N plants may be *C. nemoralis* × *C. nigra*).   Epsom Downs, *C. nemoralis*, eradiata slightly contaminated by *C. jacea* now forms the main population, but *C. nigra* also occurs. Herbarium material of various dates was scored as follows : radiata normalis 10 : eradiata normalis 46 ; N 27 : VL 3 : L 3 : S 12 : M 8 : VM 1 : C 17.   This does not represent a random sample since *C. jacea*, and hybrid plants had certainly been selected by collectors.   The interesting facts established by this material are (1) the occurrence in 1920 and 1921 of pure *C. jacea* ; and (2) the occurrence of rayed plants in 1918 and 1921.   Details for typical *C. jacea*, radiata normalis C, are Epsom Downs, 24.vii.21.   Recent sampling on a large scale on 31.vii.52 and 14.viii.52 showed that the population was essentially *C. nemoralis* with a few plants (past flowering) of *C. nigra* and of *C. nemoralis* × *C. nigra*, and some hybrids of *C. jacea* × *C. nemoralis*. All plants were eradiata.   Out of a total of 1606 plants scored all were normalis except 4 longiflora and 4 breviflora.   For phyllaries the scoring was :

	Number of plants.	Percentage.	Hybrid index value.
N . . .	1469	91·47	—
VL . . .	96	5·98	5·98
L . . .	29	1·80	3·60
S . . .	11	0·68	2·04
M . . .	1	0·06	0·24
Totals . .	1606	99·99	11·86

There was thus a low hybrid index value of 11·86 which may be compared with values obtained, for example, in Oxfordshire (V.-C.23).

Farthing Downs, 14.ix.30, *C. nemoralis*, eradiata normalis, N 34. Frensham, 17.viii.48, *C. nigra*, eradiata normalis, N 1. Between Frensham Ponds and Somerset Bridge, Peper Harow district, road verges and fields, 17.vii.48, all plants seen eradiata, N 60 (normalis 55, breviflora 1, longiflora 4 of which 1 female) : VL 48 (normalis 45, breviflora 2, longiflora 1) : L normalis 11 : S normalis 1 (total 120). Frimley, 1849, *C. nemoralis-nigra*, eradiata longiflora N 1. Ham Common, 30.viii.26 and 28.ix.29, *C. nemoralis* and *C. nemoralis-nigra*, eradiata normalis, N 33 : VL 4. Ham Pits, 14.vii.29, *C. nemoralis-nigra*, eradiata normalis, VL 2 ; *C. nemoralis-nigra*, eradiata normalis, N 3. Headley, various dates, *C. nemoralis*, *C. nigra*, and intermediates, and contamination with *C. jacea*, eradiata normalis, N 8 : VL 3 : L 1 : S 1. Headley Common, 31.vii.52, on sands and gravels, *C. nemoralis* and *C. nigra* (out of flower) with only a trace of *C. jacea* genes, all eradiata normalis, N 52 : VL 12. Between Headley Common and Epsom Downs, 31.vii.52, on chalk, road verges and field margins, *C. nemoralis* with some *C. nigra* (out of flower), and a few plants with some *C. jacea* genes, all eradiata normalis, N 202 : VL 24 : L 11 : S 1, a few plants with aborted capitula only. Between Headley and Mickleham, on chalk, road verges and grassy field bank up to open downland, 31.vii.52, *C. nemoralis* with a little *C. nigra* (out of flower) and a few intermediates and a slight trace of *C. jacea* genes, all eradiata normalis, N 199 : VL 24 : L 1. Hindhead, 22.vi.30, *C. nigra*, eradiata normalis, N 1. Hog's Back, chalk, various dates, *C. nemoralis* N 95, eradiata normalis 89 : radiata normalis 1 : eradiata longiflora 5. Horsham, St. George's Hill, *C. nemoralis*, radiata normalis, N 2, with narrow leaves. Kenley Common, 27.vii.30, *C. nigra* and hybrids with *C. jacea*, eradiata normalis, N 5 : VL 3 : L 1. Kew, banks of Thames, in 1862 and 1866, *C. jacea* × *C. nigra*, N 4 : L 2 : M 1 ; radiata 1 : eradiata 1 (rest not scorable). Between Kew and Richmond, river bank, grassy places between willows, 25.vi.29, *C. nigra*, eradiata normalis, N 1. Kew Gardens, grassy places, *C. nigra* or *C. nemoralis-nigra*, eradiata normalis, N 2 : VL 1. Kingston, 29.vi.30 and 21.ix.30, *C. nigra*, eradiata normalis, N 3. Leatherhead district to Mickleham Down, various dates, *C. nigra*, eradiata normalis 16, N 17 : VL 2 ; *C. nemoralis* × *C. nigra*, eradiata normalis, N 2 ; *C. nemoralis*, eradiata normalis, N 2. Lower Morden, 8.viii.20 and 16.vii.21, *C. jacea* × *C. nemoralis*, eradiata normalis, S 1 : radiata longiflora L 1. Malden district, various dates, *C. nigra* eradiata normalis, N 2 ; *C. nemoralis-nigra*, eradiata normalis, N 6 ; *C. nemoralis* with probable slight contamination with *C. jacea*, eradiata normalis, VL 1 ; *C. jacea* × *C. nigra*, eradiata normalis 4 : radiata normalis 1 ; L 4 : S 1. 30.vi.29, *C. jacea*, normalis, VM 1. Merton, 24.vii.27, *C. jacea* × *C. nigra*, eradiata normalis, S 1. Merrow Downs, 23.viii.03, *C. nemoralis*, radiata longiflora, N 1 : eradiata longiflora, N 1. Mitcham Downs, 8.ix.26 and 20.viii.27, *C. nemoralis-nigra*, eradiata normalis, N. Oxshott, 28.viii.27, *C. nemoralis-nigra*,

eradiata normalis, N 6. Oxted, 5.ix.09, *C. nigra*, eradiata longiflora, N 1 ; 7.ix.30, *C. nigra*, eradiata normalis, N 2. Pyrford,
25.ix.34, *C. nigra*, eradiata normalis, N 1 : eradiata longiflora, N 1.
One sheet, 11.x.10, "probably introduced with lucerne," *C. jacea*
hybrids, radiata normalis, S 1 : M 3. Ranmore, 19.xi.33, *C. nigra*,
eradiata normalis, N 1. Reigate district, 11.ix.26, *C. nemoralis*,
eradiata normalis, N 2 ; *C. nemoralis-nigra*, eradiata normalis, N 7 ;
C. jacea × *C. nigra* (?), eradiata normalis, L 1. Richmond and Sheen,
17.ix.27 and 21.ix.30, *C. nemoralis-nigra*, eradiata normalis, N 3.
Runnymede, 25.vi.27 and 28.vi.31, *C. nigra*, eradiata normalis, N 6.
Stoke and Abernon, 18.ix.26, secondary flowering, *C. nemoralis-nigra*,
eradiata normalis, N 4. Near Sunbury Lock, 1848, *C. nigra-nemoralis*,
eradiata normalis, N 1. Stokes Heath Farm, 12.vii.31 and 26.vii.31,
C. nemoralis, eradiata normalis, N 8. Below Sunbury Lock, ix.1879,
C. jacea, radiata normalis, C 1. Tadworth, 12.vi.27 and 27.vii.30,
C. nigra, eradiata normalis, N 3 ; 27.vii.30, *C. nemoralis*, eradiata
normalis, N 1 ; *C. jacea* × *C. nemoralis*, eradiata normalis, S 1. Thames
Ditton, Claygate side, ix.1853, *C. nigra*, eradiata longiflora, N 1.
Warlingham in a grass field, 24.vi.05, *C. jacea*, radiata normalis, C 1 ;
23.viii.25, *C. jacea* × *C. nemoralis*, radiata normalis, S 1. West
Horsley, 25.vi.22, *C. nigra* with slight contamination with *C. jacea*,
eradiata normalis, VL 1. Wimbledon, 23.vii.36, eradiata normalis,
VL 1, *C. nigra* possibly with slight contamination with *C. jacea*.
Woldingham, various dates, hybrid swarm, probably of *C. jacea*, *C.
nemoralis*, and *C. nigra*, eradiata normalis 7 : radiata normalis 12 ;
N 6 : VL 1 : L 6 : S 3 : M 4. Walton-on-the-Hill, 11.ix.26, *C. nigra*,
eradiata normalis, N 8. West Molesey, vii.1880, *C. nigra* (?) × *C.
jacea*, eradiata longiflora, VL 1.

*V.-C.*18: *South Essex.*—Stanford-le-Hope, 24.ix.16, *C. nigra*, eradiata
normalis, N 1. Dagenham, rubbish dumps, 28.vi.29, *C. nigra*,
eradiata normalis, N 2. Blackmore, S. of Chelmsford, grassy places
by roadsides, 4.viii.29, *C. nigra* and *C. nemoralis-nigra*, eradiata, N,
normalis 9 : longiflora 1 : breviflora 3. One and a half miles S. of
Navestock, 4.viii.29, *C. nemoralis-nigra*, eradiata normalis, N 4.
On the road verges between Ilford and Chelmsford via Navestock
and return via Ingatestone and Brentwood, knapweeds were abundant
except where there was shading by tress. Thousands of plants were
seen but all were eradiata though longiflora and breviflora plants, and
plants intermediate between breviflora and normalis, occurred amongst
the predominant normalis individuals.

*V.-C.*19 : *North Essex.*—Specimens seen from this vice-county
determined as *C. nemoralis-nigra*, eradiata normalis, N, are : Saffron
Walden, 5.ix.1899 and ix.38. Pleshey, near Dunmow, chalky boulder
clay, 10.viii.36. From Kelvedon, 1851, *C. nemoralis-nigra*, eradiata
longiflora, N 1. Flatford Mill, 8.vii.52, grass field *C. nemoralis-nigra*,
eradiata normalis, N 2 : VL 2.

*V.-C.*20 : *Herts.*—Harpenden, Mud Lane, 27.vii.00, *C. nigra*,
eradiata normalis, N 1. Rickmansworth, loam on gravel and chalk,

ix.25, *C. nigra*, eradiata normalis, N 2. Bricket Common, amongst bushes, 23.ix.27, *C. nigra*, eradiata normalis, N 6. Great Amwell, near Ware, in old gravel pit, 29.vii.36, *C. nigra*, eradiata normalis, N 4. Near Bayfordbury, grassy roadside, 29.viii.36, *C. nemoralis-nigra*, eradiata normalis, N 2. Waltham Abbey, *C. nigra*, with two to three heads close together, VL 1   (N. H. M.).

V.-C.21 : *Middlesex.*—Twickenham, grass field, 2.ix.1867, *C. jacea*, radiata normalis, C 1. Ruislip district, *C. nigra*, eradiata normalis, N 17, 11.viii.27 and x.26. R. Brent, near Boston Manor Station, *C. nigra* × *C. jacea*, eradiata normalis, VL 1 : L 2. Wembley, 27.ix.29, *C. nigra*, eradiata normalis, N 4 : VL 2. Single sheets of *C. nigra*, eradiata normalis, N, from Staines, 30.vi.23 ; Isleworth, vii.1845 ; Brentford, ix.26 ; Yiewsley, 7.vii.17 ; Twickenham, vii.12. Great West Road, west of Osterley Hotel, 2.vii.30, *C. nigra*, radiata normalis, N 1. Thames Bank between Kingston Bridge and Hampton Court, 22.vii.22, *C. jacea* × *C. nigra*, eradiata normalis, L 1. Hampstead Heath, viii.1894, *C. nemoralis*, eradiata normalis, N 1. South Kensington, 21.ix.1870 and 26.viii.1871, *C. jacea*, radiata normalis. C 2.

V.-C.22 : *Berks.*—Wellington College, playing fields, on Bagshot Sands, 22.viii.27, sample of 91 plants, a hybrid swarm of *C. jacea* × *C. nigra* ancestry, including both parent species. Phyllary analysis gave N 5 : VL 11 : L 15 : S 26 : M 23 : VM 10 : C 4. Floral analysis gave eradiata 47 : radiata 33. Twin-headed plants were present. Two neuter plants were found in the population. Other specimens, collected by several botanists, from this locality, have been seen in herbaria. Bradfield, meadows and grass verges, 9.vii.28, 9.vii.29, and 10.viii.30, 105 plants in sample analyzed, phyllaries N 33 : VL 33 : L 19 : S 10 : M 7 : VM 1 : C 2, floral characters eradiata 56 : radiata 39, normalis 75 : longiflora 4 : breviflora 16. The population is considered a hybrid swarm between *C. nigra* and *C. jacea*. In the centre of another area in the same general locality 5 plants of *C. jacea* were found. Around these hybrids occurred. Indications of hybridization decreased outwards from this centre to a distance of 100 m. Cothill, near sides of marsh, 30.vii.43 and 25.viii.44, 10 plants, eradiata 2 : radiata 8, phyllaries all N. This population has characters of *C. nigra* and *C. nemoralis* and probably represents a confluence of the two. Other plants similar to those of the Cothill population have been seen from Kingston and Burghfield, except that the former had phyllaries VL. *C. nigra* plants have been seen from Yattendon (eradiata, phyllaries N). Bourton (radiata, phyllaries N), and near Old Windsor, grassy places near Thames bank (eradiata, phyllaries VL). Cholsey, 18.viii. 1835, *C. nemoralis-nigra*, radiata normalis, N 1 (Herb. Cantab.). Cholsey, 18.viii.1835, *C. nemoralis*, radiata normalis, N 1 (Herb. Cantab.).

Wokingham District, 6.viii.53 : (1) Field near Holme Green. A grass field heavily grazed by cattle, with a very large population of *Centaurea nigra* which formed the most conspicuous " weed." At this date the plants were mostly past flowering but were fruiting freely. About one plant in five had one head, or rarely two or more heads, in flower. Samples of these were collected and scored as follows :

eradiata normalis N	
heads not twinned . .	140
heads in part twinned .	15
eradiata longiflora N	
heads not twinned . .	2
eradiata breviflora ♀ N	
heads not twinned . .	2
heads twinned . .	1
eradiata normalis VL	
heads not twinned . .	4
heads twinned . .	1
eradiata normalis L	
heads not twinned . .	2
Total . . .	167

The population was one of *C. nigra* with some slight infiltration of genes of *C. nemoralis* and, in one plant of probable *C. jacea* genes as judged by L phyllaries. There was a rather high proportion (15 to 152 or approximately 1 to 10) of plants with some heads twinned.

(2) Road verges and field margins. Plants mostly just in flower. Between Holme Green and Gard(e)ners Green. *C. nemoralis* with occasionally some genes of *C. nigra*, but no certain trace of *C. jacea* :

eradiata normalis N . . .	37
eradiata normalis VL . .	1
eradiata breviflora ♀ N . .	1
Total	39

(3) Field margin near Gard(e)ners Green. *C. nigra*. One plant, past flowering but in fruit.

eradiata normalis N . . .	1

*V.-C.*23 : *Oxford.*—The knapweed populations in parts of Oxfordshire have been intensively studied over a period of more than twenty-five years. On the soils derived from the oolitic limestones (especially Cornbrash and Forest Marble) *C. nemoralis* is the commonest species and is fairly frequently associated with hybrids of *C. jacea* × *C. nemoralis* origin. Some of the hybrid swarms have fairly high hybrid indexes. In the Woodstock district radiata plants are greatly predominant and population anaylses suggest that the radiata character may well have been introduced from *C. jacea*. *C. nemoralis* and hybrid populations have their main flowering period in August and September. In the northern and extreme western parts of the county, on limestone soils especially, the large majority or even practically all the plants are *C. nemoralis* eradiata. On the sands and clays the earlier flowering *C. nigra*, with its maximum flowering period in June or early July, is common. It may be radiata or eradiata and may or may not show some characters suggesting contamination with *C. jacea*.

Special mention must be made of the knapweed populations in the alkaline marshes of the Oxford " meads " and the Cherwell meadows. These consist of plants very similar to those of King's Sedgemoor in Somerset and like them are early (June) flowering.

We classify our data under four main headings :

1. *Woodstock district..C. nemoralis* with frequent hybridization with *C. jacea* and sometimes with *C. nigra*, and occasionally plants definitely determined as *C. jacea* (phyllaries VM or C) occur. The plants are generally radiata and late flowering. The soils, derived from the immediately underlying Cornbrash or Forest Marble, are shallow and immature. Shipton Road, 12.ix.26, radiata normalis, N 14 : VL 2 : L 1 : S 1 ; eradiata normalis N 1. Green Lane, 12.ix.26, radiata normalis, N 1 : L 2 ; eradiata normalis, VL 1 ; eradiata longiflora, L 2. Gibraltar Hill, field path, 19.viii.27, radiata normalis, N 14 : VL 6 : L 9 : S 14 : M 6. Green Lane, near Railway Bridge, 23.ix.28, radiata normalis, L 4 : S 3 : VM 2. Between Woodstock and Sturdy's Castle, 24.ix.28, radiata normalis, L 4 : S 3 : VM 2. Between Woodstock and Sturdy's Castle, 24.ix.28, radiata normalis, N 1 : L5 : S 7 : M 5 : VM 1 : C 1 ; radiata longiflora, VL 1 ; eradiata normalis, N 1 : VL 1 : L 2. "Round the Firs," 22.ix.28, radiata normalis, N 2 : VL 4 : L 16 : S 5 : M 3 : VM 1 ; eradiata normalis, N 3. "Round the Firs," 5.viii.30, radiata normalis, N 14 : VL 9 : L 10 : S 2 ; eradiata normalis N 1 : VL 2 : L 1. Gibraltar Hill, field path, 30.viii.29, radiata normalis, N 1 : VL 2 : L 3 : S 12 : M 6 : VM 3 : C 1 ; radiata longiflora, N 1 : S 1 ; eradiata normalis, N 2. Green Lane, 3.viii.30, radiata normalis, N 1 : L 2 ; radiata longiflora, N 1 ; eradiata normalis, L 1 : S 1 ; eradiata longiflora, N 1 : L 1. Woodstock, Blenheim Park, lakeside, 4.viii.30, radiata longiflora, N 1. Woodstock, near Bladon, 4.viii.30, radiata normalis, S 1.

Green Lane, 5.viii.30, all normalis :

	N.	VL.	L.	S.	M.
radiata	49	31	28	17	1
eradiata	17	8	7	5	—
Totals	66	39	35	22	1

The hybrid index is 109·81.

Near Hensington, 16.viii.33, eradiata longiflora, N 1. Green Lane, near Railway Bridge, 31.vii.40, radiata normalis, N 70 : VL 22 : L 10 : S 2 : M 1 ; eradiata normalis, N 5 : VL 4. Between Woodstock and Sturdy's Castle, 19.viii.41 eradiata normalis, N, floribus albis 1. Between Woodstock and Wootton, 31.viii.29 and 17.viii.33, radiata normalis, N 2 : VL 3 : L 2 : S 2 : M 7 : VM 1 ; eradiata normalis, S 2 ; eradiata longiflora, N 1. Gibraltar Hill, field path, 9.viii.41, radiata normalis, VL 3 : L 2 : S 3 : M 5 : VM 1 : C 1 ; eradiata normalis, S 1 : M 1. Gibraltar Hill, field path, 10.viii.41, radiata normalis, N 70 : VL 134 : L 174 : S 50 : M 19 : VM 4 : C 1 ; eradiata normalis, N 1 : VL 4 : L 1 : S 7. The hybrid index was 163·70.

Cypselas from two plants from " Round the Firs " were collected on 22.ix.28 and sown and plants grown in the Herbarium Experimental Ground at Kew where the flowering specimens were scored on 11.viii.31. All the plants were radiata normalis and the scoring for the phyllaries was : N 1 : VL 7 : L 19 : S 4 and VL 3 : L 4 : S 1 respectively. The cypselas were from open wild pollination of two plants scored on morphological characters as *C. jacea* × *C. nemoralis*, the first more closely resembling *C. jacea* and the second about intermediate.

A characteristic feature of many of the knapweeds of the Oxfordshire oolites is that they have very narrow cauline leaves. It is difficult to obtain an entirely satisfactory standard for comparing this character in different populations. After due consideration, we have taken the breadth of the widest leaf of the first six below a capitulum. Most often, but not always, this is the sixth leaf itself. The results are given here of five Oxfordshire populations so analyzed :

a. Between Woodstock and Shipton, August and September flowering, *C. jacea*, *C. nemoralis*, and hybrids, with probably a few genes of *C. nigra* in some plants from gene flow, on shallow immature soils of Cornbrash.

b. Near Yarnton, June and July flowering, *C. nigra* with some genes of *C. jacea*, on gravels and clays.

c. Pixey Mead, water meadow, August, in fruit or final stages of flowering, *C. nigra* and hybrids of *C. jacea* × *C. nigra* origin.

d. Oxey Mead, water meadow, 1 July flowering, *C. nigra* and hybrids of *C. jacea* × *C. nigra* origin.

e. Cherwell meadows, early July flowering, flood grassland, *C. nigra* and hybrids of *C. jacea* × *C. nigra* origin.

Breadth (in mm.) of widest leaf of the first six below a capitulum.

Population.	Number of plants in sample.	Maximum.	Minimum.	Mean.	Standard deviation of mean.
a	141	7	2	3·11	1·16
b	20	23	4	10·20	4·69
c	27	10	4	6·37	1·94
d	24	12	4	8·42	2·12
e	34	10	4	7·35	1·78

None of the populations was pure but the basic differences between *C. nemoralis* and *C. nigra* are particularly evident on comparing the figures for population *a* and population *b*. Had plants showing no trace of *C. jacea* genes in phyllary shape been selected (*i.e.*, with phyllaries N) and used alone the differences would have been still greater, but it would still be impossible (without breeding) to say they did not contain some genes from *C. jacea*.

2. *Oxford district.*—Especially on soils derived from sands, gravels, and clays. The populations are largely of *C. nigra* with or without contamination with *C. jacea* and/or *C. nemoralis*. Near Yarnton and near Begbroke, 1.vii.41, radiata normalis, N 4 : VL 4 : L 2 : S 1 ;

eradiata normalis, N 1 : VL 1 ; eradiata longiflora, VL 1 ; eradiata breviflora, VL 1. Barton, 20.vi.43, radiata normalis, N 1. Cassington, old gravel pit, 14.vi.44, radiata longiflora, VL 1. Field path near Yarnton, 4.vii.45, radiata normalis, N 19 : VL 5 : L 2.

3. *Meads and "water meadows," near Oxford.*—Oxey Mead, near Wolvercote, 25.vi.41, radiata normalis, N 1 : VL 2 : S 4 and 1.vii.41, radiata normalis, N 23 : VL 63 : L 100 : S 41 : M 3 ; radiata breviflora, N 3 : VL 5 : L 5 ; eradiata normalis, VL 1 : L 2. Water meadows near the Cherwell, 7.vii.41, radiata normalis, N 27 : VL 7 : L 2 ; radiata breviflora, N 1. Pixey Mead, near Wolvercote, 14.viii.41, plants mostly past flowering, capitula at anthesis on 12 plants were all radiata normalis, N 18 : VL 11 : L 3. Water meadow near Cassington, 9.vii.42, radiata normalis, VL 1.

Many of the plants in the meads and water meadows tended to be rather dwarf and often had only one capitulum or few capitula. A general ecological account of the Oxford Meads is given by H. Baker in *Journ. Ecol.* **25**, 408–20 (1937). The knapweed is there named *C. nemoralis* but, in our opinion, it has to be classified as forming hybrid swarms of *C. jacea* × *C. nigra* parentage.

4. *Miscellaneous records.*—Between Stonesfield and Blenheim Park, 5.viii.30, *C. jacea* × *C. nemoralis* eradiata normalis, N 1 : VL 1 : L 1 : S 1. Between Long Handborough and East End, Combe, 27.viii.32 ; *C. nemoralis-nigra,* eradiata normalis, N 3. Water Eaton, Kidlington district, 28.viii.32, *C. nemoralis-nigra,* radiata normalis, N 1. Near Long Handborough, 22.viii.41, *C. nemoralis,* eradiata normalis, N 4 : VL 3 : L 1. Yarnton, vii.22, *C. nemoralis,* radiata normalis, N 1. Crowell, ix.27, radiata normalis, N 1, *C. nemoralis.* Near Henley, rubbish dump, 24.vii.29, *C. jacea* × *C. nemoralis,* radiata normalis, VL 1 : S 1. S. of Yarnton, 29.vi.41, *C. jacea* × *C. nigra,* radiata normalis. VL 2 : L 1. Sibford Gower, near Banbury, 4.ix.41, *C. nemoralis,* eradiata normalis, N 1. Near Cassington, 4.vii.43, *C. nemoralis-nigra,* radiata normalis, N 1 (white rays). Near Burford, 4.ix.26, *C. nemoralis,* radiata normalis, N 6 : VL 2 ; radiata longiflora, VL 2 ; eradiata normalis, N 5 : VL 2. Near Witney, 19.viii.27, *C. nemoralis,* eradiata normalis, N 1. Near Chipping Norton, 1926 and 28.viii.29, *C. nemoralis* with some genes of *C. nigra,* eradiata normalis, N 15 ; radiata normalis, N 1. Between Chipping Norton and Churchill, 20.viii.41, *C. nemoralis* with trace of *C. jacea* and perhaps of *C. nigra,* eradiata normalis, N 34 : VL 7 : L 5 : S 3 : M 1. Near Fritwell, 28.viii.29, *C. jacea* × *C. nemoralis,* eradiata normalis, N 26 : VL 5 : L 10 : S 4 : M 1 ; eradiata longiflora, VL 1. Near Stonesfield, 5.viii.30, *C. jacea* × *C. nemoralis,* eradiata normalis, N 6 : VL 7 : L 11 : S 10 : M 6 : VM 1 ; eradiata longiflora, N 3 : VL 1. Near Kencott Lane, 6.viii.52, all *C. nemoralis,* normalis, N, radiata 28 : eradiata 10. Henley, probably *C. nemoralis* × *C. jacea,* radiata normalis, VL 1. Between Burford and Merry Month Inn, 6.viii.52, *C. nemoralis,* eradiata normalis, N 20.

The range of radiata and eradiata knapweeds, determined as *C.*

nemoralis with or without some contamination with *C. jacea*, is particularly interesting in north-west Oxfordshire. For example, along the road from Swindon to Banbury there is a change from south to north from radiata to eradiata. From Swindon (North Wilts) to Filkins (Oxfordshire) only radiata plants have been observed. Just north of Filkins for about one mile and also along the side road from Grove Wood to Kencott there is an overlap of both variants. North of this only eradiata plants (and these in abundance) were observed except for four small outliers of radiata : north of Broadwell Grove, at Fulbrook, three miles south of Chipping Norton, and two miles south of Chipping Norton. There is a similar change from radiata to eradiata between Woodstock and Chipping Norton but this has not been plotted in detail.

*V.-C.*24 : *Bucks.*—Near Chesham, 1.v.27 (cult. Kew 10.viii.27) *C. nemoralis*, eradiata normalis, N 2. Burnham Beeches, at edge of mixed wood, 23.vi.28, *C. nemoralis*, eradiata normalis, N 1. Meadow near river, Bourne End, 28.vi.30, *C. nigra*, eradiata normalis, N 2. Farnham Common, 7.viii.31, *C. nemoralis*, eradiata normalis, N 8. Near Tingewick, grassy roadside, 16.viii.29, *C. nemoralis*, eradiata longiflora, N 1. Buckingham-Bicester Road, 1 and 6 miles from Buckingham and on to 2–3 miles from Bicester, 16.viii.29, *C. nemoralis* eradiata normalis, N 15.

On 16.viii.29 a survey was made along the roads for about 50 miles from Aylesbury to Buckingham (via Winslow), returning via Bicester (in east Oxfordshire). From Aylesbury to Winslow and on to Buckingham there was a *complete absence* of knapweeds although there were wide grassy roadsides eminently suitable to their growth so far as position was concerned. Many of the roadside areas had been cut for hay, but even in the uncut parts knapweeds were absent. This area is over Middle Oolite rocks—Corallian (sandy facies) and Oxford Clay and Kellaways (Kellaways Rock) Beds—much covered with boulder-drifts. Less than a mile west of Buckingham knapweeds appeared again and were all eradiata. The rocks here are Lower Oolite (Cornbrash and Great Oolite series) and the vegetation is of a calciphilous nature (*Viburnum lantana, Cornus sanguinea,* etc.). On the Bucks–Oxon border from Buckingham to Bicester knapweeds were frequent. This tract is all on the Lower Oolite limestones. All the plants were eradiata though typical *longiflora* was also found. On the other (southern) side of Bicester knapweeds suddenly ceased again with the outcropping of clay rocks. The occurrence of knapweeds only in the limestone areas in W. Bucks and E. Oxon is a remarkable instance of their limitation by edaphic conditions. Moreover, the occurrence of only eradiata plants is striking considering the dominance of *radiata* variants on the Cornbrash round Woodstock in central Oxfordshire.

*V.-C.*25 : *East Suffolk.*—Large gravel pit near Wangford, viii.26, *C. nemoralis*, eradiata normalis, N 1. Beccles district, between Wrentham and Sotterley, 7.ix.46, *C. nemoralis*, eradiata normalis, 1000 plants ; sampled for phyllaries N 72.

6

V.-C.26 : *West Suffolk*.—Grassy lane near Cavenham Heath, 23.viii.
30, *C. nemoralis*, eradiata normalis, N 2. Chalk Pit near Bury St.
Edmunds, 24.vii.34, *C. nemoralis*, eradiata normalis, N 1.

V.-C.27 : *East Norfolk*.—Carter's Lane, near Stratton-Strawless,
7.viii.36, *C. nemoralis-nigra*, eradiata normalis, N 7.

V.-C.28 : *West Norfolk*.—Appleton district, disused pasture, banks,
and hedgerows, chalky soil, overlying chalk, 28–29.viii.27, *C. nigra*
and *C. nemoralis*, eradiata normalis, N 7. West Newton, sand pits,
29.viii.27, *C. nemoralis* eradiata normalis, N 1. Foulden Common,
13.ix.27, *C. nemoralis*, eradiata normalis, N 1. West Newton, damp
places in pasture, sandy soil, 7.vii.28, *C. nemoralis* (?), eradiata normalis, N 1. Near Snettisham, grassy place at edge of sandy heath,
21.vii.33, *C. nemoralis* and *C. nemoralis-nigra*, eradiata normalis, N 5 :
VL 2. North of Hunstanton, grassy place near edge of cliff, 27.vii.33,
C. nemoralis-nigra with some *C. jacea* genes, eradiata normalis, N 7 :
VL 2 : M 1 ; eradiata longiflora, N 1. Near Heacham, grass field and
hedge bank, 31.vii.33, *C. nemoralis*, eradiata normalis, and one plant
with *C. jacea* genes, N 10 : L 1. Near Appleton, roadside, banks, and
old sand pit, 22.vii and 1.viii.33, *C. nemoralis* and *C. nemoralis-nigra*,
eradiata normalis, N 85. Between Appleton and Flitcham, on bank
in chalk lane amongst grasses, 2.viii.33, *C. nemoralis*, eradiata normalis, VL 1. Leziute Fen, with *Cladium*, etc., 2.viii.33, *C. nemoralis*,
eradiata normalis, N 6. Stiffkey, grassy bank near hedge, 24.vii.34,
C. nemoralis-nigra, eradiata normalis, N 1. Wells, grassy creek bank,
30.vii.34, *C. nemoralis* and *C. nemoralis-nigra*, eradiata normalis,
N 18 : VL 1. Hunstanton, sandy soil over chalk, 6.viii.36, *C. nemoralis-
nigra*, eradiata normalis, N 1. Thetford, by stream, 19.vii.49, *C.
nemoralis-nigra*, eradiata normalis, N 1.

In West Norfolk the knapweeds of the *C. nigra* s.l. group are eradiata
and nearly all normalis and probably are mostly to be referred to *C.
nemoralis* though some plants show a mixture of *C. nemoralis* and *C.
nigra* characters. Little trace of hybridization with *C. jacea* was found
except near Hunstanton. It is somewhat noteworthy that no breviflora plants were recorded and only three plants of longiflora were
found amongst hundreds of normalis. The plants did not come into
flower till the last days of July. They were common on grassy road
verges, in hedges, on the margins of heaths (as near Snettisham and
Dersingham), and in grass fields, but not generally in *Calluna* and
Erica heaths. The most remarkable ecological occurrence was at
Leziute Fen, where knapweeds were common in the fen with such
plants as *Cladium mariscus* and *Schoenus nigricans*. The margins of
the fen had been reclaimed as pasture and several pasture species had
been introduced into the fen, presumably by cattle. Many of these
certainly wandered through it in the dry summer of 1933. It is possible
that *C. nemoralis* had been so introduced but it is still interesting to
know it can grow under fen conditions and compete relatively success-
fully with fen species.

V.-C.29 : *Cambridge*.—Little Linton, 4.vii.1855, *C. jacea* × *C.*

nigra, eradiata normalis, L 1 (Herb. Cantab.). Dernford Lane, near Stapleford, 19.ix.23, *C. nemoralis*, eradiata normalis, N 1 and another plant same place and date, *C. jacea* × *C. nigra* (?), M 1 (N. H. M.). Lane near Wicken Fen, grassy hedgerow, 27.viii.30, *C. nemoralis*, eradiata normalis, N 1. Near Newmarket, on chalk, grassy place on roadside 23.viii.30, *C. nemoralis*, eradiata normalis, N 1 : VL 1. Cherry Hinton district, 31.viii.32, *C. nemoralis*, eradiata normalis, N (8 sheets). Near Madingley, 3.ix.35, *C. nemoralis*, eradiata normalis, N 7. Half mile N of Isleham, grassy roadside, almost peaty earth with chalk subsoil, 12.vii.36, *C. nigra*, eradiata normalis, VL 1. Camberton, 29.viii.1853, *C. nigra*, eradiata longiflora, N 1 (Herb. Cantab.). Cambridge, 27.ix.1835, *C. nemoralis*, eradiata normalis, N 2 (Herb. Cantab.). Wicken Fen, vii.1856, *C. nigra*, eradiata normalis, VL 1 (Herb. Cantab.).

*V.-C.*30 : *Bedford.*—Grassy roadside, Thurleigh, 5.viii.36, *C. nemoralis*, eradiata normalis N 1. Roadside, 1 mile N. of Shefford, *C. nemoralis*, eradiata normalis, N 7 : eradiata longiflora, N 4. Roadside between Turvey and Carlton, on oolitic soil, *C. nemoralis*, eradiata normalis, N 30 : L (rather low) 1. The last probably indicating a slight contamination with *C. jacea*. Warden Hills, 27.vi.42, *C. nigra*, eradiata normalis, N 1. Leighton Buzzard, 8–9.vii.44, *C. nemoralis-nigra*, eradiata normalis, VL 3. Chiltern Green Station, 9.vii.44, *C. nemoralis* (?), eradiata normalis, N 1. Podington, 28.vii.44, *C. nigra*, eradiata normalis, N 1.

*V.-C.*32 : *Northampton.*—Charlton, grassy places on roadside, 28.viii.29, *C. nemoralis* and *C. nemoralis-nigra*, eradiata normalis, N 11. Near Kettering, viii.38, *C. nigra*, eradiata normalis, N 1. Deene Park, waste ground, 20.viii.38, *C. nemoralis* and *C. nigra*, eradiata normalis, N 104.

*V.-C.*33 : *East Gloucester.*—Cheltenham, 28.vii.1843, *C. nemoralis*, radiata normalis, N 1. Cheltenham, 1860, *C. nemoralis*, radiata normalis, N 1. Charlton Common, near Cheltenham, oolitic soil, 19.viii.29, *C. nemoralis* and *C. nemoralis-nigra*, eradiata normalis, N 9. Cheltenham, lower slopes of Lechampton Hill, 15.vii.48, *C. nemoralis* with trace of *C. jacea*, radiata normalis, VL 1. Cheltenham, edge of lawn, 27.vii.48, *C. nemoralis*, radiata normalis, N 1. Cheltenham, grass verge, 24.vii.48, *C. jacea* × *C. nemoralis*, radiata normalis, L 1. Near Stroud, vii.26, *C. nemoralis-nigra*, eradiata normalis, N 4. Roadside, near Badgeworth, 19.viii.29, *C. nemoralis* with some *C. jacea* genes, normalis 5, radiata N 2 : radiata VL 1 : radiata L 1 : eradiata VL 1. Roadside near Staverton, clay soil, 23.viii.29, *C. nemoralis* with some *C. jacea* genes, radiata normalis, N 4 : VL 1 : L 3. Roadside, near Uckington, 23.viii.29, *C. nemoralis*, radiata normalis, N 9 : VL 2. Near Lower Hilcot, Colesbourne, 8.ix.41, road verges, *C. nemoralis*, eradiata normalis, N 17. Near Stow-on-the-Wold, 6.viii.52, *C. nemoralis*, with some *C. jacea* genes, eradiata normalis, N 7 : VL 3 : L 1.

*V.-C.*34 : *West Gloucester.*—Near Stone, 11.viii.30, from slightly grazed green common or wide lane on Keuper Marl, *C. nemoralis* with slight contamination with *C. jacea*, radiata normalis 91 (and 8 unscorable for flowers), N 88 : VL 11. From field of mowing grass on alluvium at Rockhampton, 8.viii.30, *C. nemoralis* with slight contamination with *C. jacea*, radiata normalis, 47 (and 4 unscorable for flowers), N 42 : VL 7 : L 2. Between Hill and Rockhampton, in field, 4.viii.30, *C. nemoralis* with slight contamination with *C. jacea*, radiata normalis, 49, N 38 : VL 9 : L 2. Rough field on W. slope of May Hill, sandstone, 17.viii.29, *C. nemoralis* and *C. nemoralis-nigra*, eradiata normalis, N 13. Hill, on alluvium, 12.vii.28, *C. nemoralis-nigra*, radiata normalis, N 11. Between Rockhampton and Lower Stone, marly clay, 5.viii.30, *C. nemoralis*, radiata normalis, N 3. Falfield, cultivated at Kew, 10.vii.31, *C. nigra*, radiata breviflora, N 1, rays white tinged pink. Uley, 23.viii.33, *C. nemoralis*, radiata normalis, N 3 : VL 1. St. Vincent's Rocks, viii.1846 and 18.viii.48, *C. nemoralis*, radiata normalis, N 3. St. Vincent's Rocks, vii.1846, probably *C. nemoralis* with a slight trace of *C. jacea*, radiata normalis, VL 1. Coaley, side of cornfield, clay brash Lias, 8.vii.36, *C. nigra* (?), semiradiata normalis, N 1. Coaley, hay field, yellow clay over blue marl Lias, 8.vii.36, *C. nigra*, radiata normalis, VL 1. Coaley, Peak Lane, limestone and clay, 8.vii.36, *C. nemoralis-nigra*, radiata normalis, N 1. Hill below Amberley Parish Church, rough grassy edge of field, Great Oolite, 19.vii.36, *C. nemoralis*, radiata and eradiata normalis, N (?) 2. Alney Island, 4.vii.37, *C. nigra*, radiata normalis, N 1 (long rays).

*V.-C.*35 : *Monmouth.*—Wye Valley, near Trellech, grassy place on roadside, 6.ix.30, *C. nemoralis* and *C. nemoralis-nigra*, eradiata normalis, N 9. Near May Hill Station, Monmouth, on railway bank, 19.vii.50, sample of 121 plants, *C. nigra* eradiata. Some plants with the phyllary appendages not fully covering the pericline. Two female plants in the sample. There is a 4 weeks' range in flowering period here. Between Monmouth and Dixton Church river bank, 6.vii.51, sample of 24 plants of *C. nigra* eradiata, of which 2 were longiflora, 2 breviflora, and 20 normalis. Redbrook, grassy bank, 9.vii.51, 600 plants of *C. nigra* eradiata as sample, of which 2 were longiflora, 68 breviflora, and 530 normalis. Wyesham, railway bank, 4.vii.52, sample of 68 plants of *C. nigra* eradiata normalis with some trace of hybridization with *C. jacea* as shown by the phyllaries : N 49 : VL 12 : L 7. *C. nigra* collectings also seen from Shirenewton and the Peat Bog near Cleddon. Wyesham, railway bank, 14.viii.52, *C. nemoralis*, eradiata normalis, N 32. Wyesham, hedge bank, 14.viii.52, *C. nemoralis*, eradiata normalis, N 15. Monmouth, vii.1847, *C. nigra*, eradiata normalis, N 1 (Herb. Watson).

*V.-C.*36 : *Hereford.*—Meadow beyond Dixton Church, 7.vii.51, 1200 plants sampled, *C. nigra* eradiata, with 17 longiflora : 124 breviflora : 1059 normalis. Doward, top of limestone quarry, 8.vii.51, 45 plants, *C. nigra* × *C. jacea* swarm as shown by phyllaries N 13 : VL 18 : L 10 : S 3 : M 1. Floral characters gave the following combinations : eradiata normalis 8 : radiata normalis 11 : eradiata longiflora 1 :

radiata longiflora 12 : eradiata breviflora 9 : radiata breviflora 4. At
Pipe plants collected in July, 1927, and July, 1933, a total of four sheets,
suggest *C. nigra* × *C. jacea*. The plants are radiata. Upper Colwall,
Llandovey Beds (Silurian), west side of Malvern Hills, 12.ix.38, *C.
nigra* (?), eradiata normalis, N 1. Ross, 2.vii.29, *C. nigra* (?), radiata
normalis, N 1. Ross, cult. Kew, 29.vii.29, *C. nigra* (?), eradiata
normalis, N 1. Ross. cult. Kew, 10.vii.31, *C. nigra*, eradiata normalis, N 1.

*V.-C.*37 : *Worcester.*—Alvechurch, 11.vii.36, *C. nigra*, radiata normalis, N 1. Defford Common, near Pershore, 10.ix.38, *C. nemoralis*
with slight contamination with *C. jacea*, radiata normalis, N 18 :
eradiata normalis, N 3 : radiata normalis, VL 3 : radiata normalis,
L 3. Hayley Green district, viii.38, *C. nemoralis*, eradiata normalis,
N 3. Offmoor Green, Clent, 17.viii.38, *C. nemoralis*, eradiata normalis, N 5. Near Holy Cross, Clent, *C. nemoralis*, eradiata normalis,
N 1. Fields between St. Kenelon's Church, Romsley, and Hayley
Green, viii.38, *C. nemoralis-nigra*, eradiata normalis, N 5. Between
Broom and Belbroughton (New Red Sandstone), viii.38, *C. nemoralis-
nigra*, eradiata normalis N 1.

*V. C.*38 : *Warwick.*—Harbury, railway cutting in Lias Clay,
11.viii.35, 134 plants, *C. nemoralis* eradiata partly hybridized with
C. jacea as shown by phyllaries, N 110 : VL 20 : L 2 : S 2, all eradiata.
Wild seed from this locality sown at Potterne and the plants scored
24.viii.28 gave 86 with phyllaries of *C. nemoralis* character and 43
showing more or less influence of *C. jacea*. Specimens of *C. nemoralis*
eradiata have also been seen from near Shipston-on-Stour and Hamp-
ton-on-the-Hill   South east of Leamington, *C. nemoralis* eradiata is
abundant. Chesterton, 6.viii.52, *C. nemoralis*, eradiata normalis,
N 8 : VL 2. On the border of Worcestershire, near Stretton-on-Fosse,
6.viii.52, *C. nemoralis*, eradiata normalis, N 1 : VL 2. Trickley
Coppice, edge of coppice, 13.viii.50, *C. nigra*, eradiata normalis, N 1.
Majors Green, Canal Bank, 1.x.50, *C. nigra*, eradiata normalis, N 1.
Tow Path, Worcester Canal, Birmingham, 6.vii.51 and 1.ix.51, *C.
nigra* with trace of *C. jacea*, eradiata normalis, VL 1 ; radiata normalis, VL 1 : L 1. Heronfield, canal bank, 23.viii.52, *C. nemoralis*,
eradiata normalis, N 2. New End, 10.viii.50, *C. nemoralis* × *C.
jacea*, radiata normalis, L 1. New End, 13.viii.50, *C. nemoralis*,
radiata normalis, N 1. Newbould-on-Stour, 21.vii.51, *C. nemoralis*,
eradiata normalis, N 1. Between Chesterton and Harwood's House,
road verge, 31.vii.53, *C. nemoralis*, eradiata normalis, N 35.

*V.-C.*40 : *Shropshire.*—Ruckly Wood, viii.1830, *C. nemoralis-nigra*,
eradiata normalis, N 1. Marrington, Cherbury field, vii.01, *C.
nemoralis* (?), radiata normalis, N 1. Little Berwick, hay field, 20.vii.
36, *C. nigra* (?) eradiata normalis, N 1. Porthrywaen, near lime
quarry, 28.vii.36, *C. nemoralis-nigra*, eradiata normalis, N 1. Rose
Hill, Berwick, roadside, 18.viii.36, *C. nigra*, eradiata normalis, N 1.
Shrewsbury, 30.vii.1836, *C. nigra*, eradiata normalis, N 1 (Herb.
Cantab.).

V.-C.41 : *Glamorgan.*—Monknash Cwm, Foggitt, *C. nigra,* radiata (N. H. M.). Field near Roath Park, Cardiff, 24.viii.30, *C. nigra s.l.,* eradiata normalis, N 93 : VL 8. Roath Park, " Wild Garden,' 25.viii.30, *C. nigra s.l.,* eradiata normalis, N 52. Four miles from Cardiff, wide green roadside, 30.viii.30, *C. nigra s.l.,* eradiata normalis, N 50. The Mumbles, 5 miles from Swansea, meadow on limestone, 10.vii.36, *C. nigra,* eradiata normalis, N 1. Waste ground, Cathays Park, Cardiff, viii.36, *C. nigra,* eradiata normalis, N 1.

V.-C.42 : *Brecon.*—Penycae, roadside, 18.vii.27, *C. nigra s.l.,* eradiata normalis, N 1.

V.-C.44 : *Carmarthen.*—St. Clears, clay on Silurian, 7.viii.36, *C. nigra,* eradiata normalis, N 1.

V.-C.45 : *Pembroke.*—Fishguard, 19.ix.1851, *C. nemoralis,* probably radiata normalis, N 1 (Herb. Cantab.). Saundersfoot, in hedge 10.viii.28, *C. nemoralis,* eradiata normalis, N 16. St. David's, roadside, 8.viii.31, *C. nigra,* eradiata normalis, N 1. Valley N. of Tenby, 1.ix.32, *C. nemoralis-nigra,* eradiata normalis, N 3. Waste ground, Haverfordwest, 2.vii.39, *C. nigra,* eradiata longiflora, N 1.

V.-C.46 : *Cardigan.*—Near Aberystwyth, cultivated in the Herbarium Experimental Ground, Kew, vii–viii.29–31, *C. nigra* and *C. nemoralis-nigra,* eradiata normalis, N 7. Devil's Bridge, in wet pasture on slope of hill, 12.viii.29, *C. nigra,* eradiata normalis, N 1. Aberystwyth, on banks of R. Ystwyth, near sea, on sand and shingle, 13.viii.29, dwarf plants, *C. nemoralis* (?), eradiata normalis, N 6. Various localities in the Aberystwyth district, from sea-level at Borth, etc., into the hills near Devil's Bridge, 12–24.vii.30, *C. nigra,* eradiata, N (a few with slightly branched pectinations), normalis 16 : longiflora 3 : breviflora 3. Above Ysgubor-y-coed, 50 m., in a hay field, 24.vii.30, *C. nigra,* eradiata normalis, N 74 : VL 25, breviflora N 2. Most of the plants scored as VL were very " low," *i.e.,* with some branched rather than fused pectinations. Two plants, however, were " high " VL or even " low " L. It is possible these resulted from a lingering trace of genes infiltrated from long past hybridization with *C. jacea.*

In Cardiganshire *Centaurea nigra,* with little trace of contamination with *C. jacea* or *C. nemoralis,* is common on road verges, hay fields, grass fields, and grassy places of various kinds. It has evidently suited itself to, or was pre-suited to, and has accompanied man's cultivation and treatment of grasslands in West Wales. The general scoring for plants seen and for samples collected was *C. nigra* eradiata normalis. The plants, on the whole, were later flowering than is typical *C. nigra* in the south of England. In the middle of July, 1930, most plants were in bud with scattered individuals just in flower, though a population near Bow Street, in a grassy field nearly dominated by the knapweed and being cut for hay, was in full flower on 15 July. Bow Street is in a warm protected valley. There was considerable variation in leaf breadth and lobing. A few longiflora and breviflora variants were seen. In the hills, it was particularly noticeable that knapweeds only occurred on road verges and in hay fields and not on heaths and moorlands. Specimens were collected up to 360 m. in the higher reaches of the rivers Rheidol and Ystwyth. In the Plynlimmon district (22.vii.30) *Centaurea nigra* eradiata occurred only in grassland enclosed for hay, up to Nant-y-moch, 315 m.

*V.-C.*47 : *Montgomery.*—Glanhafren, viii.1871, *C. nigra*, eradiata normalis, N 1 (Herb. Cantab.).

*V.-C.*48 : *Merioneth.*—Harlech district, mainly between Llanbedr and Morlach, road sides and cliff side, 31.vii.38 and 1.viii.38, *C. nigra*, eradiata normalis, N 55 : normalis VL 1 : longiflora N 1 : breviflora N 7. Damp ground at bottom of pony track over Cader, 15.ix.23, *C. nemoralis-nigra*, eradiata normalis, N 1. Fairbourne, railway embankment, 21.vii.36, *C. nemoralis-nigra*, eradiata normalis, N 1.

*V.-C.*49 : *Carnarvon.*—Great Orme's Head, 14.ix.10, plants only 13·5 cm. tall, *C. nigra*, eradiata. Rolven, near Conway, on grassy roadside, siliceous soil, 11.viii.36, *C. nemoralis*, eradiata normalis, N 1. Llanberis,4.ix.1847, *C. nigra*, eradiata normalis, N 2 (Herb. Cantab.).

*V.-C.*50 : *Denbigh.*—Near Ruabon, viii.1835, probably *C. nemoralis* × *C. jacea*, radiata normalis, S 1 (Herb. Cantab.).

Above Loggerheads Inn, on ridge of Carboniferous Limestone, above the Alyn River and forming one of the foothills of the Clwyd Range. The knapweeds (*Centaurea nemoralis* with slight introgression of *C. nigra* and *C. jacea*) occur at wood margins and in wood clearings and in gorse-heather heathland on the lower slopes where the soil is presumably leached and more or less acid. They do not occur in the limestone grassland of the upper part of the ridge. Sample taken on 5.ix.53. All plants normalis eradiata. N 118 : VL 1 : L 1 : S 1. Many of the capitula were heavily galled and there was a very low average setting of apparently viable cyselas. Of heads with ripe cypselas examined (N phyllaries) 24 had well developed pappus and 14 had the pappus vestigial or absent in different cypselas of the same capitulum. None has cypselas all of which had no pappus and no vestiges. One (L phyllaries) had vestigial pappus. (The S and VL plants were too badly galled to score cypselas.)

Denbigh, Graig Quarry, Carboniferous Limestone, in the quarry, 5.ix.53, *Centaurea nemoralis* with slight infiltration of *C. nigra*. All plants eradiata normalis. N 195 : VL 4. The VL plants were " very weak VL," with slight fusion or branching of a few pectinations, and probably did not indicate any hybridization with *C. jacea*. Many of the plants were past flowering. Most had cypselas with well developed pappus but in two there was little or no development of pappus but the heads were badly galled and the pappus may have been destroyed.

*V.-C.*52 : *Anglesey.*—Near Llangoed, clay over sand, 13.vii.36, *C. nigra*, eradiata normalis, N 1.

*V.-C.*54 : *North Lincoln.*—Louth, grassy roadside bank on chalk, and edge of cornfield, clay above chalk, 18.viii.36, *C. nemoralis-nigra*, eradiata normalis, N 2. Near Waddington, grassy roadside on oolite, 20.viii.30, *C. nemoralis*, eradiata normalis, N 1. Near Osgodby,

Market Rasen, grassy roadside, blown sand over Kimmeridge Clay, 21.viii.36, *C. nemoralis*, eradiata normalis, N 1 : longiflora N 1. Near Kingerby, grassy roadside, near wood, Oxford Clay, 21.viii.36, *C. nemoralis-nigra*, eradiata normalis, N 1. Holton-le-Moor, grassy hedgeside of field, blown sand over Kimmeridge Clay, 23–26.viii.36, *C. nemoralis*, eradiata normalis, N 2. Tealby, Horncastle to Barton-on-Humber Roman road, 24.viii.36, *C. nemoralis*, eradiata normalis, N 2.

*V.-C.*55 : *Leicester with Rutland.*—From Herbarium of the Leicester Literary and Philosophical Society the following specimens have been seen :

C. nigra, eradiata normalis, N : Lutterworth, 2.vii.1896 ; Between Redmite and Belvoir, 7.ix.1915 ; Ashby de la Zouch, 15.ix.1902 ; Enington, near Leicester, neutral grassland, 15.vii.1935 ; Ayleston ; Brooksby, 26.vi.1895 ; Canal near Kilby Bridge, vii.1945 ; Embankment, Balby, 1.vii.1948 ; East Norton, 6.viii.1903 ; Market Harborough, vi.1895 ; Sysonby, 28.vii.1903 ; Cropston, 29.viii.1891, longiflora : Thurlaston, vii.1898, longiflora.

C. nigra-nemoralis, eradiata normalis, N : near Kirby Muxloe, 31.vii.1915 ; Cropston Reservoir, 24.viii.1894 ; Cropston, 20.vii.1891 ; Buckminster Park, 19.vii.1905 ; Debdale Wharf, 2.viii.1901.

C. nemoralis, eradiata normalis, N : Rutland, Casterton Rings, 28.viii.1951 ; Watling Street Road, 1914 ; Wymondham, 6.ix.1904 ; Thurcaston Road, ix.1874 ; Ravenstone, 4.viii.1896 ; Rutland, Great Casterton, roadside, 10.viii.1952 ; The Drift, Croxton-Keyrial, 13.vii.1952 ; Knol and Bassett, 1914 ; The Drift, Croxton-Keyrial, 13.vii.1952, longiflora.

Hybrid *nemoralis* (?) × *jacea*, radiata normalis VL : Muston, 9.1894.

*V.-C.*56 : *Nottingham.*—*C. nigra*, eradiata normalis, N 5, from Everton Carr, 13.vii.52, peaty fenland ; Farndon, 30.vi.52, sandy loam ; Misson, 11.vi.52, peat land ; Cossall, 19.vi.52, Coal Measures. *C. nigra* (with trace of *C. nemoralis*), eradiata longiflora, Newark Wharf, 19.vii.52, waste land, N 2. *C. nigra* (with trace of *C. nemoralis*), eradiata normalis, Sookholme, 3.vii.52, Magnesian Limestone, N 1 ; Muskham, 21.vi.52, N 1. *C. nemoralis*, eradiata normalis, N 1, Coddington, 26.viii.52, Lias Clay ; Barnstone, 7.viii.52, Lias lime pits, N 2. *C. nemoralis*, eradiata longiflora, N 1. Barnstone, 7.viii.52, Lias lime pits ; Balderton, 9.viii.52, railway bank, clay N 1.

*V.-C.*57 : *Derby.*—Near Stony Middleton, 5.viii.11, *C. nigra*, eradiata normalis, N 1 : eradiata longiflora, VL 1. Near Ashover, N.E. of Matlock, in old quarry, 8.ix.33, *C. nigra* and *C. nemoralis-nigra*, eradiata normalis, N 8. Matlock district, above Via Gellia, in grass field, 8.ix.33, *C. nemoralis* (?), eradiata normalis, N 1. Cample Bridge, Closeburn, 3.viii.36, *C. nigra*, eradiata normalis, N 1. Corbar Hill, Buxton, edge of hay field on clay soil with grit stone outcrops, 17.viii.36, *C. nigra*, eradiata normalis, N. 1.

*V.-C.*58 : *Cheshire.*—Northwich, Hartford Village, grassy roadside, sandy subsoil, Keuper Marl, 1.viii.36, *C. nigra*, eradiata normalis, N 2. Dunkerfield, Chester, in a cemetary, *C. jacea*, C (N.H.M.). Lower Wych, 13.viii.1894, *C. nigra*, longiflora, N 1 (see B.E.C.Rep.) (N.H.M.).

*V.-C.*59 : *South Lancashire.*—Orrell, 20.vii.23 and 1.viii.23, *C. nigra*, eradiata normalis, N 2. Bolton, 14.viii.35, *C. nigra*, eradiata normalis, N 1.

*V.-C.*60 : *West* (or *Mid*) *Lancashire.*—Cork, 4.viii.1870, *C. nigra* (N.H.M.). On face of cliff between Hest Bank and Red Bank, Bolton-le-Sands, 5.viii.33, *C. nemoralis* and *C. nigra*, eradiata normalis, N 3 : VL 1. Cliff facing Cockerham salt-marsh, near Blackpool, 10.ix.36, *C. nigra*, eradiata normalis, N 5.

*V.-C.*62 : *North-east York.*—*C. nigra*, eradiata normalis, near York, ix.1859, N 1 ; valley near Bride Stones, Cleveland, in pasture field, 8.ix.27, N 4 ; between Pickering and Fox and Rabbits Inn, 8.ix.27, N 10 ; between Rievaulx and Beckdale Woods, Cleveland, 9.ix.27, N 4 ; Beckdale Woods, 9.ix.27, valley bottom in grassy places, N 3 ; Allerton Forest, path side, 10.ix.27, N 3 ; Forge Valley, E. Cleveland, 11.ix.27, grassy places in valley, N 67 ; near Levisham, Clevelands, railway embankment, 12.ix.27, N 2. Thirsk, 1952, Magnesian Limestone Quarry, *C. nemoralis*, eradiata normalis, N 2. Rievaulx, near the village, 9.ix.27, *C. nemoralis-nigra*, eradiata normalis, N 2.

*V.-C.*64 : *Mid-west York.*—*C. nigra*, eradiata normalis : near Roundhay, Leeds in grass field, 1.ix.27, N 2 ; Dacre, N. of Leeds, grassy place by roadside, 3.ix.27, N 4 ; between Ripon and Knaresborough, grassy place on roadside, 3.ix.27, N 8 ; meadow by Slaidburn Bridge, 8.vii.32, N 2 ; Askham Bog, near York, at edge of marsh, 1.ix.32, N 2 ; Pallathorpe, Bolton Percy, pasture field, 26.vii.36, N 1. Pallathorpe, Bolton Percy, pasture field, 26.vii.36, *C. nigra*, eradiata longiflora, N 1.

The knapweed surveys made in 1927 in vice-counties 62 and 64 showed that *Centaurea nigra* eradiata was common on road verges and other artificial or greatly modified grassy places. This was true both of Millstone Grit and Carboniferous Limestone areas and also where Corallian rocks (often leached at the surface) outcrop. A few *Centaurea* plants were found amongst gorse and in valley pastures but none on the " moors " proper. Where there was vegetation of *Calluna*, *Erica*, *Vaccinium*, *Pteridium*, etc., knapweeds were absent. In woods, also, knapweeds are not usually found, except now and again in the grass of " drives." The conclusion one reaches is that in Yorkshire the knapweeds are not constituents of the original vegetation. They are a relatively recent invasion from the south and can only establish themselves in places opened up by man and in competition with " semi-ruderals " in the less exposed situations.

*V.-C.*65 : *North-west York.*—Cotherstone, viii.1882, *C. nigra*, eradiata longiflora, N 1. Red Scar, 3 miles from Richmond, on face of limestone cliff, 3.ix.32, *C. nigra*, eradiata normalis, N 1. Garsdale, Sedbergh, 7.vii.34, *C. nigra*, eradiata normalis, N 1.

*V.-C.*66 :   *Durham.*—Castle Eden Dene, 2.viii.32, *C. nigra*, eradiata normalis, N 1.   Rookchope Burn, 1939, *C. nigra*, eradiata normalis, N 1.   Teesdale, High Force, by side of river, 3.ix.49, *C. nigra*, eradiata normalis, N 6.

*V.-C.*67 :   *Northumberland, South.*—Tynesdale, Newton Hall, 1937, *C. nigra*, N 88, eradiata normalis 58 (rest not scorable for florets). Cultivated at Kew, from seeds from same population, 11.viii.39, *C. nigra*, eradiata normalis, N 23 : curly longiflora 1.   St. Swinburn, ix.38, *C. nigra*, eradiata normalis, N 1.   Black Callerton, 1939, *C. nigra*, eradiata normalis, N 1.   On Walker Ballast Hills, ix.1845, *C. nemoralis* with trace of *C. jacea*, radiata normalis, VL 1.

*V.-C.*69 :   *Westmorland.*—Near Kendal, 1838, *C. nigra*, radiata, N 1 (Herb. Edinb.).   Near Blindbeck Bridge, Barbondale, meadow, 6.viii.33, *C. nigra*, eradiata normalis, N 4 : VL 1.   From seed collected near Wray Castle, Windermere, 15.ix.34. cultivated in Herbarium Experimental Ground, Kew, 10.viii.36, *C. nigra*, and one or two with some genes of *C. jacea*, eradiata normalis, N 15 : VL 1 : L 1.   Kendal, grassy roadside, heavy dark soil, 21.vii.36, *C. nigra*, eradiata normalis, N 1.   Kendal, roadside bank, limestone rock, 7.viii.36, *C. nigra*, eradiata normalis, N 1.

*V.-C.*70 :   *Cumberland.*—St. Bees, hedgerow, 30.vii.16, *C. nigra*, eradiata normalis, N 1.   Caldbeck, stony bed by side of river, glacial gravel overlying limestone, 17.vii.36, *C. nigra*, eradiata normalis, N 1.   Hutton Roof, Greystoke, grassy roadside, limestone, 18.vii.36, *C. nigra*, eradiata normalis, N 1.   Cockermouth, grassy roadside, clay soil, 27.vii.36, *C. nigra*, eradiata normalis, N 5.   Dockray, Penrith, 30.vii.36, *C. nigra*, eradiata normalis, N 1.   Wastwater, peatland, 1952, *C. nigra*, eradiata longiflora, N 1.

*V.-C.*71 :   *Isle of Man.*—Port St. Mary, grassy roadside, old sod bank, margin of shore shingle, 13.viii.36, *C. nigra*, eradiata normalis, N 5.

*V.-C.*72 :   *Dumfries.*—Hightoe Lockerbie, 20.viii.36 and Closeburn, 3.viii.36, *C. nigra*, eradiata normalis, N 2.

*V.-C.*73 :   *Kirkcudbright.*—Near Gatehouse, viii.1887, *C. nigra*, eradiata normalis, N 1.   Castle Douglas, ix.27 and 20.viii.36, *C. nigra*, radiata normalis, N 1 : eradiata normalis, N 2 : eradiata breviflora, N 1.

*V.-C.*77 :   *Lanark.*—Without locality and date, *C. nigra*, eradiata normalis, N 1.

*V.-C.*83 :   *Edinburgh.*—Near Blackshiels, 5.viii.36, *C. nigra*, eradiata, N 1.   Near Edinburgh, 1841, *C. jacea* × *C. nigra*, radiata.

V.-C..85 :   *Fife and Kinross.*—Near Taypost, 8.viii.36, *C. nigra*, eradiata normalis, N 3.   One with florets Marguerite Yellow.   Tentsmuir, grassy place by roadside, 4.ix.28, *C. nigra*, eradiata normalis, N 9.   St. Andrews, grassy places on cliffs to east of town, 31.viii.47, *C. nigra*, eradiata, N 41.

*V.-C.*86 :   *Stirling.*—Balmaha, side of Loch Lomond, 4.viii.27, *C. nigra*, eradiata normalis, N 3.   Gartness, grassy places at edge of field, 9.ix.28, *C. nigra*, eradiata normalis, N 9.   Near Stirling, 23.ix.31,

C. nigra, eradiata normalis, N 45, two plants exceptional in having phyllaries narrower with smaller appendages which do not completely cover the pericline at anthesis, 31 with leaves more or less entire, 9 with leaves toothed, and 5 with leaves lobed.

*V.-C.*87 : _West Perth.—Callender, grassy places on railway bank, 1.ix.28, *C. nigra*, eradiata normalis, N 9. Port of Monteith (Menteith), Ballochraggan, amongst bracken, 12.viii.51, *C. nigra*, eradiata normalis, N 6.

*V.-C.*88 : *Mid-Perth.*—Kenniel Park, Killin, 7.viii.1882, *C. jacea*, radiata normalis, or near to this, a peculiar plant unlike any of our southern stocks (Herb. Edinb.). At foot of Ben Lawers, fields and hedgebank, 1.viii.27, *C. nigra*, radiata normalis, N 7. Grassy slope near side of Loch Tay, 12.ix.34, in fruit, *C. nigra*, eradiata normalis with few genes of *C. jacea*, N 3 : VL 2 : L 1 ; plants grown at Kew from seeds of these gave N 11 : VL 4 : L 1. Fortingal, *C. nigra*, eradiata normalis, N 1 (N.H.M.). Side of hill road leading from Dumbuils to the village of Forgandenny, viii.1870, *C. jacea* × *C. nigra*, normalis, L 1 (N.H.M.).

*V.-C.*90 : *Angus.*—Brechin, 8.viii.36, *C. nigra*, eradiata normalis, VL 1, with suggestion of hybridization with *C. jacea*. Kinnoul Hills, near Perth, *C. nigra*, eradiata normalis, N 1.

*V.-C.*91 : *Kincardine.*—Near Kingcausie, viii.1837, *C. nigra*, eradiata normalis, N 1 (Herb. Edinb.).

*V.-C.*92 : *South Aberdeen.*—Braemar, vii.1855, *C. nigra*, eradiata normalis, N 2. Peterculter, ix.1879, *C. nigra*, eradiata normalis, N 1 (Herb. Cantab.). Aberdeen, ix.1879, *C. nigra*, radiata normalis, N 1 (N.H.M.).

*V.-C.*93 : *North Aberdeen.*—Oldmeldrum, 1.ix.27, *C. nigra*, eradiata normalis, N 1.

*V.-C.*94 : *Banff.*—Banff, 25.vii.27, *C. nigra*, eradiata normalis, N 3.

*V.-C.*96 : *Easterness.*—Rothiemurchus, *C. nigra*, eradiata normalis, N 1 (N.H.M.). Castle Urquhart, road verges, in fruit 12.ix.34 and plants grown at Kew from seeds from this population, 25.viii.36, *C. nigra*, eradiata normalis with slight contamination with *C. jacea*, N 14 : VL 3.

*V.-C.*98 : *Argyll.*—Loch Sunart, *C. nigra*, eradiata normalis, N 1 (N.H.M.). Between Kilmun and Ben More, grassy places by roadsides, 8.ix.28, *C. nigra*, eradiata, N 10, normalis 9 : longiflora 1.

*V.-C.*99 : *Dumbarton.*—Garelochhead, amongst bracken, etc., near roadside, 13.ix.28, *C. nigra*, eradiata normalis, N 2. Baldernock, grassy place by roadside, 3.viii.27, *C. nigra*, eradiata, N 3, longiflora 1 : normalis 2. Near Milngavie, grassy places, 7.ix.1927 and 1928, *C. nigra*, eradiata normalis, N 48.

*V.-C.*104 : *Skye.*—Near Broadford, wet field, 20.viii.34, *C. nigra*, eradiata normalis, N 37. Vaternish, N. of Stein, 29.viii.34, *C. nigra*, eradiata, normalis, N 18. Portree, 30-31.viii.34, *C. nigra*, eradiata normalis, N 65 : L 1, indicating a trace of *C. jacea* in one plant. Glen

Brittle, river bank on sandy alluvium and stream bank on peaty ground, 5–6.viii.36, *C. nigra*, eradiata normalis, N 2. Isle of Rum, viii.38, *C. nigra*, eradiata normalis, N 1.

*V.-C.*106 : *East Ross.*—Muir of Ord, grassy roadside, 20.vii.36, *C. nigra*, eradiata normalis, N 5, 3 with deeply lobed leaves.

*V.-C.*108 : *West Sunderland.*—Melness Sands, Tongue Bay, *C. nigra*, eradiata normalis, N.1 (N.H.M.).

*V.-C.*111 : *Orkneys.*—Crafty, Firth, Mainland, 15.ix.28, with phyllaries pale, radiata, VL 1, introduced with clover seed in 1922 or 1923. The Loons, Stromness, Mainland, 13.ix.28, black phyllaries, eradiata, L 1, probably *C. jacea* × *C. nigra*. Eleven plants grown at Kew, 29.vii.30, from seed received as from the same locality gave *C. nigra* eradiata, black phyllaries, N. Firth, Mainland, artificial grass field, 8.xi.28, *C. nemoralis* radiata, VL 1, suggesting past hybridization with *C. jacea*. 16 plants were recorded as occurring in the field. Of these 1 had phyllaries N and one VL. 9 plants grown at Kew, 29.vii.29, from seed received as from the same source, *C. nemoralis*, radiata with phyllaries N. Near St. Margarets Hope, grassy roadside, 13.viii.36, probably *C. nigra* × *C. jacea*, with black phyllaries, L 1. Sanday, Orkney, 1817–18, *C. nigra*, eradiata normalis, N 1.

Throughout much of southern and central Scotland plants of *Centaurea nigra* eradiata are often common along road verges, on railway banks, and in some other habitats much modified by man. They have not been seen in woods or on moors or heaths away from roads and paths. There is usually a striking and abrupt limitation of their distribution to habitats made or greatly altered by man. A partial exception is the occurrence on sea cliffs under at least semi-natural conditions.

IRELAND.

*V.-C.*2 : *North Kerry.*—Killarney district, near stream and grassy places, 19–20.viii.36, *C. nemoralis-nigra*, eradiata normalis, N 21.

*V.-C.*3 : *West Cork.*—Near Timoleague, gravel pit, 8.viii.36, *C. nemoralis-nigra*, eradiata normalis, N 1. Near Bantry, grassy roadside, 12.viii.36, *C. nemoralis-nigra*, eradiata normalis, N 3. Near Baltimore, heaths, 12.viii.36, *C. nemoralis-nigra*, eradiata normalis, N 51. Near Tragumna, heaths near coast, 13.viii.36, *C. nemoralis-nigra*, eradiata normalis, N 38. Near Gougane Barra, hillsides, 15.viii.36, *C. nemoralis-nigra*, eradiata normalis, N 1. Between Glengariff and Skibbereen, hillside in gorge, 15.viii.36, *C. nigra*, eradiata normalis, N 1. Bryce's Island, Bantry Bay, 16.viii.36, *C. nemoralis-nigra*, eradiata normalis, N 16.

*V.-C.*5 : *East Cork.*—Fermoy, grassy roadside, 29.vii.36, *C. nigra*, eradiata normalis, N 1.

*V.-C.*11 : *Kilkenny.*—Lyrath, very old pasture, 19.viii.36, *C. nemoralis-nigra*, eradiata normalis, N 1.

*V.-C.*16 : *West Galway.*—Connemara, near Roundstone, 28.viii.35, pasture near sea-shore, *C. nemoralis-nigra*, eradiata normalis, N 1.

*V.-C.*20 : *Wicklow.*—Co. Wicklow, July, *C. nigra*, eradiata normalis, N 1 (N.H.M.).

*V.-C.*21 : *Dublin.*—Greenhills, 22.vii.28, *C. nigra*, eradiata normalis, N 1. Knockannabra, near Tullagh(t), ix.26, *C. nigra*, eradiata normalis, N 4. Chapelizod, ix.26, *C. nigra*, eradiata normalis, N 1. Killiney, ix.26, *C. nigra*, eradiata normalis, N 3.

*V.-C.*33 : *Fermanagh.*—Levally, Enniskillen, hay field on limestone soil, 28.vii.36, *C. nigra*, eradiata normalis, N 1. Roadside at Ely Lodge, near Enniskillin, 14.vii.53, *C. nigra*, eradiata longiflora, N 1. By side of bog road near Killyrover, Lisnaskea, 16.vii.53, *C. nigra*, eradiata longiflora, N 1.

*V.-C.*38 : *Down.*—Holywood Hills, 25.ix.28, *C. nigra*, eradiata normalis, N 1. Slidderyford, 6.ix.52, on grassy sides of a deserted railway, *C. nigra*, N 50 : VL 4, eradiata normalis 33 (21 entirely past flowering, only 3 in full flower, the rest with one or two flowering capitula). Tollymore Park, 6.ix.52, on grassy road verges and amongst bushes, *C. nigra*, eradiata, N. 97, normalis 95 : breviflora 2.

*V.-C.*39 : *Antrim.*—Shane's Castle, Lough Neagh, on walls and at base of walls, 7.ix.52, *C. nigra* s.l. with possible slight contamination with *C. jacea*, eradiata normalis 3, out of flower 9, N 11 : L 1 (rather " low " L). Selsham, near Lough Neagh, on road verges and amongst tall herbage of damp meadow, 7.ix.52, *C. nigra* s.l., N 239 : VL 10 : L 1 (rather " low "). Of the N plants eradiata normalis 123 : eradiata breviflora 5, the remainder past flowering ; of the VL plants eradiata normalis 6, the remainder past flowering ; the L plant eradiata normalis.

No radiata plants and no longiflora plants were seen in N. Ireland. There was a very slight indication in two or three of the populations of infiltration of *C. jacea* genes as judged by a low degree of phyllary fusion in, at most, 16 out of the 413 plants scored in Northern Ireland. The Tollymore Park sample was entirely uncontaminated. Adding together the 4 samples from Co. Down and from Co. Antrim, the hybrid index was only 4·4.

It is possible that populations with a higher hybrid index occur or have occurred in Northern Ireland. Praeger (' The Botanist in Ireland,' paragraph group 470 : 1934) says that *Centaurea jacea* " collected by John Templeton near Drum Bridge nearly 150 years ago (see Britton in ' Bot. Exch. Club Rep., 1920,' 164), has not been recognized in Ireland since." A specimen in the Smith Herbarium of the Linnean Society of London is *C. jacea* radiata normalis VM and has the particulars " Ireland, Mr. Templeton, 1796 " on the sheet. In the Cambridge Univerity Herbarium is a sheet of *C. nigra* eradiata longiflora N, " Belfast, 1846, W. Thompson." It is interesting to record the occurrence of *C. jacea* in 1796 and *C. nigra* in 1846 in the Belfast area and slight traces of *C. jacea* genes in 1952.

Jersey.—St. Catherine's Bay, viii.1854, *C. nigra*, eradiata normalis, N 2. Waterworks Valley, 30.vi.1898, *C. nigra*, eradiata normalis,

N 1. St. Ouen's Bay, 26.vii.1899, *C. nigra* × *C. jacea*, radiata normalis L. Also cultivated from the same locality, 22.viii.24. Sands of St. Ouen's Bay, 15.vii.26, *C. nigra* with trace of *C. jacea*, radiata normalis, VL 1. Bouley Bay, amongst gorse and bracken on igneous rocks, 14.vii.29, *C. nigra*, eradiata normalis, N 2. St. Lawrence, 22.vii.29, *C. nigra*, radiata normalis, N 1. St. Catherine's Bay, amongst gorse and bracken, 21.vii.29, *C. nigra*, eradiata normalis, N 3. Don Bridge, near the station, 17.vii.29, 24.vii.29 and (cultivated at Kew from seeds) 11.viii.31. A hybrid swarm with strong admixture of *C. jacea* and the local *C. nigra*, radiata normalis, N 6 : VL 9 : L 11 : S 16 : M 10 : VM 4 : C 1. Noirmont, St. Brelade's, 1.vii.49, *C. jacea*, radiata normalis, C 1. Grown at Kew, 10.vii.51, from seeds collected, 1.vii.49, Noirmont, St. Brelade's, *C. jacea* × *C. nigra*, radiata normalis, M 6 : C 4. Noirmont, x.1842, *C. jacea* × *nigra*, radiata normalis, L 1 (Herb. Cantab.).

In Jersey knapweed populations are local. They especially occur in grassy and heathy places near the sea. The common variant appears to be *C. nigra* eradiata normalis, where there has not been contamination with *C. jacea*. Two particularly interesting populations studied were those at Don Bridge and Noirmont. At Don Bridge there was on 24.vii.29, a considerable population that was sampled and shown to consist of *C. nigra*, *C. jacea*, and various hybrids. Don Bridge was the station for the Jersey race course and it is suggested that *C. jacea* might have been introduced with horse fodder. In July, 1949, not a single *Centaurea* plant could be found in the neighbourhood. The railway had been replaced by a path and the station had disappeared. With these changes the knapweed population had been exterminated.

Guernsey.—St. Saviour's Parish, ix.27, *C. jacea*, radiata normalis, VM 1 ; 1927, *C. nigra*, eradiata normalis, N 2, florets Marguerite Yellow, very hairy leaves, pale phyllaries. Cultivated at Kew, 11.viii.31, from seeds collected on cliffs at Moulin, Honet, 20.ix.28, *C. nigra*, eradiata normalis, N 16 : VL 1, radiata normalis, VL 3. Sommeillenses, grassy side of cliff path, 8.vii.36, *C. nigra*, N 1. St. Peter's Port, 8.vii.36, *C. nemoralis-nigra*, radiata normalis, VL 1. Forest Parish, 8.vii.36, *C. nigra*, radiata normalis, VL 1. Forest Parish, 8.vii.36, *C. nigra*, eradiata normalis, VL 1. St. Saviour's, 9.vii.36, *C. nigra*, eradiata normalis, N 1. St. Martin's, 22.vi.36, *C. nigra*, eradiata normalis, VL 1. Forest Parish, 30.viii.36, *C. nigra*, eradiata normalis, N 3 (2 with Marguerite Yellow florets and pale phyllaries). Near St. Peter Port, 30.viii.36, *C. nigra*, eradiata normalis, N 5. Lancresse Common, 2.ix.36, *C. nigra*, eradiata normalis, N 3 : VL 1, radiata normalis, N 1. Petit Bot, 6.ix.36, *C. nigra*, eradiata normalis, N 22.

Alderney.—Platte Saline, among gorse, 16.viii.32, *C. nemoralis-nigra*, radiata normalis, N 1. Cliffs near Telegraph Tower, 2.ix.32, *C. nemoralis-nigra*, eradiata normalis, N 5 ; radiata normalis, N 1.

Pasture at base of quarry dump near foot of Mount Hale, 21.vi.34, *C. nigra*, radiata normalis, N 4.

Sark.—Hedgerow of Coupée Road, 10.ix.28, *C. nemoralis-nigra*, eradiata normalis, N 2. Without exact locality, seeds collected ix.28, cultivated at Kew, 11.viii.31, *C. nemoralis-nigra* with slight contamination with *C. jacea*, eradiata normalis, N 7 : VL 1 : L 1. Sufield, near Seigneurie, seeds collected 19.ix.28, cultivated Kew, 5.viii.29, *C. nigra*, radiata normalis, and hybrids, N 1 : VL 2 : L 1 : S 5 ; eradiata normalis, N 1. Above Port à la Jument, waste land with gorse, bracken, etc., 15.vii.30, *C. nigra*, eradiata normalis, N 1. Field near Beau Regard, 17.vii.30, *C. nigra*, eradiata normalis, N 1. Coupée Road, 8.vii.36, *C. nemoralis-nigra*, eradiata normalis, N 7.

Centaurea jacea in France.—We have collected this species in several localities in eastern France, in the French Alps, particularly in the Briançon and La Grave districts and have grown plants at Kew from seed from La Grave. It is interesting to record the occurrence of variants of the usual radiata normalis in a pure *C. jacea* population. Thus in Dauphiné, between Briançon and Prelles, 23.vii.31, in the one population of *C. jacea* in an alder wood in the river valley there were plants with normal, longiflora, and breviflora disc florets.

Knapweeds in Western America.—Examination of herbarium specimens, as well as a consideration of published accounts of knapweeds on the European continent, has led us to conclude that hybridization is not infrequent in several countries of western Europe between members of the *Jacea* section. A considerable number of names have been applied to plants that we should judge to be hybrids from a comparison of their phenotypic characters with those of plants we have experimentally analyzed or synthesized. We are not, however, here attempting a review of European species and hybrids of *Centaurea*, but consider it worth while recording the occurrence of *Centaurea* hybrids in western North America. Mr. J. T. Howell, of the California Academy of Sciences, has sent us six specimens from Oregon and California. Specimens of *C. jacea* and *C. nigra* s.l. have been seen from eastern North America, though not from Oregon, or California. They are alien introductions. The new Oregon specimens are all radiata normalis and are as follows :

28380. Meadowy roadside, 4 miles south of Sutherlin, Douglas County, Oregon, 16.vi.52, phyllaries VL.

28453. Roadside, 3 miles south of Hillsboro, Washington County, Oregon, 23.vi.52, phyllaries S.

28817. Field, 6 miles south of Roseburg, Douglas County, Oregon, 10.vii.52. Plant A, phyllaries M ; Plant B, phyllaries S ; Plant C, phyllaries M.

28847. Along highway in Douglas fir forest, 10 miles north-east of Patrick Creek, Del Norte County, California, phyllaries S.

Mr. Howell informs us that in western North America the knapweeds do not generally occur as large or continuous populations but " usually as isolated or few individuals along roads and on the edges of fields." Plants A, B, and C of 28817 were, however, growing together.   In the scattered sample, plants with phyllaries VL, S, and M are represented and we have to conclude that they are of hybrid origin.   Whether pure species were introduced and hybridized in western North America or whether hybrids from Europe started the knapweeds in Oregon and California we cannot say.

CHAPTER VI

GENETICAL EXPERIMENTS

ABOUT one hundred plants were grown as stocks. With only two or three exceptions, these were collected from wild British populations. Approximately forty are concerned in the breeding experiments dealt with in this chapter, the others were used for comparison or for other experiments.

It has been a difficult matter to know how best to present the results of our genetical work. Attempts at tabulation were frustrated by the range of characters and by the occurrence of aberrations which had to be recorded. It was, therefore, decided to describe, in summary form, those characters of the reproductive parts we have particularly studied. Many more details occur in our scoring records and may be useful either for working out special problems or for extended general research on the knapweeds.

The following is the scheme of this chapter :

A. Characters of the Stock Plants (S.P.) used.

B. Selfings and crossings with *Centaurea nigra* or *C. nemoralis*.

    a. Selfings. Using Stock Plants 1, 7, 8·1, 10, 13·7, 27·1, 27·3, 36, 3, 4, 5, 15, 17, and some carried on to F_2.

    b. Crossings (including F_2 families).

    S.P.1 × S.P.23
    S.P.1 × S.P.27·1
    S.P.1 × S.P.36   S.P.13·7 × S.P.24·5
    S.P.8·1 × S.P.26·1   S.P.21 × S.P.26·1
    S.P.13·7 × S.P.13·3   S.P.24·5 × S.P.13·7
    S.P.25·2 × S.P.26·1   S.P.24·5 × S.P.26·1
    S.P.27·3 × S.P.36   S.P.25·2 × S.P.24·5
    Crosses involving S.Ps. 2, 3, 4, 5, 15
    Crosses involving S.Ps. 1, 6, 7, 15, 17

C. Selfing of a Guernsey plant.

D. Selfings and crossings involving *C. jacea*.

    a. Only *C. jacea* involved.

    b. Involving *C. jacea* and *C. nigra* or *C. nemoralis.*

    S.P.34·1 × S.P.36   S.P.1 × S.P.48
    S.P.34·1 × S.P.15   S.P.27·3 × S.P.48
    S.P.15 × S.P.34·1   T.2·5 × S.P.48

S.P.34·1 × T.2·5   S.P.15 × S.P.48
T.2·5 × S.P.34·1
Crossings involving S.P.34·2
S.P.27·3 × S.P.45·2
S.P.45·2 × T.2·2
Crosses involving S.P.45·1
Crosses involving S.P.35·1
Crosses involving S.P.33
Crosses involving S.P.49
Crosses involving S.P.30

   c. Involving hybrids, that is so-called *C. jungens* and *C. pratersis.*

   E. Experiments involving Guernsey (putative) hybrids.

A. CHARACTERS OF STOCK PLANTS USED IN CONTROLLED SELFINGS AND CROSSINGS.

(Hybridization or gene flow scored solely on phyllary characters.)

S.P.1. Hampshire: Christchurch, Wick Ferry, 1922.
Pericline broadly ovoid. Disc Bone Brown ; N. Florets Marguerite Yellow ; radiata ; normalis. (*C. nigra.*)

S.P.2. Wiltshire, Roundway Down, 1924.
Pericline ovoid. Disc Bone Brown ; N. Florets Dull Dark Purple ; radiata ; normalis. (*C. nemoralis.*)

S.P.3. Wiltshire, Roundway Down, 1924.
Pericline ovoid. Disc Bone Brown ; N. Florets Dull Dark Purple ; radiata ; normalis. (*C. nemoralis.*)

S.P.4. Wiltshire, Roundway Down, 1924.
Pericline ovoid. Disc Black ; N. Florets Dull Dark Purple ; radiata ; normalis. (*C. nemoralis.*)

S.P.5. Wiltshire, Horse and Jockey Bog, near Box, 1924.
Pericline ovoid. Disc Bone Brown ; N. Florets rays white tinged at tips, disc Dull Dark Purple ; radiata ; normalis. (*C. nemoralis.*)

S.P.6. Warwickshire, Harbury Cutting, 1934.
Pericline ovoid. Disc Bone Brown ; N. Florets Bishop's Purple ; eradiata ; normalis. (*C. nemoralis.*)

S.P.7. Warwickshire, Harbury Cutting, 1924.
Pericline elongate-ovoid. Disc Black ; N. Florets Rood's Violet ; eradiata ; normalis. (*C. nemoralis.*)

S.P.8·1. Warwickshire, Harbury Cutting, 1925.
Pericline ovoid. Disc Black ; VL. Florets Rood's Violet ; eradiata ; longiflora. (*C. nemoralis,* with probably a few genes of *C. jacea.*)

S.P.8·2. Warwickshire, Chesterton, 1925.
Pericline ovoid. Disc Bone Brown ; N. Florets Rood's Violet ; eradiata ; normalis. (*C. nemoralis.*)

S.P.10. Warwickshire, Harbury Cutting, 1925.
Pericline ovoid. Disc Black ; VL. Florets Rood's Violet ; eradiata ; normalis. (*C. nemoralis*, with a few genes of *C. jacea.*)

S.P.13·3. Warwickshire, Harbury Cutting, 1925.
Pericline ovoid. Disc Black ; N. Florets Rood's Violet ; eradiata ; normalis. (*C. nemoralis.*)

S.P.13·6. Warwickshire, Harbury Cutting, 1925.
Pericline elongate-ovoid. Disc Bone Brown ; VL. Florets Dull Dark Purple ; eradiata ; normalis. (Possibly *C. nemoralis* with a few genes of *C. jacea*).

S.P.13·7. Warwickshire, Harbury Cutting, 1925.
Pericline ovoid. Disc Bone Brown ; VL. Florets Dull Dark Purple ; eradiata ; normalis. (*C. nemoralis*, with a few genes of *C. jacea.*)

S.P.15. Oxfordshire, between Burford and Filkins, 1925.
Pericline ovoid. Disc Bone Brown ; VL. Florets Marguerite Yellow ; radiata ; normalis. (*C. nemoralis*, with a few genes of *C. jacea.*)

S.P.16. Oxfordshire, between Burford and Filkins, 1925.
Pericline elongate-ovoid. Disc Bone Brown ; N. Florets rays white flushed Bishop's Purple, disc Bishop's Purple ; radiata ; normalis. (*C. nemoralis.*)

S.P.17. Oxfordshire, between Burford and Filkins, 1925.
Pericline ovoid. Disc Prout's Brown ; VL. Florets Rood's Violet ; semiradiata ; normalis. (*C. nemoralis*, with a few genes of *C. jacea.*)

S.P.21. Oxfordshire, between Burford and Filkins, 1925.
Pericline ovoid. Disc Bone Brown ; VL. Florets Dull Dark Purple ; radiata ; longiflora. (*C. nemoralis*, with a few genes of *C. jacea.*)

S.P.23. Wiltshire, Potterne, 1925.
Pericline broadly ovoid. Disc Black ; N. Florets probably Dull Dark Purple ; eradiata ; longiflora. (*C. nigra.*)

S.P.24·5. Wiltshire, Near Devizes, 1925.
Pericline ovoid. Disc Bone Brown ; N. Florets probably Bishop's Purple ; radiata ; normalis. (*C. nemoralis.*)

S.P.25·2. Warwickshire, Harbury, 1925.
Pericline broadly ovoid. Disc Bone Brown; N. Florets Dull Dark Purple; eradiata; normalis. (*C. nigra.*)

S.P.26·1. Warwickshire, Harbury, 1925.
Pericline elongate-ovoid. Disc Black; VL. Florets Rood's Violet; eradiata; longiflora. (*C. nigra*, with a few genes of *C. jacea.*)

S.P.27·1. Sussex, Crowborough, 1925.
Pericline broadly ovoid. Disc Black; N. Florets Dull Dark Purple; eradiata; normalis. (*C. nigra.*)

S.P.27·3. Sussex, Crowborough, 1925.
Pericline broadly ovoid. Disc Black; N. Florets Dull Dark Purple; eradiata; normalis. (*C. nigra.*)

S.P.30. Surrey, 1926.
Pericline ovoid. Disc Russet; VL. Florets Bishop's Purple; semiradiata; normalis. (*C. nigra*, with a few genes of *C. jacea.*)

S.P.33. Surrey, Epsom Downs, 1926.
Pericline, ovoid. Disc Prout's Brown; S (rather low). Florets Dull Dark Purple; semiradiata; normalis. (*C. jacea* × *C. nemoralis.*)

S.P.34·1. Kew, cultivated, 1926.
Pericline ovoid. Disc Prout's Brown; VM. Florets Dull Dark Purple; radiata; normalis. (*C. jacea.*)

S.P.34·2. Kew, cultivated, 1926.
Pericline ovoid. Disc Prout's Brown; VM. Florets Argyle Purple; semiradiata; normalis. (*C. jacea.*)

S.P.35·1. Surrey, Byfleet, 1926.
Pericline broadly ovoid. Disc Bone Brown; M. Florets Dull Dark Purple; radiata; normalis (*C. jacea* × *C. nigra.*)

S.P.35·2. Surrey, Byfleet, 1926.
Pericline broadly ovoid. Disc Prout's Brown; S. Florets Dull Dark Purple; eradiata; normalis. (*C. jacea* × *C. nigra.*)

S.P.36. Surrey, Malden, 1926.
Pericline ovoid. Disc Bone Brown; VL. Florets Marguerite Yellow; eradiata; normalis. (*C. nigra*, with a few genes of *C. jacea.*)

S.P.38·3. Oxfordshire, near Burford, 1926.
Pericline ovoid. Disc Black; N. Florets Bishop's Purple; eradiata; normalis. (*C. nemoralis.*)

S.P.45·1–45·8. Berkshire, Wellington College, 1926.
Pericline elongate-ovoid. Disc Prout's Brown ; C. Florets Bishop's
Purple ; radiata ; normalis. (*C. jacea.*)

S.P.47. Jersey, 1926.
Pericline ovoid. Disc Bone Brown ; L. Florets Rood's Violet ;
eradiata ; normalis. (*C. jacea × C. nigra.*)

S.P.48. Surrey, 1926.
Heads twinned. Pericline ovoid. Disc Bone Brown ; C. Florets
Bishop's Purple ; semiradiata ; normalis. (*C. jacea.*)

S.P.49. Surrey, 1926.
Pericline broadly ovoid. Disc Bone Brown ; M. Florets Rood's
Violet ; eradiata ; normalis. (*C. jacea × C. nigra.*)

S.P.58·2. Guernsey, 1927.
Pericline ovoid. Disc Tawny Olive ; N. Florets Marguerite
Yellow ; eradiata ; normalis. (*C. nigra.*)

S.P.79·1–79·2. Guernsey, 1927.
Pericline broadly ovoid. Disc Pront's Brown ; M. Florets Bishop's
Purple ; radiata ; normalis. (*C. jacea,* with genes of *C. nigra.*)

B. SELFINGS AND CROSSINGS WITH *C. nigra* OR *C. nemoralis,* THAT IS
NOT DELIBERATELY INTRODUCING *C. jacea.*

a. *Selfings.*

T.8. S.P.1 selfed. 21 plants.
Pericline broadly ovoid 21. Phyllaries Bone Brown 21 ; N 21.
Florets Marguerite Yellow 21 ; radiata normalis 21.

T.53. S.P.7 selfed. 13 plants.
Pericline elongate-ovoid 13. Phyllaries Black 13 ; N 13. Florets
Rood's Violet 13 ; eradiata normalis 13.

T.202. T.53, plant 1 selfed. 17 plants.
Pericline elongate-ovoid 17. Phyllaries Bone Brown 13 : Prout's
Brown 4 ; N 17. Florets Rood's Violet 16, eradiata normalis 16.

T.26. S.P.8·1 selfed. 5 plants.
Pericline ovoid 3 : broadly ovoid 2. Phyllaries Black 2 : Bone
Brown 3 ; N 5. Florets Rood's Violet 3 : Dull Dark Purple 1 : Bishop's
Purple 1 ; eradiata normalis 3 : eradiata longiflora 2.
Plants 2 and 3 had pericline ovoid, phyllaries Bone Brown, florets
(probably) Rood's Violet, longiflora.

T.22. S.P.10 selfed. 44 plants.

Pericline ovoid 44, with a tendency for twinning of capitula. Phyllaries Black 44 ; N 24 : VL 18 : L 2. Florets Rood's Violet 44 ; eradiata normalis 44. Many of the plants had at least some capitula that more or less aborted.

Plant 5 had phyllaries N and plants 2 and 3 had phyllaries VL.

T.130. T.22, plant 5 selfed. 1 plant.

This plant was similar to its parents in vegetative characters but the capitula remained small and aborted without expanding.

T.148. T.22, plant 5 × T.22, plant 3. 3 plants.

Pericline ovoid. Phyllaries Black 3 ; N 2 : VL 1. Florets Rood's Violet 3 ; eradiata normalis 3.

T.32. S.P.13·7 selfed. 3 plants.

Percline ovoid 3. Phyllaries Bone Brown 3 ; N 3. Florets Dull Dark Purple 3 ; eradiata normalis 3.

T.192. T.32, plant 1 selfed. 1 plant.

Pericline ovoid. Phyllaries Bone Brown ; VL. Florets Dull Dark Purple ; eradiata normalis.

T.167. T.32, plant 1 × T.32, plant 2. 2 plants.

Pericline ovoid. Phyllaries Bone Brown 1 : Prout's Brown 1 ; N 2. Florets Dull Dark Purple 2 ; eradiata normalis 2.

T.35. S.P.27·1 selfed. 1 plant.

Pericline broadly ovoid. Phyllaries Black ; N. Florets Dull Dark Purple ; eradiata normalis.

T.72. S.P.27·3 selfed. 81 plants.

Pericline broadly ovoid 81. Phyllaries Black 81 ; N 81. Florets Dull Dark Purple 81 ; eradiata normalis 81.

T.60. S.P.36 selfed. 8 plants.

Pericline ovoid 8. Phyllaries Bone Brown 8 ; VL 5 : L 3. Florets Marguerite Yellow 8 ; eradiata normalis 8.

T.10. S.P.3 selfed. 4 plants.

Pericline ovoid 4. Phyllaries Bone Brown 4 ; N 4. Florets Dull Dark Purple 4 ; radiata normalis 4.

T.11. S.P.4 selfed. 3 plants.

Pericline ovoid 3. Phyllaries Black 3 ; N 3. Florets Dull Dark Purple 3 ; radiata normalis 3.

T.12. S.P.5 selfed. 12 plants.
Pericline ovoid 12. Phyllaries Bone Brown 12 ; N 12. Florets Dull Dark Purple 2 : Dull Dark Purple but rays white flushed or tipped Dull Dark Purple 9 ; radiata normalis 11.

T.86. S.P. 15 selfed. 4 plants.
Pericline ovoid 4. Phyllaries Bone Brown 4 ; N 4. Florets Marguerite Yellow 4 ; radiata normalis 4.

T.24. S.P.17 selfed. 36 plants.
Pericline ovoid 36. Phyllaries Prout's Brown 36 ; N 6 : VL 2. Florets Rood's Violet 36 ; radiata normalis 12 : semiradiata normalis 16 : eradiata normalis 8.
Plant 1 had phyllaries N, florets radiata normalis.
Plants 3, 4, and 5 had phyllaries N, florets semiradiata normalis.

T.158. T.24, plant 7 × T.24, plant 3. 47 plants.
Pericline ovoid 47. Phyllaries Prout's Brown 47 ; N 40 : VL 3 : L 4. Florets Rood's Violet 47 ; radiata 19 : semiradiata 7 : eradiata 21 ; normalis 31 : longiflora 16.

T.161. T.24 plant 7 × T.37 plant 3. 16 plants.
Pericline ovoid 16. Phyllaries Bone Brown 13 : Prout's Brown 3 ; N 8 : VL 7. Florets Dull Dark Purple 16 ; radiata 7 : eradiata 8 ; normalis 12 : longiflora 2 : breviflora 1.

T.171. T.24, plant 3 × T.24, plant 4. 1 plant.
Pericline ovoid. Phyllaries Prout's Brown ; N. Florets Rood's Violet ; semiradiata longiflora.

T.169. T.24, plant 7 × T.24, plant 4. 31 plants.
Pericline ovoid 31 : Phyllaries Prout's Brown 31 ; N 17 : VL 11 : L 3. Florets Rood's Violet 30 ; radiata 22 : eradiata 8 ; normalis 7 : longiflora 23.

T.189. T.24, plant 7 selfed. 3 plants.
Pericline ovoid 3. Phyllaries Black 1 : Prout's Brown 2 ; N 1 : VL 2. Florets Rood's Violet 3 ; radiata 2 : eradiata 1 ; normalis 3.

T.187. T.24, plant 1 selfed. 4 plants.
Pericline ovoid 4. Phyllaries Prout's Brown 4 ; N 4. Florets Rood's Violet 4 ; normalis 4.

Comments on Selfings within C. nigra *or* C. nemoralis.
Selfings of stock plants of *C. nigra* and *C. nemoralis* have shown that these breed true, to most of the characters we have studied in F_1 and, when made, F_2 generations. S.P.8·1 segregated for pericline shape. S.P.10, S.P.36, and S.P.17 (all three scored VL for phyllaries) segregated

for phyllary shapes with some plants as high as L. These three stock plants were certainly " low-grade " hybrids of *C. jacea* × *C. nigra* or *C. nemoralis*, in the sense that while the majority of genes were those of *C. nigra* or *C. nemoralis*, some genes derived from a previous cross with *C. jacea* were present. S.P.17 segregated for presence or absence and length of ray florets and, in F_2, for normalis, longiflora, and breviflora disc florets. It was unexpected that S.P.8·1 on selfing gave 5 plants with normalis disc florets and none with longiflora disc florets, for it had itself longiflora disc florets.

b. *Crossings.*

T.13. S.P.1 × S.P.23. 31 plants.
Pericline broadly ovoid 31. Phyllaries Black 31 ; N 31. Florets Dull Dark Purple 31 ; radiata normalis 31.

T.291. T.13, plant 29 × T.13, plant 8. 90 plants.
Pericline broadly ovoid 90. Phyllaries Black 88 : Bone Brown 2 ; N 77 : VL 12. Florets Dull Dark Purple 85 : Marguerite Yellow 2 ; radiata normalis 87.

T.255. T.13, plant 27 selfed. 87 plants.
Pericline broadly ovoid 87. Phyllaries Black 86 : Bone Brown 1 ; N 87. Florets Dull Dark Purple 86 : Marguerite Yellow 1 ; radiata 81 : semiradiata 5 : eradiata 1 ; normalis 87.

T.261. T.13, plant 8 selfed. 120 plants.
Pericline broadly ovoid 120. Phyllaries Black 117 : Bone Brown 3 ; N 99 : VL 20. Florets Dull Dark Purple 116 : Marguerite Yellow 3 ; radiata 115 : semiradiata 4 ; normalis 119.

T.280. T.13, plant 29 selfed. 67 plants.
Pericline broadly ovoid 67. Phyllaries Black 67 ; N 57 : VL 10. Florets Dull Dark Purple 67 ; radiata normalis 63.

T.279. T.13, plant 27 × T.13, plant 29. 87 plants.
Pericline broadly ovoid 87. Phyllaries Black 86 : Bone Brown 1 ; N 79 : VL 7. Florets Dull Dark Purple 86 : Marguerite Yellow 1 ; radiata 83 : semiradiata 4 ; normalis 87.

Comments on the Cross S.P.1 × S.P.23.

F_1 and F_2 families bred true to pericline shape, phyllaries colour, except for a few with Bone Brown phyllaries, and disc florets. There was segregation in F_2 for phyllaries shape into N and VL in four families and for floret colour. The original cross was between M.Y. and D.D.P. plants. In F_1 all the offspring had D.D.P. florets and in the five F_2 families the figures probably represent D.D.P. 63 : M.Y.

1 ratios. The original cross was radiata normalis × eradiata longiflora. The 31 F_1 plants were radiata normalis. In the five F_2 families all the 442 plants had normalis disc florets and all except one were either radiata or semiradiata. It was expected that longiflora plants and more eradiata plants would have appeared in F_2 families. The five F_2 families were produced by three selfings of F_1 plants and by two crossings of F_1 sibs. The eradiata longiflora characters of S.P.23 are not only recessive to the radiata normalis characters of the maternal parent S.P.1 but are pheno-typically overwhelmed by them in F_2.

T.14. S.P.1 × S.P.27·1. 39 plants.

Pericline broadly ovoid 39. Phyllaries Bone Brown 39 ; N 22 : VL 16. Florets Dull Dark Purple 39 ; radiata normalis 1 : radiata longiflora 3 : semiradiata normalis 4 : semiradiata longiflora 1 : eradiata normalis 30.

Plant 27 had phyllaries VL, florets radiata longiflora.

Plant 30 had phyllaries N, florets eradiata normalis.

Plant 39 had phyllaries N, florets semiradiata normalis.

T.326. T.14, plant 39 selfed. 81 plants.

Pericline ovoid 3 : broadly ovoid 62. Phyllaries Black 10 : Bone Brown 55 ; N 55 : VL 13. Florets Dull Dark Purple 61 : Rood's Violet 3 : Marguerite Yellow 1 ; radiata 28 : semiradiata 21 ; normalis 37 : longiflora 3 : quilled 4 : breviflora 5. 13 plants were " blind," *i.e.*, they produced only abortive capitula which remained small and did not open. Some " quilled " and some " breviflora " plants showed the one or other character incompletely.

Plant 11 had pericline broadly ovoid, phyllaries Black, N, florets Rood's Violet, semiradiata, quilled.

Plant 16 had pericline broadly ovoid, phyllaries Bone Brown, N, florets Dull Dark Purple, semiradiata, normalis.

Plant 64 had pericline broadly ovoid, phyllaries Black, N, florets Dull Dark Purple, semiradiata, longiflora more or less quilled.

T.528. T.326, plant 64 selfed. 9 plants.

Pericline broadly ovoid 7. Phyllaries Black 7 ; N 4 : VL 2. Florets Dull Dark Purple 6 ; radiata 5 : eradiata 1 ; normalis 1 : longiflora 5 (2 of which were more or less " quilled ").

Two plants had only aborted heads and one was past flowering when scored.

T.538. T.326, plant 16 × T.326, plant 64. 8 plants.

Pericline broadly ovoid 8. Phyllaries Black 8 ; N 4 : VL 4. Florets Dull Dark Purple 8 ; radiata 3 : semiradiata 1 ; longiflora 4.

The plants showed more or less abortion at production of capitula.

T.543. T.326, plant 11 selfed. 1 plant.

The only plant completely aborted at production of capitula.

T.541. S.P.1 × T.326 plant 64.   49 plants.
Pericline broadly ovoid 49.   Phyllaries Bone Brown 49 ; N 30 :
VL 19.   Florets Dull Dark Purple 7 : Bishop's Purple 31 : Marguerite
Yellow 7 ; radiata 44 : semiradiata 1 ; normalis 43 : longiflora 2.

T.327. T.14 plant 30 selfed.   16 plants.
Pericline broadly ovoid 16.   Phyllaries Black 7 : Bone Brown 9 ;
N 15 : VL 1.   Florets Dull Dark Purple 12 : Marguerite Yellow 2 ;
semiradiata 1 : eradiata 13 ; normalis 14.

T.329. T. 14 plant 39 × T.14 plant 30.   85 plants.
Pericline ovoid 72 : broadly ovoid 8.   Phyllaries Black 8 : Bone
Brown 72 ; N 70 : VL 10.   Florets Dull Dark Purple 79 : Marguerite
Yellow 1 ; radiata 31 : semiradiata 22 : eradiata 20 ; normalis 67 :
quilled 2 : breviflora 3.
Plant 28 had pericline ovoid.   Phyllaries Bone Brown, N, florets
Dull Dark Purple, eradiata normalis.

T.532. T.329 plant 28 selfed.   3 plants.
Pericline ovoid 3.   Phyllaries Bone Brown 3 ; VL 2.   Florets Dull
Dark Purple 2 ; semiradiata 1 : eradiata 1 ; normalis 2.

T.332. T.14 plant 27 selfed.   8 plants.
Pericline broadly ovoid 8.   Phyllaries Black 1 : Bone Brown 7 ;
N 6 : VL 2.   Florets Dull Dark Purple 8 ; radiata 6 : semiradiata 2 ;
normalis 5 : longiflora 3.

Comments on the Cross S.P.1 × S.P.27·1.

Pericline shape was BO in the parents, in F_1, and mostly in F_2
except in T.329 and in an F_3 from this (T.532)   The F_1 and all the F_2
and the one back cross and two F_3 families segregated into N and VL
for phyllary shape but no plants with phyllaries showing pronounced
C. jacea characters appeared.   Phyllary colour was entirely limited
in all the families to Black and Bone Brown.   Floret colour is interesting
in the series of families raised from this cross since the original parents
were M.Y. and D.D.P., the maternal parent being the same as in the
last series of families, but with a different pollen parent.   Again, we
note the small numbers of M.Y. plants appearing in F_2 families.
In two of these the numbers approximate to a D.D.P. 63 : M.Y. 1
ratio.   T.327 (from a plant of F_1 selfed) gave D.D.P. 12 and M.Y. 2.
A once removed backcross, S.P.1 (M.Y.) crossed with a plant F_2
(D.D.P.) gave the instructive figures D.D.P. 7, B.P. 31, M.Y. 7.   The
results for ray floret development are different from those obtained in
the last series of families.   The cross radiata × eradiata gave an F_1
of radiata (R) 4, semiradiata (S) 5, eradiata (E) 30. F_2 families gave
results varying according to the character of the immediate F_1 parent
or parents used.   A once removed backcross, R × S, gave R 44 and
S 1.   For disc florets, the exceptional interest was the appearance in

two F_2 and one F_3 families of the rare " quilled " plants. The parents had normalis disc florets but a minority of plants with longiflora florets appeared in the F_1 family and in five later offspring families.

T.65. S.P.1 × S.P.36. 73 plants.
Pericline ovoid 73. Phyllaries Black 73 ; N 19 : VL 47 : L 7. Florets Dull Dark Purple 73 ; semiradiata normalis 8 : eradiata normalis 63.
Plants 2 and 9 had phyllaries VL, florets semiradiata normalis.
Plants 4 and 13 had phyllaries VL, florets eradiata normalis.

T.214. T.65 plant 2 selfed. 70 plants.
Pericline ovoid 70. Phyllaries Black 70 ; N 62 : VL 8. Florets Dull Dark Purple 67 : Marguerite Yellow 3 ; radiata 5 : semiradiata 14 : eradiata 49 ; normalis 68.
Plant 37 had phyllaries N, florets Dull Dark Purple, eradiata normalis.
Plant 63 had phyllaries N, florets Marguerite Yellow, eradiata normalis.

T.535. T.214 plant 37 selfed. 1 plant.
Pericline ovoid. Phyllaries Black ; N. Florets Dull Dark Purple ; eradiata normalis.

T.544. T.214 plant 63 selfed. 3 plants.
Pericline ovoid 2 : broadly ovoid 1. Phyllaries Black 3 ; N 1 : VL 2. Florets Marguerite Yellow 3 ; eradiata normalis 3.

T.548. T.214, plant 63 × T.214, plant 37. 1 plant.
Pericline ovoid. Phyllaries Bone Brown ; N. Florets Dull Dark Purple ; eradiata intermediate between normalis and breviflora.

T.217. T.65, plant 4 × T.65, plant 2. 81 plants.
Pericline ovoid 81. Phyllaries Black 79 : Bone Brown 2 ; N 76 : VL 5. Florets Dull Dark Purple 77 : Marguerite Yellow 4 ; radiata 6 : semiradiata 3 : eradiata 72 ; normalis 81.
Plants 11 and 81 had phyllaries Black, N, florets Dull Dark Purple, eradiata normalis.
Plant 64 had phyllaries Black, N, florets Marguerite Yellow, eradiata normalis.

T.498. T.217, plant 81 selfed. 29 plants.
Pericline ovoid 29. Phyllaries Black 29 ; N 29 (of which 4 had some high up lateral branchings to the phyllaries). Florets Dull Dark Purple 27 ; eradiata normalis 27.

T.477. T.217, plant 11 × T.217, plant 64. 20 plants.
Pericline ovoid 20. Phyllaries Black 20 ; N 20 (with pectinations sometimes branched high up). Florets Dull Dark Purple 19 : Marguerite Yellow 1 ; radiata normalis 1 : eradiata normalis 18 : eradiata breviflora 1.

T.466. T.217, plant 64 selfed. 22 plants.
Pericline ovoid 22. Phyllaries Black 22 ; N 22. Florets Marguerite Yellow 22 ; radiata 1 : eradiata 21 ; normalis 22.

T.481. T.217, plant 64 × T.217, plant 11. 29 plants.
Pericline ovoid 29. Phyllaries Black 27 : Bone Brown 2 ; N 29 (of which 9 had some high up lateral branchings to the phyllaries). Florets Dull Dark Purple 21 : Marguerite Yellow 8; radiata 1 : eradiata 28 ; normalis 29.

T.497. T.217, plant 81 × T.217, plant 64. 6 plants.
Pericline ovoid 6. Phyllaries Black 6 ; N 6. Florets Dull Dark Purple 6 ; eradiata normalis 6.

T.502. T.217, plant 81 × T.217, plant 11. 7 plants.
Pericline ovoid 7. Phyllaries Black 7 ; N 7 (of which 4 with pectinations sometimes branched high up). Florets Dull Dark Purple 7 ; radiata 1 : eradiata 6 ; normalis 7.

T.465. T.217, plant 11 selfed. 11 plants.
Pericline ovoid 11. Phyllaries Black 11 ; N 6 : VL 5. Florets Dull Dark Purple 11 ; radiata 1 : eradiata 10 ; normalis 11.

T.485. T.217, plant 64 × T.217, plant 81. 42 plants.
Pericline ovoid 42. Phyllaries Black 38 : Bone Brown 4 ; N 42 (of which 14 had some high up lateral branchings to the pectinations in some of the phyllaries). Florets Dull Dark Purple 34 : Marguerite Yellow 8 ; eradiata 42 ; normalis 41 : breviflora 1.

T.219. T.65, plant 13 selfed. 23 plants.
Pericline ovoid 23. Phyllaries Black 23 ; N 22 : VL 1. Florets Dull Dark Purple 23 ; semiradiata 3 : eradiata 20 ; normalis 23.

T.206. T.65 plant 4 selfed. 17 plants.
Pericline ovoid 17. Phyllaries Black 17 ; N 16 : VL 1. Florets Dull Dark Purple 17 ; eradiata normalis 17.

T.218. T.65, plant 9 × T.65, plant 13. 1 plant.
Pericline broadly ovoid. Phyllaries Black ; VL. Florets Dull Dark Purple ; eradiata normalis.

Comments on the Cross S.P.1 × S.P.36.

For pericline shape, the cross BO × O gave, with two exceptions only, O offspring in F_1, F_2, and F_3 families. The F_1, from N × VL for phyllary shape, showed segregation, including 7 L plants. Only VL plants were used to produce F_2 families, all of which and all F_3 families gave either N or VL or only N and VL. Phyllary colour throughout the series was limited to the Black and Bone Brown classes. Floret colour in F_1 gave a result so far unique in our experiments, that a cross M.Y. × M.Y. gave only D.D.P. plants, suggesting complementary factors. Two F_2 families segregated (D.D.P. 67 and M.Y. 3 ; D.D.P. 77 and M.Y. 4) and three others bred true to D.D.P. F_3 families bred true to D.D.P. or M.Y. or segregated variously, the F_2 parents being sometimes D.D.P. and sometimes M.Y. The scorings for ray florets gave different results from those of the two previous series of families though the ovule parent was the same in all three series and the pollen parent in every one was (a different) eradiata stock plant. F_1 gave semiradiata 8 and eradiata 63. In F_2 and F_3 families there was a very strong preponderance of eradiata plants, contrasting strongly with the preponderance of radiata plants in the families derived from the cross S.P.1 × S.P.23. The cross S.P.1 × S.P.27·1 was intermediate in this respect. It would appear that S.P.36 was genetically a " stronger " eradiata plant than either S.P.23 or S.P.27·1. For disc florets, there was true breeding throughout for the normalis condition, except for the appearance of two breviflora plants and one intermediate, in F_3 families.

T.41. S.P.8·1 × S.P.26·1.   32 plants.
Pericline elongate-ovoid 32.   Phyllaries Black 32 ; N 32.   Florets Rood's Violet 32 ; radiata longiflora 30 : eradiata curly longiflora 2.
Plant 1 had florets eradiata curly longiflora.
Plants 2 and 3 had florets radiata longiflora.

T.125. T.41, plant 3 selfed.   3 plants.
Pericline ovoid 2 : broadly ovoid 1.   Phyllaries Black 3 ; N 3.   Florets Rood's Violet 3 ; radiata longiflora 3.

T.153. T.41, plant 1 × T.41, plant 2.   55 plants.
Pericline ovoid 55.   Phyllaries Black 55 ; N 50 : VL 5.   Florets Dull Dark Purple 4 : Rood's Violet 51 ; radiata 28 : eradiata 27 ; normalis 8 : longiflora 33 : curly longiflora 14.

Comments on the Cross S.P.8·1 × S.P.26·1.

The original cross was O × EO for pericline shape and F_1 gave only EO. One F_2 family gave only O, and one segregated. Phyllary shape, from VL × VL gave N 32 in F_1 and segregation in one F_2 in the ratio N 10 : VL 1. Phyllary colour was Black without exception. Floret colour from R.V. × R.V. gave R.V. only in F_1 and some segregation in one F_2. For florets, the cross was eradiata longiflora × eradiata longiflora. F_1 gave the surprising result radiata 30 and eradiata 2, with a 1 : 1 segregation in one F_2 from F_1 eradiata × F_1 radiata. For the longiflora character all the F_1 were longiflora, two of them being curly longiflora. One F_2 family segregated, normalis 8 : longiflora 33 : curly longiflora 14.

T.44.   S.P.13·7 × S.P.13·3.   15 plants.
Pericline ovoid 15.   Phyllaries Black 8 : Bone Brown 7 ;   N 15.
Florets colour Dull Dark Purple 15 ;   radiata longiflora 2 : radiata
curly longiflora 1 : eradiata normalis 11 : eradiata longiflora 1.
Plant 1 had phyllaries Bone Brown, florets eradiata normalis.
Plant 3 had phyllaries Bone Brown, florets radiata longiflora.
Plant 4 had phyllaries Bone Brown, florets radiata curly longiflora.

T.200.   T.44, plant 1 selfed.   14 plants.
Pericline ovoid 14.   Phyllaries Bone Brown 14 ;   N 14.   Florets
Dull Dark Purple 11 :   Rood's Violet 3 ;   radiata 2 : semiradiata 3 :
eradiata 9 ;   normalis 9 : longiflora 5.

T.201.   T.44, plant 3 selfed.   5 plants.
Pericline ovoid 5.   Phyllaries Bone Brown 5 ;   N 5.   Florets Dull
Dark Purple 5 ;   radiata 4 : semiradiata 1 ;   longiflora 4 : curly longi-
flora 1.

T.168.   T.44, plant 3 × T.44, plant 4.   3 plants.
Pericline ovoid 3.   Phyllaries Bone Brown 3 ;   N 3.   Florets Dull
Dark Purple 3 ;   radiata longiflora 3.

T.176.   T.44, plant 3 × T.44, plant 1.   3 plants.
Pericline ovoid 3.   Phyllaries Bone Brown 3 ;   N 3.   Florets Dull
Dark Purple 3 ;   radiata longiflora 3.

Comments on the Cross S.P.13·7 × S.P.13·3.

This cross between two plants from Harbury Cutting, Warwickshire,
gave uniform F_1 and F_2 families for ovoid periclines and N phyllary
shape (though one parent was VL). F_1 was scored Black 8 : Bone
Brown 7 and all F_2 families were scored Bone Brown for phyllary
colour.   For floret colour, the original cross was D.D.P. × R.V.   The
F_1 gave only D.D.P. but R.V. segregated in one F_2 family.   The parents
were both eradiata normalis.   Unfortunately the resulting families of
F_1 and F_2 were small but some radiata plants appeared in every one
of them as did also some longiflora plants.   Of particular interest was
the occurrence of one curly longiflora plant in F_1 and one in an F_2
family.   Both longiflora and curly longiflora are in some sense recessive
to normalis in these plants.

T.49.   S.P.13·6 selfed.   1 plant.
Pericline elongate-ovoid.   Phyllaries Bone Brown ;   VL.   Florets
Dull Dark Purple ;   eradiata normalis.

T.29.   S.P.25·2 × S.P.26·1.   41 plants.
Pericline ovoid 41.   Phyllaries Black 6 : Bone Brown 35 ;   N 41.
Florets Dull Dark Purple 41 ;   eradiata normalis 41.

T.127.   T.29, plant 1 selfed.   15 plants.
Pericline ovoid 15.   Phyllaries Black 15 ; N 15.   Florets Dull Dark Purple 15 ; eradiata 15 ; normalis 14 : longiflora 1.

T.184.   T.29, plant 1 × T.24, plant 3.   4 plants.
Pericline ovoid 4.   Phyllaries Black 4 ; N 4.   Florets Dull Dark Purple 4 ; eradiata normalis 4.

Comments on the Cross S.P.25·2 × S.P.26·1.

The F_1 and F_2 families were uniform for ovoid periclines (though the original cross was broadly ovoid × elongate-ovoid), phyllary shape N, and D.D.P. floret colour (though the original cross was D.D.P. × R.V.), and eradiata capitula.   The scoring for phyllary colour was Black 6 and Bone Brown 35 in F_1 and only Black in F_2.   In F_1 normalis was completely dominant and in one F_2 family there were normalis 14 and longiflora 1, suggesting a 15 : 1 ratio.

T.74.   S.P.27·3 × S.P.36.   54 plants.
Pericline ovoid 54.   Phyllaries Black 54 ; N 51 : VL 3.   Florets Dull Dark Purple 54 ; eradiata normalis 54.
Plants 1, 6, 15, 16, and 22 had phyllaries N.

T.341.   T.74, plant 15 × T.74, plant 22.   65 plants.
Pericline ovoid 65.   Phyllaries Black 63 : Bone Brown 2 ; N 65. Florets Dull Dark Purple 58 : Marguerite Yellow 2 ; eradiata normalis 60.

T.344.   T.74, plant 16 × T.74, plant 22.   80 plants.
Pericline ovoid 80.   Phyllaries Black 77 : Bone Brown 3 ; N 80. Florets Dull Dark Purple 77 : Marguerite Yellow 3 ; eradiata normalis 66.
The seven families immediately below agree with T.341 and T.344 in all essential characters.   The plants (noted) with flowers of Marguerite Yellow colour have phyllaries Bone Brown the remainder have them Black.

T.356.   T.74, plant 1 selfed.   6 plants.   N 5 : VL 1.

T.360.   T.74, plant 1 × T.74, plant 15.   52 plants.
One Marguerite Yellow flowered plant.   N 52 : VL 1.

T.342.   T.74, plant 15 × T.74, plant 16.   66 plants.
One Marguerite Yellow flowered plant.   N 59 : VL 4.

T.343.   T.74, plant 16 × T.74, plant 1.   56 plants.
N 53 : VL 2.

T.337.   T.74, plant 6 selfed.   17 plants.   N 17.

T.361. T.74, plant 1 × T.74, plant 16.   19 plants.
N 19.

T.338. T.74, plant 15 selfed.   16 plants.
One Marguerite Yellow flowered plant.   N 16.

Comments on the Cross S.P.27·3 × S.P.36.

There were uniform F_1 and F_2 families for ovoid periclines and eradiata normalis floret characters.   Only slight segregation if such it was, occurred for N and VL phyllary shapes and Black and Bone Brown phyllary colours.   The main interest in the cross was floret colour, since it was D.D.P. × M.Y.   In F_1 only D.D.P. plants appeared. The ratio of the summated figures for the nine F_2 families was 45·1 : 1. Figures for individual families suggest 63 : 1 ratios and, in one, a 15 : 1 ratio.

T.1. S.P.2 × S.P.3.   10 plants.
Pericline ovoid 10.   Phyllaries Bone Brown 10 ;   N 10.   Florets Dull Dark Purple 10 ;   radiata normalis 10.

T.5. S.P.3 × S.P.2.   61 plants.
Pericline ovoid 61.   Phyllaries Bone Brown 61 ;   N 61.   Florets Dull Dark Purple 61 ;   radiata normalis 61.

T.6. S.P.3 × S.P.5.   33 plants.
Pericline ovoid 33.   Phyllaries Bone Brown 33 ;   N 33.   Florets Dull Dark Purple 30 : Dull Dark Purple rays partly white 3 ;   radiata normalis 33.

T.2. S.P.5 × S.P.3.   63 plants.
Pericline ovoid 63.   Phyllaries Bone Brown 63 ;   N 63.   Florets Dull Dark Purple 31 : Dull Dark Purple but rays white and more or less flushed or tipped with colour 32 ;   radiata normalis 63.
Plants 4 and 5 had rays white or white flushed colour.

T.92. T.2, plant 4 selfed.   7 plants.
Pericline ovoid 7.   Phyllaries Bone Brown 7 ;   N 7.   Florets Dull Dark Purple 2 : Dull Dark Purple but rays white 3 : Dull Dark Purple but rays white flushed colour 2 ;   radiata normalis 7.

T.93. T.2, plant 3 × T.2, plant 4.   17 plants.
Pericline ovoid 17.   Phyllaries Bone Brown 17 ;   N 17.   Florets Dull Dark Purple 7 : Dull Dark Purple but rays white 1 : Dull Dark Purple but rays white flushed colour 9 ;   radiata normalis 17.

T.96. T.2, plant 3 × T.2, plant 5.   7 plants.
Pericline ovoid 7.   Phyllaries Bone Brown 7 ;   N 7.   Florets Dull

Dark Purple 3 : Dull Dark Purple but rays white 1 : Dull Dark Purple but rays white flushed colour 3 ; radiata normalis 7.

T.88. T.2, plant 3 selfed. 1 plant.
Pericline ovoid. Phyllaries Bone Brown ; N. Florets Dull Dark Purple ; radiata normalis.

T.3. S.P.4 × S.P.5 65 plants.
Pericline ovoid 65. Phyllaries Black 32 : Bone Brown 33 ; N 65. Florets Dull Dark Purple 64 : Dull Dark Purple but with few ray florets partly white 1 ; radiata normalis 65.

T.7. S.P.5 × S.P.4. 85 plants.
Pericline ovoid 85. Phyllaries Black 40 : Bone Brown 45 ; N 85. Florets Dull Dark Purple 81 : Dull Dark Purple but with one ray floret white flushed colour 4 ; radiata normalis 85.

T.105. S.P.15 × S.P.5. 10 plants.
Pericline ovoid 10. Phyllaries Bone Brown 10 ; N 5 : VL 5. Florets Dull Dark Purple 7 : Dull Dark Purple but rays white flushed colour 3 ; radiata normalis 10.

Comments on a Series of Crosses Involving
Stock Plants 2, 3, 4, 5, and 15.

This somewhat miscellaneous series of families, was uniform for ovoid pericline, N phyllary shape (except for a segregation in the ratio 1 : 1 for N : VL phyllary shape in T.105), D.D.P. floret colour (except for some plants with ray florets partially white, a character due to genes introduced from Stock Plant 5) and for radiata normalis floret characters. Phyllary colour was all Bone Brown except for S.P.4 × S.P.5 and its reciprocal where there was, as scored, segregation for Black and Bone Brown.

T.47. S.P.1 × S.P.15. 29 plants.
Pericline ovoid 29. Phyllaries Bone Brown 29 ; N 29. Florets Marguerite Yellow 29 ; radiata normalis 29.

T.57. S.P.6 × S.P.17. 43 plants.
Pericline ovoid 43. Phyllaries Bone Brown 39 : Prout's Brown 4 ; N 43. Florets Dull Dark Purple 43 ; eradiata normalis 43.

T.56. S.P.7 × S.P.17. 38 plants.
Pericline elongate-ovoid 38. Phyllaries Black 4 : Bone Brown 6 : Prout's Brown 28 ; N 38. Florets Dull Dark Purple 38 ; radiata longiflora 1 : semiradiata normalis 3 : eradiata normalis 34.
Plant 1 had phyllaries Prout's Brown, florets semiradiata normalis.
Plant 2 had phyllaries Prout's Brown, florets radiata longiflora.
Plant 4 had phyllaries Black, florets eradiata normalis.

T.174. T.56, plant 4 × T.56, plant 1. 20 plants.
Pericline elongate-ovoid 17 : ovoid 3. Phyllaries Black 12 : Prout's
Brown 6 ; N 11 : VL 7. Florets Dull Dark Purple 19 ; radiata 2 :
eradiata 17 ; normalis 19.

T.185. T.56, plant 2 × T.56, plant 4. 14 plants.
Pericline elongate-ovoid 14. Phyllaries Prout's Brown 14 ; N 9.
Florets Dull Dark Purple 6 : Rood's Violet 3 ; radiata 1 : semiradiata
1 : eradiata 7 ; normalis 7 : longiflora 1 : breviflora 1.

T.182. T.56, plant 2 × T.56, plant 1. 42 plants.
Pericline elongate-ovoid 42. Phyllaries Prout's Brown 42 ; N 32.
Florets Rood's Violet 32 ; radiata 18 : eradiata 14 ; normalis 23 :
longiflora 9.

T.203. T.56, plant 1 selfed. 18 plants.
Pericline elongate-ovoid 17 : ovoid 1. Phyllaries Prout's Brown 18 ;
N 18. Florets Dull Dark Purple 16 ; radiata 6 : eradiata 9 ; normalis
13 : longiflora 2.

T.204. T.56, plant 2 selfed. 3 plants.
Pericline ovoid 3. Phyllaries Prout's Brown 3 ; N 2 : VL 1. Florets
Dull Dark Purple 3 ; radiata 3 ; normalis 1 : longiflora 2.

T.205. T.56, plant 4 selfed. 33 plants.
Pericline elongate-ovoid 33. Phyllaries Black 33 ; N 26 : VL 1.
Florets Dull Dark Purple 27 ; radiata 2 : eradiata 25 ; normalis 27.

Comments on a Series of Crosses Involving
Stock Plants 1, 6, 7, 15 *and* 17.

F_1 families were uniform for pericline shape O (from BO × O and
O × O) or for EO (from EO × O). From the last, F_2 families consisted
mostly of EO plants, *i.e.*, plants similar in this character to the immediate parent or parents, but a very few O plants appeared in three
families. For the phyllary shape, the original crosses were all N × VL
and all F_1 families were uniformly N. There was some segregation in
three F_2 families from S.P.7 × S.P.17. S.P.1 × S.P.15 bred true to
Bone Brown for phyllary colour. S.P.6 × S.P.17 and S.P.7 × S.P.17
in F_1 families, and in F_2 families from the latter, segregated plants with
Prout's Brown phyllaries. The genes for this colour came, at least in
part, from S.P.17 which was Prout's Brown. S.P.1 × S.P.15, that is
M.Y. × M.Y. for floret colour gave only M.Y. plants. S.P.6 × S.P.17,
that is B.P. × R.V., and S.P.7 × S.P.17, that is R.V. × R.V. gave
only D.D.P., but in F_2 families from the latter the results varied.
Three selfings and one sib cross gave only D.D.P. plants, while one
cross gave D.D.P.6 and R.V.3 and another gave R.V.32 only. There
are obviously definite gene combinations needed to give this or that

colour. In the cross S.P.1 × S.P.15, the F_1 bred true to the radiata character of both parents. In S.P.6 × S.P.17 (eradiata × semi-radiata) eradiata was dominant in F_1, but in S.P.7 × S.P.17 (eradiata × radiata) there was segregation in F_1 and in all F_2 families, except one small one. The only cross segregating in F_1 and F_2 families for disc floret characters was S.P.7 × S.P.17. In this series of experiments it is of particular interest to note the different results of using S.P.17 as a pollen parent with two different ovule parents.

T.37. S.P.13·7 × S.P.24·5. 33 plants.
Pericline ovoid 33. Phyllaries Bone Brown 32 : Prout's Brown 1 ; N 33. Florets Bishop's Purple 33 ; radiata longiflora 22 : eradiata normalis 11.
Plants 1 and 7 had phyllaries Bone Brown, florets radiata longiflora.
Plant 2 had phyllaries Bone Brown, florets eradiata normalis.
Plants 3 and 5 had phyllaries Bone Brown, florets radiata normalis.

T.196. T.37, plant 7 selfed. 5 plants.
Pericline ovoid 5. Phyllaries Bone Brown 5 ; N 4 : VL 1. Florets Bishop's Purple 5 ; radiata longiflora 5.

T.183. T.37, plant 3 × T.37, plant 1. 23 plants.
Pericline ovoid 23. Phyllaries Bone Brown 23 ; N 18. Florets Dull Dark Purple 3 : Bishop's Purple 15 ; radiata 17 : eradiata 1 ; normalis 7 : longiflora 11.

T.165. T.37, plant 2 × T.24, plant 4. 29 plants.
Pericline ovoid 29. Phyllaries Bone Brown 29 ; N 29. Florets Dull Dark Purple 21 : Bishop's Purple 8 ; radiata 5 : eradiata 24 ; normalis 24 : longiflora 5.

T.164. T.37, plant 2 × T.37, plant 3. 18 plants.
Pericline ovoid 18. Phyllaries Bone Brown 18 ; N 17. Florets Dull Dark Purple 1 : Bishop's Purple 16 ; radiata 3 : eradiata 14 ; normalis 12 : longiflora 5.

T.163. T.37, plant 2 × T.37, plant 5. 12 plants.
Pericline ovoid 12. Phyllaries — ; N 11 : VL1. Florets Dull Dark Purple 2 : Bishop's Purple 10 ; radiata 4 : semiradiata 2 : eradiata 6 ; normalis 8 : longiflora 2.

T.166. T.37, plant 7 × T.30, plant 4. 5 plants.
Pericline ovoid 5. Phyllaries Bone Brown 5 ; N 4 : VL 1. Florets Dull Dark Purple 5 ; radiata longiflora 5.

T.175. T.37, plant 3 × T.37, plant 7. 41 plants.
Pericline ovoid 41. Phyllaries Bone Brown 41 ; N 10 : VL 17 : L 5. Florets Dull Dark Purple 22 : Rood's Violet 10 ; radiata 19 : eradiata 12 ; normalis 17 : longiflora 14.

T.173. T.37, plant 1 × T.37, plant 3.   8 plants.
Pericline ovoid 8.   Phyllaries Bone Brown 8 ;   N 2 : VL 6.   Florets
Bishop's Purple 8 ;   radiata 8 ;   normalis 3 : longiflora 5.

T.180. T.37, plant 3 × T.56, plant 1.   14 plants.
Pericline ovoid 14.   Phyllaries Prout's Brown 14 ;   N 13 : VL 1.
Florets Dull Dark Purple 14 ;   radiata 11 : eradiata 3 ;   normalis 10 :
longiflora 4.

T.195. T.37, plant 3 selfed.   34 plants.
Pericline ovoid 34.   Phyllaries Bone Brown 34 ;   N 24 : VL 5.   Florets
Dull Dark Purple 14 : Bishop's Purple 14 ;   radiata 18 : eradiata 10 ;
normalis 24 : longiflora 4.

T.194. T.37, plant 2 selfed.   29 plants.
Pericline ovoid 29.   Phyllaries Bone Brown 29 ;   N 29.   Florets
Bishop's Purple 29 ;   radiata 3 : eradiata 26 ;   normalis 29.

T.193. T.37, plant 1 selfed.   3 plants.
Pericline ovoid 3.   Phyllaries Bone Brown 3 ;   N 3.   Florets
Bishop's Purple 3 ;   radiata longiflora 3.

Comments on the Cross $S.P.13 \cdot 7 \times S.P.24 \cdot 5$.

There was true breeding throughout for ovoid periclines. $S.P.13 \cdot 7$
had VL and $S.P.24 \cdot 5$ N phyllary shape. All F_1 plants were N, but
five F_2 families segregated and one included five L plants. The
original parents had Bone Brown phyllaries. In F_1 only one plant had
phyllaries Prout's Brown, while 32 had them Bone Brown. This Prout's
Brown plant crossed with a Bone Brown sib yielded 14 Prout's Brown
plants only. The other F_2 families gave only Bone Brown offspring.
$S.P.13 \cdot 7$ had florets of D.D.P. colour. The colour of those of $S.P.24 \cdot 5$
was, by oversight, not recorded. The breeding results suggest they
were B.P. since this was the floret colour of all F_1 plants and of some
plants in most F_2 families. The original cross was between eradiata
and radiata plants and there was segregation in F_1 and most F_2
families. Each of the original parents had normalis florets, but there
were longiflora plants in F_1 and all but one of the F_2 families.

T.43. S.P.21 × S.P.26·1.   13 plants.
Pericline ovoid 13.   Phyllaries Black 8 : Bone Brown 5 ;   N 11 :
VL 2.   Florets Rood's Violet 13 ;   radiata longiflora 11 :   eradiata
longiflora 2.
Plant 2 had phyllaries Bone Brown, N, florets radiata longiflora.
Plant 3 had phyllaries Black, N, florets eradiata longiflora.

T.156. T.43, plant 2 × T.43, plant 3.   5 plants.
Pericline ovoid 5.   Phyllaries Black 4 : Bone Brown 1 ;   N 3 : VL 2.
Florets Rood's Violet 5 ;   radiata longiflora 5.

T.159. T.43, plant 3 × T.24, plant 1. 44 plants.

Pericline ovoid 44. Phyllaries Black 2 : Bone Brown 42 ; N 40 : VL 4. Florets Rood's Violet 8 : Dull Dark Purple 36 ; radiata longiflora 36.

T.155. T.26, plant 2 × T.43, plant 3. 3 plants.

Pericline ovoid 3. Phyllaries Black 2 : Bone Brown 1 ; N 2 : VL 1. Florets Bishop's Purple 2 : Rood's Violet 1 ; radiata longiflora 3.

Comments on the Cross S.P.21 × S.P.26·1.

The original cross was between plants with O and EO periclines, but in the F_1 and F_2 families, and in a backcross, only plants with ovoid (O) periclines appeared. Both parents had VL phyllary shape and there was segregation into N and VL in all offspring families. Phyllary colour throughout was Black or Bone Brown. The original cross was between D.D.P. and R.V. floret colours. The F_1 gave only R.V. One small F_2 family gave only R.V. but when two plants derived from other crosses were used there was segregation. The F_1 segregated into radiata 11 and eradiata 2, but the other families bred true to radiata. All families gave only longiflora disc florets, like those of the original parents, even when one parent (in T.24·1) had normalis florets.

T.42. S.P.24·5 × S.P.13·7. 16 plants.

Pericline ovoid 16. Phyllaries Bone Brown 16 ; N 16. Florets Dull Dark Purple 16 ; radiata normalis 4 : radiata longiflora 5 : eradiata normalis 7.

Plant 1 had florets eradiata normalis.

Plant 3 had florets radiata longiflora.

T.160. T.42, plant 3 × T.24, plant 4. 19 plants.

Pericline ovoid 19. Phyllaries Bone Brown 19 ; N 14 : VL 4. Florets Dull Dark Purple 14 : Rood's Violet 5 ; radiata 16 : eradiata 3 ; normalis 16 : longiflora 2 : curly longiflora 1.

T.198. T.42, plant 1 selfed. 93 plants.

Pericline ovoid 93. Phyllaries Bone Brown 93 ; N 81 : VL 6. Florets Dull Dark Purple 87 ; radiata 29 : semiradiata 19 : eradiata 39 ; normalis 63 : longiflora 24.

T.199. T.42, plant 3 selfed. 7 plants.

Pericline ovoid 7. Phyllaries Bone Brown 7 ; N 7. Florets Dull Dark Purple 7 ; radiata longiflora 7.

Comments on the Cross S.P.24·5 × S.P.13·7.

This was the reciprocal of the cross considered on p. 102, but with only two F_2 families. There was true breeding for ovoid periclines and Bone Brown phyllaries. All F_1 plants had N phyllary shape but one

F_2 family segregated for N and VL, though no L plants appeared. One family gave five R.V. coloured florets, otherwise all the plants in F_1 and F_2 had D.D.P. florets. There was segregation in F_1 and one F_2 family for presence or absence of rays. The second F_2 family was obtained by selfing an eradiata F_1 plant and gave 7 radiata plants only. The F_1 family and two F_2 families segregated for normalis and longiflora disc florets and one curly longiflora plant occurred in one family. One can say that the behaviour in the reciprocal crosses, and their F_2 families, was essentially similar, except for floret colour.

T.30. S.P.24·5 × S.P.26·1. 39 plants.
Pericline elongate-ovoid 39. Phyllaries Bone Brown 39 ; N 39. Florets Dull Dark Purple 39 ; radiata longiflora 14 : semiradiata longiflora 25.
Plants 1, 2, 3, and 4 had florets radiata longiflora.

T.140. T.30, plant 1 selfed. 21 plants.
Pericline elongate-ovoid 21. Phyllaries Black 7 : Bone Brown 14 ; N 16 : VL 5. Florets Dull Dark Purple 20 : Rood's Violet 1 ; radiata 21 ; normalis 1 : longiflora 20.

T.154. T.30, plant 2 × T.30, plant 3. 5 plants.
Pericline ovoid 5. Phyllaries Bone Brown 5 ; N 5. Florets Dull Dark Purple 5 ; radiata 5 ; normalis 1 : longiflora 4.

Comments on the Cross S.P.24·5 × S.P.26·1.

The cross O × EO for pericline shape gave only EO in F_1 and one F_2 family. Another small F_2 family gave five O plants only. Phyllary colour was Black or Bone Brown. Floret colour was entirely D.D.P. except for the appearance of one R.V. plant in one F_2 family. Radiata and semiradiata plants appeared in F_1 but only radiata plants in F_2. All F_1 and all except two F_2 plants were longiflora.

T.21. S.P.25·2 × S.P.24·5. 46 plants.
Pericline broadly ovoid 46. Phyllaries Bone Brown 46 ; N 46. Florets Bishop's Purple 46 ; eradiata normalis 46.

T.190. T.21, plant 1 selfed. 7 plants.
Pericline ovoid 7. Phyllaries Bone Brown 7 ; N 7. Florets Bishop's Purple 7 ; eradiata normalis 7.

T.170. T.21, plant 1 × T.21, plant 2. 2 plants.
Pericline ovoid 1 : broadly ovoid 1. Phyllaries Bone Brown 2 ; N 2. Florets Bishop's Purple 2 ; eradiata normalis 2.

T.181. T.21, plant 1 × T.24, plant 3. 20 plants.

Pericline ovoid 20. Phyllaries Black 3 : Bone Brown 17 ; N 20. Florets Dull Dark Purple 17 : Rood's Violet 2 ; radiata 4 : eradiata 15 ; normalis 19.

T.150. T.22, plant 2 × T.21, plant 1. 4 plants.

Pericline ovoid 3 : broadly ovoid 1. Phyllaries — ; N 4. Florets Dull Dark Purple 4 ; eradiata normalis 4.

T.151. T.21, plant 5 × T.24, plant 7. 47 plants.

Pericline ovoid 47. Phyllaries Bone Brown 7 : Prout's Brown 40 ; N 42 : VL 3. Florets Dull Dark Purple 45 ; radiata 7 : eradiata 38 ; normalis 45.

Comments on the Cross S.P.25·2 × S.P.24·5.

Broadly ovoid (BO) × ovoid (O) pericline gave only BO in F_1. The two F_2 families were small ; one segregated into BO and O and one gave only O. Crossed with other derived plants of varied origin, F_1 plants gave only offspring with ovoid periclines. Only plants with N phyllaries that were Bone Brown in colour appeared in F_1 and F_2 families though there was some segregation when other plants were crossed with F_1 individuals. Of particular interest was the appearance of 40 plants with phyllaries Prout's Brown in T.151 after the crossing of an F_1 with a Prout's Brown plant, though this did not happen in T.181 where two other plants, phenotypically like those used in T.151, were used. F_1 and the two F_2 families gave only plants with Bishop's Purple for floret colour. Introducing other plants resulted in Dull Dark Purple florets only, except for two with Rood's Violet florets. The eradiata character was completely dominant over the radiata character and the latter only appeared in some plants in crosses of F_1 with other (semiradiata) plants. The disc florets all through were normalis.

c. Selfing of a Guernsey Plant.

T.247. S.P.58·2 selfed. 6 plants.

Pericline ovoid 6. Phyllaries Tawny Olive 6 ; N 6. Florets Marguerite Yellow 6 ; eradiata normalis 6.

Comments on S.P.58·2 Selfed.

Only one very small family was obtained but in this there was true breeding for ovoid pericline, N-shaped and Tawny Olive coloured phyllaries, Marguerite Yellow florets, absence of ray florets, and normalis disc florets.

Some General Comments.

The series of selfings and crossings were made of or between plants that had been determined, not by us, as either *C. nigra* or *C. nemoralis*.

It was hoped to obtain some light on the genetics of intraspecific, or what were for long considered to be intraspecific, variations. This matter is discussed later. Here it must be pointed out that certain Stock Plants used above were shown not to be pure *C. nigra* or *C. nemoralis* but to have *C. jacea* genes in their genoms, as based upon phyllary shape in F_1 and/or F_2 families. Such were Stock Plants 10, 13·7, 17, and 36. This does not mean that all the other stock plants used were homozygous for all specific characters.

D. SELFINGS AND CROSSINGS INVOLVING *C. jacea*.

a. *Only* C. jacea *Involved*.

T.95. S.P.34·1 selfed. 3 plants.
Pericline ovoid 3. Phyllaries Prout's Brown 3 ; VM 3. Florets Dull Dark Purple 3 ; radiata normalis 3.

T.115. S.P.34·2 selfed. 2 plants.
Pericline ovoid 2. Phyllaries Prout's Brown 2 ; C 2. Florets Argyle Purple 2 ; semiradiata normalis 2.

T.102. S.P.34·1 × S.P.34·2. 10 plants.
Pericline ovoid 10. Phyllaries Prout's Brown 10 ; VM 5 : C 5. Florets Dull Dark Purple 10 ; radiata 6 : semiradiata 4 ; normalis 9 : breviflora 1.

T.75. S.P.45·1 × S.P.45·2. 38 plants.
Pericline elongate-ovoid 38. Phyllaries Prout's Brown 38 ; C 38. Florets Bishop's Purple 38 ; radiata 26 : semiradiata 7 ; normalis 24 : breviflora 9 (of which 4 are radiata and 5 semiradiata).

T.71. S.P.45·1 × S.P.45·3. 11 plants.
Pericline elongate-ovoid 11. Phyllaries Prout's Brown 11 ; C 11. Florets Bishop's Purple 11 ; radiata 11 ; normalis 10 : breviflora 1.

T.408. S.P.48 selfed. 1 plant.
Pericline ovoid. Phyllaries Bone Brown ; VM. Florets Bishop's Purple ; radiata normalis.

T.97. S.P.45·2 × S.P.34·1. 1 plant.
Pericline ovoid. Phyllaries Prout's Brown ; VM. Florets Dull Dark Purple ; radiata normalis.

Comments on Selfings and Inter-crossings of C. jacea *Stock Plants.*

None of the families in the above section was large and four of the seven were very small. The results indicate true or essentially true breeding for the characters studied, except for the appearance in three families from crosses of breviflora plants and slight variations between

VM and C for phyllary shape and for radiata and semiradiata for ray florets. For floret colour, Dull Dark Purple is dominant over both Bishop's Purple and Argyle Purple, the former in a very small and the latter in a small family.

With the next group of families we commence a study of interbreeding deliberately between *C. jacea* and *C. nigra* s.l., using stock plants either thought to be "specifically pure" or putative hybrids. The shape of the phyllaries is, from some points of view, the most important character for generally evaluating the hybridity of a plant in the following experiments, most of which were designed to aid in interpreting field work on wild populations.

b. *Involving* C. jacea *and* C. nigra *or* C. nemoralis.

T.100. S.P.34·1 × S.P.36. 11 plants.
Pericline ovoid 11. Phyllaries Bone Brown 4 : Prout's Brown 7 ; N 1 : VL 5 : L 3 : S 2. Florets Dull Dark Purple 11 ; semiradiata 4 : eradiata 7 ; normalis 11.
Plant 3 had phyllaries Prout's Brown, VL, florets eradiata nomalis.
Plant 6 had phyllaries Prout's Brown, S, florets eradiata normalis.
Plant 8 had phyllaries Prout's Brown, L, florets eradiata normalis.

T.274. T.100, plant 3 selfed. 14 plants.
Pericline ovoid 14. Phyllaries Prout's Brown 14 ; N 2 : VL 4 : L 5 : S 3. Florets Dull Dark Purple 7 : Rood's Violet 4 ; radiata 1 : semiradiata 1 : eradiata 9 ; normalis 11.

T.275. T.100, plant 6 selfed. 13 plants.
Pericline ovoid 10 : broadly ovoid 3. Phyllaries Prout's Brown 9 : Russet 4 ; VL 2 : L 3 : S 3 : M 4. Florets Dull Dark Purple 12 ; radiata 1 : semiradiata 1 : eradiata 7 ; normalis 9.

T.298. T.100, plant 6 × T.100, plant 8. 69 plants.
Pericline ovoid 69. Phyllaries Prout's Brown 69 ; N 2 : VL 13 : L 14 : S 21 : M 17 : VM 2. Florets Dull Dark Purple 59 : Marguerite Yellow 1 ; eradiata normalis 60.

Comments on the Cross *S.P.*34·1 × *S.P.*36.

The F_1 has periclines all ovoid and so had all F_2 families except one. In one of these, from a selfing of an F_1 plant, three plants with broadly ovoid periclines were scored. The original cross was between parents with VM and VL phyllaries and there was segregation in the F_1 and all F_2 families. The largest of the latter (69 plants) was derived from the cross, of F_1 plants, S × L and gave a hybrid index of 263·3. F_1 was between plants with Prout's Brown and Bone Brown phyllaries. The F_1 family and one of the F_2 families segregated for phyllary colour, but plants with phyllaries Prout's Brown were most numerous. In F_1, Dull Dark Purple floret colour was dominant over Marguerite Yellow.

Only one M.Y. plant appeared in F_2 families, but in another F_2 family there were four plants with Rood's Violet florets. The figures in T.298 were D.D.P. 59 and M.Y. 1. For ray florets from the original cross, radiata × eradiata, there was segregation in F_1 and three F_2 families. One F_2 family, from eradiata × eradiata, gave eradiata 60 only. Disc florets throughout were normalis.

T.98. S.P.34·1 × S.P.15. 39 plants.
Pericline ovoid 39. Phyllaries Bone Brown 39 ; N 4 : VL 13 : L 5 : S 7 : M 5 : VM 5. Florets Bishop's Purple 39 ; radiata 38 : semiradiata 1 ; normalis 39. 2 plants (nos. 9 and 31) had peculiarly elongated phyllaries.
Plants 19 and 37 had phyllaries N, florets radiata normalis.
Plants 29 and 31 had phyllaries S, florets radiata normalis.

T.389. T.98, plant 19 selfed. 4 plants.
Pericline ovoid 4. Phyllaries Bone Brown 4 ; VL 3 : S 1. Florets Dull Dark Purple 4 ; radiata normalis 4.

T.390. T.98, plant 31 selfed. 4 plants.
Pericline ovoid 4. Phyllaries Bone Brown 4 ; VL 2 : S 1 : M 1. Florets Dull Dark Purple 3 ; radiata normalis 3.

T.407. T.98, plant 19 × T.98, plant 29. 45 plants.
Pericline elongate-ovoid 1 : ovoid 44. Phyllaries Bone Brown 20 : Prout's Brown 25 ; N 8 : VL 11 : L 6 : S 10 : M 9 : elongated M 1. Florets Rood's Violet 3 : Bishop's Purple 38 : Argyle Purple 3 ; radiata 43 : semiradiata 1 ; normalis 21 : intermediate between normalis and breviflora 23.

T.385. T.98, plant 19 × T.98, plant 31. 39 plants.
Pericline elongate-ovoid 1 : ovoid 38. Phyllaries Bone Brown 13 : Prout's Brown 26 ; N 11 : VL 8 : L 9 : S 10 : M 1. Florets Dull Dark Purple 32 : Bishop's Purple 2 : Marguerite Yellow 1 ; radiata 35 ; normalis 28 : longiflora 1 : intermediate between normalis and breviflora 6.

T.384. T.98, plant 19 × T.98, plant 37. 49 plants.
Pericline ovoid 49. Phyllaries Bone Brown 25 : Prout's Brown 24 ; N 12 : VL 9 : L 6 : S 16 : M 6. Three plants had very elongated discs to the phyllaries. Florets Bishop's Purple 46 : Argyle Purple 1 ; radiata 47 ; normalis 43 : intermediate between normalis and breviflora 3 : longiflora 1.

T.388. T.98, plant 31 × T.98, plant 37. 38 plants.
Pericline ovoid 38. Phyllaries Bone Brown 18 : Prout's Brown 20 ; N 5 : VL 4 : L 2 : S 11 : M 15. Florets Bishop's Purple 37 ; radiata normalis 37.

T.402. T.98, plant 37 × T.98, plant 29.   22 plants.

Pericline ovoid 22.   Phyllaries Bone Brown 7 : Prout's Brown 15 ;
VL 3 : L 2 : S 8 : M 9.   Florets Rood's Violet 1 : Bishop's Purple 18 :
Mallow Purple 1 ; radiata 20 ; normalis 13 : intermediate between
normalis and breviflora 7.

T.386. T.98, plant 37 × T.98, plant 31.   20 plants.

Pericline ovoid 20.   Phyllaries Bone Brown 12 : Prout's Brown 8 ;
N 1 : VL 5 : L 3 : S 11 : M 6.   Florets Rood's Violet 1 : Bishop's
Purple 16 : Argyle Purple 2 ; radiata 19 ; normalis 17 : intermediate
between normalis and breviflora 2.

Comments on the Cross S.P.34·1 × S.P.15.

There was true breeding for ovoid periclines except for the appearance of a plant with elongate-ovoid periclines in each of two F_2 families.
For phyllary shape, the original cross was between VM and VL.   Every
family showed segregation.   It is worth noting that two F_2 families
were reciprocals, S × M and M × S and gave hybrid indexes 272·7
and 261·9 respectively.   One plant in one F_2 family and three plants
in another had narrow elongated discs to the phyllary appendages.
It is interesting that this character appeared in F_2 families from
an interspecific cross, because it has been recorded in wild hybrid
swarms and has been given taxonomic value.   In F_1, Bone Brown was
dominant over Prout's Brown and there was segregation in six F_2
families, the other two were very small.   The figures suggest a 1 : 1
ratio, and this may be correct.   The F_1 gave only plants whose florets
were Bishop's Purple in colour from the cross D.D.P. × M.Y.   There
was segregation in most F_2 families but only one M.Y. plant appeared.
One plant with florets of the rare Mallow Purple occurred in an F_2
family from two F_1 plants crossed together.   All plants had ray
florets, all except two 2·5 cm. or more in length.   Two longiflora plants
segregated in two F_2 familes.   Most interesting was the appearance in
five F_2 families of a total of 41 plants with disc florets intermediate
between normalis and breviflora.

T.99. S.P.15 × S.P.34·1.   61 plants.

Pericline ovoid 61.   Phyllaries Bone Brown 39 : Prout's Brown 22 ;
N 19 : VL 13 : L 9 : S 17.   Florets Bishop's Purple 61 ; radiata 60 :
semiradiata 1 ; normalis 58 : breviflora 3.

Comments on the Cross S.P.15 × S.P.34·1.

This is the reciprocal of the last stock plant cross considered but no
F_2 family was raised.   It bred true for ovoid periclines.   Segregation
occurred for all other characters except floret colour.   The hybrid
index for phyllary shape was only 143·4 as compared with 228·1 which
was the H.I. for the reciprocal.   There was segregation in F_1 for
Phyllary colour, though in the reciprocal this occurred only in F_2

families. The original cross was M.Y. × D.D.P. for floret colour and all the F_1 offspring were Bishop's Purple (B.P.). From R × R, the F_1 had R 60 and S 1, for ray florets. Three plants with breviflora disc florets occurred in F_1.

T.101. S.P.34·1 × T.2, plant 5. 29 plants.
Pericline ovoid 29. Phyllaries Bone Brown 1 : Prout's Brown 28 ; L 1 : S 8 : M 17 : VM 3. Florets Rood's Violet 29 ; radiata 14 : semi-radiata 15 ; normalis 1 : breviflora 27 (in addition, 1 plant, no. 1, had some heads breviflora but mostly normalis).

T.103. T.2, plant 5 × S.P.34·1. 77 plants.
Pericline ovoid 77. Phyllaries Bone Brown 65 : Russet 12 ; N 2 : VL 16 : L 21 : S 34 : M 4. Florets Dull Dark Purple 74, in 22 of which a few odd white petals in the ray florets ; radiata normalis 74.
Plant 31 had phyllaries Bone Brown, S.
Plant 42 had phyllaries Bone Brown, L, a few odd ray petals white.

T.244. T.103, plant 31 selfed. 1 plant.
Pericline ovoid. Phyllaries Bone Brown ; VL. Florets Rood's Violet ; radiata longiflora.

T.246. T.103, plant 31 × T.103, plant 42. 14 plants.
Pericline ovoid 14. Phyllaries Bone Brown 2 : Russet 12 ; N 6 : VL 5 : L 2 : S 1. Florets Dull Dark Purple 14 ; of which 3 had partially white rays ; radiata normalis 14.

Comments on the Crosses S.P.34·1 × T.2·5 and the Reciprocal.

Pericline shape was ovoid in all families. Segregation occurred for phyllaries shape and the hybrid indexes for the two reciprocal crosses were 375·5 and 228·8 respectively. For phyllary colour there was segregation in both F_1 families and in one F_2 family but the results were not exactly comparable. Floret colour was "linked" with structure of disc florets to a high degree. In S.P.34·1 × T.2·5, only plants (29) with Rood's Violet florets appeared and of these 1 had normalis, 27 breviflora, and 1 intermediate disc florets. In the reciprocal, the florets of all plants (77) were Dull Dark Purple, though 22 had odd petals of the ray florets white or flushed, and the disc florets were normalis. In S.P.34·1 × T.2·5 there were radiata 14 and semi-radiata 15, but in the reciprocal and its F_2 families all the plants were radiata.

T.112. T.2, plant 5 × S.P.34·2. 5 plants.
Pericline ovoid 5. Phyllaries Bone Brown 1 : Prout's Brown 4 ; S 4 : M 1. Florets Dull Dark Purple 5 ; radiata normalis 5.

T.110. S.P.34·2 × S.P.2. 13 plants.
Pericline ovoid 13. Phyllaries Bone Brown 5 : Prout's Brown 8 ; S 6 : M 6. Florets — ; radiata 9 : semiradiata 2 ; normalis 6 : breviflora 5. One plant had many aborted capitula.

T.108. S.P.2 × S.P.34·2. 33 plants.
Pericline ovoid 33. Phyllaries Bone Brown 20 : Prout's Brown 13 ; S 16 : M 15 : VM 1 : C 1. Florets Bishop's Purple 30 ; radiata normalis 30. 4 of the plants produced many aborted capitula.

T.113. S.P.34·2 × S.P.5. 25 plants.
Pericline ovoid 25. Phyllaries Prout's Brown 23 ; L 1 : S 6 : M 7 : VM 2 : C 6. Florets Bishop's Purple 25, but rays white flushed pink in one plant ; radiata 8 : semiradiata 10 ; normalis 16 : breviflora 3.
Plant 5 had phyllaries S, florets radiata normalis, rays white flushed pink.
Plants 7 and 19 had phyllaries M, florets semiradiata breviflora.
Plant 8 had phyllaries M, florets radiata normalis.
Plant 9 had phyllaries —, florets semiradiata normalis.

T.243. T.113, plant 5 selfed. 52 plants.
Pericline ovoid 52. Phyllaries Bone Brown 4 : Prout's Brown 48 ; N 1 : VL 3 : L 7 : S 20 : M 9 : VM 10 : C 2. Florets Dull Dark Purple 9 : Bishop's Purple 14 : Rood's Violet 29 ; white rays 5 : partially white or tinged rays 12 ; radiata 40 : semiradiata 12 ; normalis 38 : breviflora 14.

T.233. T.113, plant 19 × T.113, plant 8. 2 plants.
Pericline ovoid 2. Phyllaries Prout's Brown 2 ; M 1 : C 1. Florets Dull Dark Purple 2 ; radiata breviflora 2.

T.242. T.113, plant 9 × T.113, plant 5. 39 plants.
Pericline ovoid 39. Phyllaries Prout's Brown 39 ; VL 3 : L 2 : S 9 : M 16 : VM 5 : C 4. Florets Dull Dark Purple 7 : Rood's Violet 32 ; with some to all white or partially white rays 8 (no. 10 had white rays slightly flushed Rood's Violet) ; radiata 16 : semiradiata 23 ; normalis 16 : breviflora 22 : some heads normalis and some breviflora 1.
Plant 20 had phyllaries VL, florets Rood's Violet, radiata normalis.
Plant 23 had phyllaries VM, florets Dull Dark Purple, semiray petals white flushed colour, semiradiata normalis.
Plant 27 had phyllaries L, florets Rood's Violet, semiray petals white flushed colour, semiradiata breviflora.
Plant 29 had phyllaries C, florets Rood's Violet, semiradiata breviflora.

T.524. T.242, plant 23 selfed. 1 plant.
Pericline ovoid. Phyllaries Prout's Brown ; M. Florets Rood's Violet ; radiata ; intermediate between normalis and breviflora.

T.520. T.242, plant 20 × T.242, plant 23. 9 plants.
Pericline ovoid 9. Phyllaries Prout's Brown 9 ; VL 1 : L 1 : S 5 : M 2. Florets Dull Dark Purple 1 : Rood's Violet 1 : rays white 2 : rays white flushed 5 ; radiata 9 ; normalis 5 : intermediate between normalis and breviflora 3 : breviflora 1.

T.518. T.242, plant 27 × T.242, plant 23. 23 plants.
Pericline ovoid 23. Phyllaries Prout's Brown 23 ; L 1 : S 8 : M 14. Florets Dull Dark Purple 2 : Rood's Violet 3 : rays white 4 : rays white flushed 14 ; radiata 23 ; normalis 6 : intermediate between normalis and breviflora 5 : breviflora 12.

T.522. T.242, plant 29 × T.242, plant 20. 64 plants.
Pericline ovoid 64. Phyllaries Prout's Brown 64 ; L 4 : S 26 : M 32 : VM 1. Florets Dull Dark Purple 24 : Rood's Violet 23 : rays white 4 : rays white flushed 13 ; radiata 63 : semiradiata 1 ; normalis 30 : intermediate between normalis and breviflora 5 : breviflora 29.

T.527. T.242, plant 29 × S.P.45·6. 78 plants.
Pericline ovoid (slightly elongated) 78. Phyllaries Bone Brown 78 ; S 3 : M 26 : VM 41 : C 8. Florets Dull Dark Purple 78 ; radiata 78 ; normalis 66 : intermediate between normalis and breviflora 12.

T.229. T.113, plant 19 × T.113, plant 7. 77 plants.
Pericline ovoid 77. Phyllaries Bone Brown 4 : Prout's Brown 73 ; N 1 : VL 4 : L 3 : S 8 : M 32 : VM 21 : C 8. Florets Dull Dark Purple 16 : Bishop's Purple 61 ; with some white or partially white rays 10 ; radiata 45 : semiradiata 32 ; normalis 11 : breviflora 65 : some heads normalis and some breviflora 1.
Plant 7 had phyllaries Prout's Brown, VM, florets Bishop's Purple, radiata normalis.
Plant 32 had phyllaries Prout's Brown, C, florets Bishop's Purple, semiradiata breviflora.
Plant 36 had phyllaries Prout's Brown, M, florets Bishop's Purple, ray petals white flushed colour, radiata breviflora.

T.521. T.229, plant 36 × 229, plant 7. 6 plants.
Pericline ovoid 6. Phyllaries Bone Brown 1 : Prout's Brown 5 ; L 2 : S 1 : M 3. Florets Bishop's Purple 4 : rays white flushed 2 ; radiata 6 ; normalis 2 : intermediate between normalis and breviflora 3 : longiflora 1.

T.519. T.229, plant 32 × S.P.45·6. 74 plants.
Pericline ovoid (slightly elongated) 74. Phyllaries Bone Brown 8 : Prout's Brown 66 ; M 10 : VM 22 : C 42. Florets Bishop's Purple 74 ; radiata 74 ; normalis 69 : intermediate between normalis and breviflora 4 : breviflora 1.

T.468. T.229, plant 36 × S.P.45·6. 60 plants.
Pericline ovoid (slightly elongated) 60. Phyllaries Bone Brown 44 : Prout's Brown 16 ; L 1 : S 3 : M 32 : VM 21 : C 3. Florets Bishop's Purple 60 ; radiata 60 ; normalis 54 : intermediate between normalis and breviflora 6.

T.517. T.229, plant 32 × T.230, plant 1. 55 plants.
Pericline ovoid 2 : broadly ovoid 53. Phyllaries Prout's Brown 55 ; S 3 : M 40 : VM 9 : C 2. Florets Rood's Violet 4 : Bishop's Purple 50 ; radiata 55 ; normalis 17 : intermediate between normalis and breviflora 8 : breviflora 30.

Comments on Crosses Involving S.P.34·2.

These are a somewhat miscellaneous set of crosses, but may be considered together. All the families bred true to ovoid pericline shape, except when S.P.45·6 was introduced when the pericline became sli htly elongated. There was segregation in all families for phyllary shape, except in one family with only one plant. There was segregation into Bone Brown and Prout's Brown or only the latter appeared for phyllary colour, except in T.527, a family of complicated origin involving three stock plants. Here, unexpectedly, Prout's Brown × Prout's Brown gave only Bone Brown offspring. Floret colour ranged, with or without segregation, from Dull Dark Purple to Bishop's Purple, but the interesting result was the appearance in many plants, in eight families, of some white or flushed petals in some ray florets. This apparently very minor character was due to genes from S.P.5. All the plants had ray or semiray florets. There was, in most families segregation for normalis and breviflora and/or intermediate disc florets. It would appear that interspecific crossing sometimes upsets the development of normal reproductive systems with the production of female or " intermediate " disc florets.

T.77. S.P.27·3 × S.P.45·2. 23 plants.
Pericline elongate-ovoid 23. Phyllaries Black 2 : Prout's Brown 21 ; N 8 : VL 9 : L 5 : S 1. Florets Dull Dark Purple 23 ; semiradiata 2 : eradiata 21 ; normalis 20 : breviflora 2.
Plants 1 and 6 had phyllaries Prout's Brown, L, florets eradiata normalis.
Plants 2 and 22 had phyllaries Prout's Brown, S, florets eradiata normalis.
Plant 11 had phyllaries Prout's Brown, VL, florets eradiata normalis.

T.368. T.77, plant 1 selfed. 4 plants.
Pericline elongate-ovoid 4. Phyllaries Prout's Brown 4 : L 3 : S 1. Florets Dull Dark Purple 4 ; radiata 2 : eradiata 2 ; normalis 2 : longiflora 2.

T.380.   T.77, plant 1 × T.77, plant 2.   20 plants.
Pericline elongate-ovoid 18 : ovoid 2.   Phyllaries Black 3 : Prout's
Brown 17 ;   VL 3 : L 12 : S 3 : M 2.   Florets Dull Dark Purple 20 ;
radiata 4 : eradiata 16 ; normalis 16 : longiflora 4.

T.377.   T.77, plant 1 × T.77, plant 6.   28 plants.
Pericline elongate-ovoid 25 : ovoid 3.   Phyllaries Black 3 : Prout's
Brown 25 ;   N 1 : VL 8 : L 12 : S 7.   Florets Dull Dark Purple 28 ;
radiata 4 : semiradiata 1 : eradiata 23 ; normalis 23 : longiflora 5.

T.378.   T.77, plant 1 × T.77, plant 11.   86 plants.
Pericline elongate-ovoid 86.   Phyllaries Black 16 : Prout's Brown
70 ;   N 3 : VL 18 : L 22 : S 39 : M 4.   Florets Dull Dark Purple 84 ;
radiata 13 : eradiata 71 ; normalis 72 : longiflora 12.

T.383.   T.77, plant 2 × T.77, plant 6.   10 plants.
Pericline elongate-ovoid 10.   Phyllaries Black 2 : Prout's Brown 8 ;
N 1 : VL 1 : L 6 : S 2.   Florets Dull Dark Purple 10 ;   radiata 2 :
eradiata 8 ; normalis 9 : longiflora 1.

T.379.   T.77, plant 6 × T. 77. plant 2.   54 plants.
Pericline elongate-ovoid 6 : ovoid 48.   Phyllaries Black 6 : Prout's
Brown 48 ;   N 3 : VL 6 : L 23 : S 18 : M 4.   Florets Dull Dark Purple
52 : Rood's Violet 1 ; radiata 7 : eradiata 46 ; normalis 48 : longiflora 5.

T.381.   T.77, plant 6 × T.77, plant 11.   58 plants.
Pericline elongate-ovoid 54 : ovoid 4.   Phyllaries Black 9 : Prout's
Brown 49 ;   N 3 : VL 5 : L 11 : S 34 : M 5.   Florets Dull Dark Purple
57 ; radiata 18 : eradiata 39 ; normalis 42 : longiflora 15.

T.374.   T.77, plant 2 × T.77 plant 1.   14 plants.
Pericline elongate-ovoid 14   Phyllaries Prout's Brown 14 ; VL 2 :
L 7 : S 4 : M 1   Florets Dull Dark Purple 14 ; radiata 4 : eradiata 10 ;
normalis 10 : longiflora 4.

T.376.   T.77 plant 22 × T.77 plant 11.   16 plants.
Pericline elongate-ovoid 16.   Phyllaries Black 1 : Prout's Brown 15 ;
N 1 : VL 3 : L 5 : S 4 : M 3.   Florets Dull Dark Purple 15 ; radiata 8 :
eradiata 7 ; normalis 7 : longiflora 8.

Comments on the Cross S.P.27·3 × S.P.45·2.

The cross broadly ovoid × elongate-ovoid gave only the latter in F_1
but four F_2 families segregated for ovoid and elongate-ovoid and five gave
only the latter.   If the phenotypic scoring correctly reflects genotypic
differences all except one of the nine F_2 families may represent an
elongate-ovoid 15 : ovoid 1 ratio.   The one exception, T.379 is not
explained since it gave a ratio of ovoid 8 : elongate-ovoid 1.   For

phyllary shape, the cross was between extremes, N × C. All families showed segregation but the F_1 was rather nearer to N than might have been expected in spite of its not being a very large family. As a consequence, the immediate parent or parents of the F_2 families did not score " higher " towards C than S. However, in five families some M plants appeared. The reciprocals, T.383 (S × L) and T.379 (L × S) had hybrid indexes 190 and 225·5 respectively. The small family T.377, L × L, 28 plants scored, had a hybrid index of 189·24, while T.378, L × VL, 86 plants scored, had a hybrid index of 226·74. One would have expected a higher figure in the former, but the discrepancy probably illustrates the limits of reliability of the hybrid index unless a large family or population has been scored. The F_1 was produced by crossing plants with phyllary colours Black and Prout's Brown. There was segregation in every family for these two colours except in two F_2 families. The summated totals for the nine F_2 families, all derived from F_1 parents with phyllaries Prout's Brown in colour, gave a ratio of Black 1 : Prout's Brown 6·07. The original cross for floret colour of D.D.P. × B.P. gave only D.D.P. in all families except for the segregation of a single plant with Rood's Violet florets in one F_2 family. It is surprising that Bishop's Purple was " swamped " so completely in a total of 290 plants. F_1 was derived from crossing eradiata and radiata stock plants. There was segregation for presence or absence of ray or semiray florets in all families, only eradiata F_1 plants being used to produce the F_2 families which gave the summated figures radiata 56 : semiradiata 7 : eradiata 212, a ratio of rays or semirays to none approximating to 1 : 3. The F_1 and all F_2 families were produced from immediate parents with normalis disc florets. The appearance in F_2 families of a total of 56 longiflora plants is significant, though the ratios varied greatly for individual families.

T.87. S.P.45·2 × T.2, plant 2. 12 plants.
Pericline elongate-ovoid 5 : ovoid 7. Phyllaries Bone Brown 12 ; VL 4 : L 4 : S 2 : M 2. Florets Bishop's Purple 12 ; radiata normalis 12.
Plant 4 had pericline elongate-ovoid, phyllaries VL.
Plant 10 had pericline ovoid, phyllaries L.

T.398. T.87, plant 4 selfed. 7 plants.
Pericline ovoid 7. Phyllaries Bone Brown 7 ; S 3 : M 3 : VM 1. Florets Dull Dark Purple 7 ; radiata normalis 7.

T.401. T.87, plant 10 selfed. 4 plants.
Pericline ovoid 4. Phyllaries Bone Brown 3 : Prout's Brown 1 ; VL 1 : L 2 : S 1. Florets Dull Dark Purple 3 ; radiata normalis 3.

Comments on the Cross $S.P.45\cdot2 \times T.2\cdot2$.

The families were small and ratios may not be significant. There was segregation for pericline shape in F_1 but not in F_2 families, for phyllary shape in all families, and for phyllary colour in one F_2 family. For floret colour, B.P. × D.D.P. gave only B.P. in F_1 and only D.D.P. in the small F_2 families. There was true breeding throughout for radiata normalis floret characters.

T.109. S.P.15 × S.P.45·1. 26 plants.
Pericline elongate-ovoid 26. Phyllaries Prout's Brown 26 ; N 1 : VL 1 : L 6 : S 11 : M 7. Florets Bishop's Purple 26 ; radiata normalis 26.
Plants 11 and 14 had phyllaries S.
Plant 23 had phyllaries M.

T.456. T.109, plant 11 selfed. 4 plants.
Pericline ovoid 4. Phyllaries Prout's Brown 4 ; L 1 : S 1 : M 1 : VM 1. Florets Argyle Purple 4 ; radiata normalis 4.

T.458. T.109, plant 14 selfed. 4 plants.
Pericline elongate-ovoid 4. Phyllaries Prout's Brown 4 ; S 2 : M 2. Florets Bishop's Purple 4 ; radiata normalis 4.

T.457. T. 109, plant 23 selfed. 5 plants.
Pericline elongate-ovoid 1 : ovoid 4. Phyllaries Prout's Brown 5 ; S 1 : M 3 : VM 1. Florets Argyle Purple 5 ; radiata 5 ; normalis 4 : breviflora 1.

T.451. T.109, plant 11 × T.109, plant 14. 12 plants.
Pericline elongate-ovoid 2 : ovoid 10. Phyllaries Prout's Brown 12 ; VL 4 : L 4 : S 4. Florets Bishop's Purple 4 : Argyle Purple 7 : Marguerite Yellow 1 ; radiata normalis 12.

T.447. T.109, plant 23 × T.109, plant 14. 12 plants.
Pericline elongate-ovoid 5 : ovoid 7. Phyllaries Bone Brown 1 : Prout's Brown 11 ; VL 1 : L 1 : S 5 : M 5. Florets Argyle Purple 10 ; radiata normalis 10.

T.111. T.2, plant 5 × S.P.45·1. 87 plants.
Pericline elongate-ovoid 18 : ovoid 69. Phyllaries Bone Brown 81 : Prout's Brown 6 ; VL 8 : L 31 : S 44 : M 3. Florets Bishop's Purple 87, one plant with rays white flushed pink ; radiata normalis 84.
Plant 9 had pericline ovoid, phyllaries Bone Brown, VL.
Plant 36 had pericline ovoid, phyllaries Bone Brown, S, ray petals white flushed colour.
Plants 80 and 84 had pericline ovoid, phyllaries Bone Brown, S.
Plant 85 had pericline ovoid, phyllaries Prout's Brown, VL.

T.453. T.111, plant 36 selfed. 2 plants.
Pericline ovoid 2. Phyllaries Bone Brown 2 ; L 1 : S 1. Florets Bishop's Purple 2 ; radiata normalis 2.

T.454. T.111, plant 85 selfed. 5 plants.
Pericline elongate-ovoid 1 : ovoid 3. Phyllaries Bone Brown 5 ; N 1 : VL 4, discs narrow and elongated. Florets Bishop's Purple 5 ; radiata normalis 5.

T.455. T.111, plant 84 selfed. 13 plants.
Pericline ovoid 2 : broadly ovoid 11. Phyllaries Bone Brown 12 : Prout's Brown 1 ; VL 1 : L 1 : S 8 : M 3. Florets Bishop's Purple 5 : rays white flushed Bishop's Purple 3 ; radiata normalis 13.

T.444. T.111, plant 9 × T.111, plant 80. 60 plants.
Pericline ovoid 60. Phyllaries Bone Brown 33 : Prout's Brown 27 ; VL 4 : L 16 : S 34 : M 5. Florets Bishop's Purple 46 (two with white rays tinged Argyle Purple)) : Argyle Purple 1 ; radiata normalis 47.

T.445. T.111, plant 36 × T.111, plant 80. 12 plants.
Pericline elongate-ovoid 2 : ovoid 10. Phyllaries Bone Brown 8 : Prout's Brown 4 ; L 3 : S 8 : M 1. Florets Bishop's Purple 10 (five with white rays tinged Argyle Purple) ; radiata normalis 10.

T.446. T.111, plant 84 × T.111, plant 9. 18 plants.
Pericline ovoid 18. Phyllaries Bone Brown 12 : Prout's Brown 6 ; L 1 : S 8 : M 8. Florets Bishop's Purple 12 (two with white rays tinged Argyle Purple) ; radiata normalis 12.

T.449. T.111, plant 85 × T.111, plant 84. 10 plants.
Pericline elongate-ovoid 1 : ovoid 9. Phyllaries Bone Brown 3 : Prout's Brown 7 ; VL 6 : L 4. Florets Bishop's Purple 8 (one with white rays tinged Argyle Purple) ; radiata 8 ; normalis 7 : longiflora 1.

T.80. S.P.45·1 × S.P.16. 14 plants.
Pericline elongate-ovoid 14. Phyllaries Bone Brown 14 ; VL 6 : L 5 : S 2 : M 1. Florets Bishop's Purple 14 ; radiata normalis 14.
Plant 2 had phyllaries M.
Plants 3 and 7 had phyllaries L.
Plant 12 had phyllaries S.

T.241. T.80, plant 2 selfed. 75 plants.
Pericline elongate-ovoid 75. Phyllaries Bone Brown 62 : Prout's Brown 13 ; VL 1 : L 2 : S 11 : M 29 : VM 19 : C 12. Florets Bishop's Purple 75 ; rays white flushed Bishop's Purple at apex 1 ; radiata 75 ; normalis 73 : breviflora 2.

T.240. T.80, plant 7 selfed. 32 plants.
Pericline elongate-ovoid 32. Phyllaries Bone Brown 32 ; VL 1 : L 2 : S 23 : M 6. Florets Bishop's Purple 24 ; radiata 24 ; normalis 20 : breviflora 4.

T.235. T.80, plant 12 selfed. 25 plants.
Pericline elongate-ovoid 25. Phyllaries Bone Brown 25 ; VL 1 : L 2 : S 4 : M 15 : VM 3. Florets Bishop's Purple 25 ; radiata normalis 25.

T.236. T.80, plant 7 × T.80, plant 3. 21 plants.
Pericline elongate-ovoid 21. Phyllaries Bone Brown 21 ; VL 1 : L 7 : S 9 : M 4. Florets Bishop's Purple 19 ; radiata 19 ; normalis 18 : breviflora 1.

T.234. T.80, plant 7 × T.80, plant 12. 26 plants.
Pericline elongate-ovoid 26. Phyllaries Bone Brown 26 ; VL 3 : L 7 : S 13 : M 3. Florets Bishop's Purple 26, 2 with ray lobes white flushed Bishop's Purple ; radiata 26 ; normalis 23 : breviflora 3.

Comments on Crosses Involving S.P.45·1.

Three groups of crosses may, for purposes of comparison, be considered together.

The pericline shape of S.P.45·1 was scored as elongate-ovoid. When this plant was used as pollen parent on ovule parents with ovoid periclines it was either dominant or there was segregation in F_1 and, with one exception, either segregation or true breeding for ovoid periclines in F_2 families. When crossed with S.P.16 (elongate-ovoid periclines) as pollen parent all families had only elongate-ovoid periclines. There was segregation for phyllary shape in every family. In three F_2 families, from selfing three F_1 plants of S.P.45·1 × S.P.16 (C × N), scored as M, S, and L respectively, the following hybrid indexes were obtained 434·0, 368·0, and 316·4 respectively. These are very closely comparable one with another on the basis of the F_1 scorings but are all somewhat higher than might have been anticipated. Two of the F_1 families were for phyllary colour derived from Bone Brown × Prout's Brown and one from Prout's Brown × Bone Brown. There is a considerable difference in the results following the use of different Bone Brown parents : S.P15 × S.P.45·1 (Bone Brown × Prout's Brown) gave in F_1 and F_2 families only Prout's Brown offspring except for one plant in an F_2 family scored as Bone Brown ; T.2·5 × S.P.45·1 (Bone Brown × Prout's Brown), gave families that segregated (apart from two very small families) ; S.P.45·1 × S.P.16 (Prout's Brown × Bone Brown) gave families with only Bone Brown plants, except for one segregating family. For floret colour, the F_1 from M.Y. × B.P. gave only B.P. plants ; F_2 families had florets Bishop's Purple or Argyle Purple, apart from one family that segregated. Unfortunately, the F_2 families were small but only one M.Y. plant occurred in a total of 35 plants. The special interest of floret colour in the other two groups of families was in the appearance of a total of 17 plants with some petals of some ray florets either white or flushed, characters genetically derived from T.2·5 or S.P.16, respectively. There was true breeding throughout for radiata floret character and for normalis disc florets except for the appearance of ten plants with breviflora florets in F_2 families from the cross S.P.45·1 × S.P.16 and one longiflora plant in an F_2 family.

T.68.   S.P.1 × S.P.48.   15 plants.
(7 of the plants were as S.P.1 and were discarded as " rogues.")
Percline ovoid 6 : broadly ovoid 2. Phyllaries Bone Brown 8 ; VL 5 : L 1 : S 2. Florets Bishop's Purple 8 ; radiata normalis 8.
Plant 10 had pericline ovoid, phyllaries S.
Plant 15 had pericline —, phyllaries L.

T.212.   T.68, plant 10 selfed.   7 plants.
Pericline ovoid 7. Phyllaries Bone Brown 7 ; N 2 : VL 2 : L 1 : S 1 : M 1. Florets Dull Dark Purple 5 : Bishop's Purple 2 ; radiata normalis 7.

T.224.   T.68, plant 15 selfed.   93 plants.
Pericline ovoid 14 : broadly ovoid 79. Phyllaries Bone Brown 65 : Light Ochraceous-Buff 27 ; N 4 : VL 19 : L 18 : S 29 : M 23.   Florets Bishop's Purple 65 : Argyle Purple 8 : Purplish Lilac 15 : Marguerite Yellow 4 ; radiata normalis 92.
Plant 10 had pericline broadly ovoid, phyllaries Light Ochraceous-Buff, N, florets Purplish Lilac.
Plant 13 had pericline broadly ovoid, phyllaries Light Ochraceous-Buff, S, florets Purplish Lilac.
Plant 26 had pericline broadly ovoid, phyllaries Bone Brown, M, florets Bishop's Purple.
Plant 29 had pericline broadly ovoid, phyllaries Light Ochraceous Buff, L, florets Marguerite Yellow.
Plant 55 had pericline broadly ovoid, phyllaries Light Ochraceous-Buff, M, florets Argyle Purple.
Plant 58 had pericline broadly ovoid, phyllaries Bone Brown, M, florets Bishop's Purple.
Plant 67 had pericline broadly ovoid, phyllaries Light Ochraceous-Buff, M, florets Marguerite Yellow.
Plant 69 had pericline broadly ovoid, phyllaries Bone Brown, L, florets Bishop's Purple.
Plant 76 had pericline broadly ovoid, phyllaries Light Ochraceous-Buff, S, florets Argyle Purple.
Plant 89 had pericline broadly ovoid, phyllaries Light Ochraceous-Buff, M, florets Marguerite Yellow.

T.494.   T.224, plant 13 selfed.   29 plants.
Pericline broadly ovoid 29. Phyllaries Light Ochraceous-Buff 29 ;

S 9 : M 13 : VM 4 : C 3.   Florets Purplish Lilac 23 : Marguerite Yellow 6 ; radiata 29 ; normalis 28 : breviflora 1.

T.505.   T.224, plant 55 selfed.   2 plants.
Pericline broadly ovoid 2.   Phyllaries Light Ochraceous-Buff 2 ; VM 2.   Florets Argyle Purple 2 ; radiata 2 ; intermediate between normalis and breviflora 2.

T.486.   T.224, plant 58 selfed.   15 plants.
Pericline broadly ovoid 15.   Phyllaries Bone Brown 14 ; L 1 : S 5 : M 8 : VM 1.   Florets Bishop's Purple 14 ; radiata 14 ; normalis 11 : intermediate between normalis and breviflora 3.

T.536.   T.224, plant 67 selfed.   11 plants.
Pericline broadly ovoid 11.   Phyllaries Light Ochraceous-Buff 11 ; VL 1 : L 1 : S 4 : M 4 : VM 1.   Florets Marguerite Yellow 10 ; radiata 10 ; normalis 7 : intermediate between normalis and breviflora 1 : breviflora 2.

T.475.   T.224, plant 89 selfed.   3 plants.
Pericline broadly ovoid 3.   Phyllaries Light Ochraceous-Buff 3 ; S 1 : M 2.   Florets Marguerite Yellow 3 ; radiata normalis 3.

T.493.   T.224, plant 10 × T.224, plant 13.   43 plants.
Pericline broadly ovoid 43.   Phyllaries Light Ochraceous-Buff 43 ; L 13 : S 23 : M 7.   Florets Purplish Lilac 24 : Marguerite Yellow 19 ; radiata normalis 43.

T.482.   T.224, plant 13 × T.224, plant 89.   12 plants.
Pericline broadly ovoid 12.   Phyllaries Light Ochraceous-Buff 12 ; S 5 : M 6.   Florets Purplish Lilac 6 : Marguerite Yellow 6 ; radiata normalis 12.

T.496.   T.224, plant 29 × T.224, plant 67.   2 plants.
Pericline broadly ovoid 2.   Phyllaries Light Ochraceous-Buff 2 ; S 2.   Florets Marguerite Yellow 2 ; radiata normalis 2.

T.506.   T.224, plant 58 × T.224, plant 13.   57 plants.
Pericline broadly ovoid 57.   Phyllaries Bone Brown 48 : Light Ochraceous-Buff 8 ; L 7 : S 25 : M 24.   Florets Bishop's Purple 42 : Argyle Purple 6 : Purplish Lilac 6 : Marguerite Yellow 2 ; radiata normalis 56.

T.503.   T.224, plant 67 × T.224, plant 13.   58 plants.
Pericline broadly ovoid 58.   Phyllaries Light Ochraceous-Buff 58 ; L 7 : S 24 : M 23 : VM 4.   Florets Purplish Lilac 24 : Marguerite Yellow 34 ; radiata 58 ; normalis 57 : intermediate between normalis and breviflora 1.

T.500.   T.224, plant 67 × T.224, plant 58.   12 plants.
Pericline broadly ovoid 12. Phyllaries Bone Brown 5 : Light
Ochraceous-Buff 7 ; N 1 : VL 1 : L 1 : S 6 : M 2.   Florets Bishop's
Purple 5 : Marguerite Yellow 7 ; radiata 12 ; normalis 6 : breviflora
3 : intermediate between normalis and breviflora 1.

T.508.   T.224, plant 67 × T.224, plant 76.   49 plants.
Pericline broadly ovoid 49. Phyllaries Light Ochraceous-Buff 49 ;
VL 3 : L 7 : S 24 : M 15.   Florets Argyle Purple 45 : Marguerite Yellow
4 ; radiata normalis 49.

T.490.   T.224, plant 67 × T.224, plant 89.   21 plants.
Pericline broadly ovoid 21.   Phyllaries Light Ochraceous-Buff 21 ;
L 3 : S 6 : M 10 : VM 2.   Florets Marguerite Yellow 21 ; radiata 21 ;
normalis 16 : breviflora 5.

T.504.   T. 224, plant 76 × T.224, plant 67.   56 plants.
Pericline broadly ovoid 56. Phyllaries Light Ochraceous-Buff 56 ;
N 1 : VL 4 : L 10 : S 23 : M 15 : VM 3.   Florets Argyle Purple 54 :
Marguerite Yellow 2 ; radiata 56 ; normalis 53 : intermediate between
normalis and breviflora 3.

T.501.   T.224, plant 89 × T.224, plant 10.   5 plants.
Pericline ovoid 2 : broadly ovoid 3. Phyllaries Bone Brown 3 :
Light Ochraceous-Buff 2 ; N 2 : S 2 : M 1.   Florets Bishop's Purple 3 :
Marguerite Yellow 2 ; radiata normalis 5.

T.492.   S.P.1 × T.224, plant 13.   58 plants.
Pericline broadly ovoid 58. Phyllaries Bone Brown 58 ; N 3 :
VL 12 : L 19 : S 18 : M 6.   Florets Bishop's Purple 55 ; radiata nor-
malis 55.

T.489.   S.P.1 × T.224, plant 58, 2 plants.   (One " with only aborted
    capitula.")
Pericline broadly ovoid 1. Phyllaries Bone Brown 1 ; VL 1.
Florets Bishop's Purple 1 ; radiata 1 ; intermediate between normalis
and breviflora 1.

T.483.   T.224, plant 58 × S.P.1.   59 plants.
Pericline broadly ovoid 59. Phyllaries Black 1 : Bone Brown 58 ;
N 15 : VL 18 : L 17 : S 7 : M 1 : VM 1.   Florets Bishop's Purple 59 ;
radiata normalis 59. Three plants had most heads aborted.

T.539.   S.P.1 × T.224, plant 69.   20 plants.
Pericline ovoid 18 : broadly ovoid 1. Phyllaries Black 2 : Bone
Brown 18 ; N 2 : VL 7 : L 5 : S 5.   Florets Bishop's Purple 3 : Argyle
Purple 9 : Marguerite Yellow 3 ; radiata normalis 15.
One plant had only aborted capitula.

T.478. S.P.1 × T.224, plant 76. 47 plants.
Pericline broadly ovoid 47. Phyllaries Bone Brown 47 ; N 7 :
VL 19 : L 20 : S 10 : M 1. Florets Bishop's Purple 42 : Argyle Purple
4 : Purplish Lilac 1 ; radiata normalis 47.

T.484. T.224, plant 76 × S.P.1. 43 plants.
Pericline ovoid 9 : broadly ovoid 34. Phyllaries Bone Brown 43 ;
N 9 : VL 21 : L 12 : S 1. Florets Bishop's Purple 2 : Argyle Purple 41 ;
radiata 43 ; normalis 41 : breviflora 2.

T.471. T.224, plant 89 × S.P.1. 60 plants.
Pericline ovoid 7 : broadly ovoid 53. Phyllaries Bone Brown 60 ;
N 14 : VL 31 : L 9 : S 6. Florets Bishop's Purple 60 ; radiata normalis
60.

T.488. T.224, plant 10 × S.P.1. 59 plants.
Pericline broadly ovoid 59. Phyllaries Bone Brown 59 ; N 29 :
VL 29 : S 1. Florets Bishop's Purple 59 ; radiata normalis 59.

T.476. T.224, plant 29 × S.P.1. 59 plants.
Pericline broadly ovoid 59. Phyllaries Bone Brown 59 ; N 16 :
VL 33 : L 10. Florets Bishop's Purple 56 : Marguerite Yellow 3 ;
radiata 59 ; normalis 55 : intermediate between normalis and breviflora 3 : breviflora 1.

T.550. T.224, plant 26 × S.P.1. 70 plants.
Pericline broadly ovoid 70. Phyllaries Bone Brown 61 : Prout's
Brown 7 : Light Ochraceous-Buff 2 ; N 7 : VL 13 : L 21 : S 24 : M 5.
Florets Bishop's Purple 68 : Marguerite Yellow 2 ; radiata 69 ; nor-
malis 68 : breviflora 1.

T.509. T.224, plant 89 × S.P.45·6. 55 plants.
Pericline elongate-ovoid 9 : broadly ovoid 46. Phyllaries Bone
Brown 21 : Prout's Brown 34 ; L 1 : S 14 : M 24 : VM 16. Florets
Bishop's Purple 55 ; radiata normalis 55.

T.473. T. 224, plant 89 × S.P.48. 58 plants.
Pericline broadly ovoid 58 ; with many " double " heads. Phyl-
laries Bone Brown 58 ; N 1 : VL 4 : L 8 : S 33 : M 12. Florets Bishop's
Purple 58 ; radiata normalis 58.

Comments on the Cross S.P.1 × S.P.48, and Backcrosses.

The small F_1 from the cross for pericline shape broadly ovoid × ovoid
gave a 1 : 3 ratio. One F_2 family from ovoid F_1 gave only ovoid and
another F_2 family segregated. F_3 families from broadly ovoid F_2
plants gave only broadly ovoid plants, with one exception. F_3 plants
backcrossed with S.P.1 either gave only broadly ovoid plants or the

families segregated into ovoid and broadly ovoid plants. Crossing a broadly ovoid F_3 with S.P.45·6 (elongate-ovoid) gave a segregation of broadly ovoid 46 and elongate-ovoid 9. For phyllaries shape, there was segregation throughout, except in two exceedingly small families, and, possibly, in one backcross. The hybrid indexes of reciprocals are : M × S 304·1, S × M 301·5 and N × S 163·1, S × N 111·5. The original cross was, for phyllary colour, Bone Brown × Bone Brown. In one F_2 family, in most F_3 families, and in one backcross family, plants with phyllaries of a new colour, Light Ochraceous-Buff, appeared. The F_1 was, for floret colour, produced by crossing M.Y. × B.P. There was segregation in F_2 and many F_3 families. The appearance of plants with Purplish Lilac florets is noteworthy. There was true breeding throughout for the radiata character, but some plants with breviflora and some with intermediate disc florets appeared in some F_3 and backcross families.

T.79. S.P.27·3 × S.P.48. 32 plants.
Pericline elongate-ovoid 1 : ovoid 31. Phyllaries Bone Brown 32 ; N 24 : VL 7 : S 1. Florets Dull Dark Purple 32 ; semiradiata 6 : eradiata 26 ; normalis 32.
Plants 2, 15, and 23 had pericline ovoid, phyllaries N, florets eradiata.
Plants 9 and 25 had pericline ovoid, phyllaries VL, florets eradiata.
Plant 10 had pericline ovoid, phyllaries S, florets eradiata.

T.251. T.79, plant 9 selfed. 7 plants.
Pericline ovoid 7. Phyllaries Black 3 : Bone Brown 4 ; N 4 : L 1 : S 2. Florets Dull Dark Purple 7 ; radiata 6 : eradiata 1 ; normalis 3 : longiflora 4.

T.256. T.79, plant 10 selfed. 20 plants.
Pericline ovoid 20. Phyllaries Black 5 : Bone Brown 15 ; N 1 : VL 1 : L 5 : S 12 : M 1. Florets Dull Dark Purple 19 ; radiata 4 : semiradiata 3 : eradiata 12 ; normalis 17 : longiflora 2.

T.264. T.79, plant 25 selfed. 14 plants.
Pericline ovoid 14. Phyllaries Bone Brown 14 ; N 6 : VL 4 : L 3 : S 1. Florets Dull Dark Purple 14 ; radiata 3 : eradiata 11 ; normalis 14.

T.281. T.79, plant 10 × T.79, plant 9. 12 plants.
Pericline ovoid 12. Phyllaries Bone Brown 12 ; N 3 : VL 2 : L 3 : S 4. Florets Dull Dark Purple 1 : Bishop's Purple 9 : Purplish Lilac 2 ; radiata 4 : semiradiata 2 : eradiata 6 ; normalis 12.

T.262. T.79, plant 10 × T.79, plant 15. 13 plants.
Pericline ovoid 13. Phyllaries Bone Brown 13 ; N 3 : VL 4 : L 2 : S 4. Florets Dull Dark Purple 13 ; radiata 3 : eradiata 10 ; normalis 13.

T.263. T.79, plant 10 × T.79, plant 25. 11 plants.

Pericline ovoid 11. Phyllaries Bone Brown 11 ; N 2 : L 1 : S 5 : M 3. Florets Dull Dark Purple 11 ; radiata 1 : semiradiata 2 : eradiata 8 ; normalis 11.

T.278. T.79, plant 25 × T.79, plant 10. 13 plants.

Pericline ovoid 13. Phyllaries Black 3 : Bone Brown 7 : Prout's Brown 3 ; N 2 : VL 3 : L 3 : S 5. Florets Dull Dark Purple 11 : Bishop's Purple 2 ; radiata 1 : semiradiata 1 : eradiata 11 ; normalis 12 : longiflora 1.

T.265. T.79, plant 23 × T.79, plant 9. 6 plants.

Pericline ovoid 6. Phyllaries Bone Brown 1 : Prout's Brown 5 ; N 2 : VL 3 : L 1. Florets Dull Dark Purple 4 : Bishop's Purple 2 ; radiata 4 : eradiata 2 ; normalis 6.

Comments on the Cross *S.P.*27·3 × *S.P.*48.

The original cross was between plants with periclines scored as broadly ovoid and ovoid. Except for one plant with elongate-ovoid periclines in F_1 all plants in F_1 and F_2 families had ovoid periclines. Crossing N and C for phyllary shape there was less influence of the *C. jacea* (C) parent shown in F_1 than was expected, but in F_2 families segregation occurred much as was expected for the class into which the immediate parents had been scored. Only Bone Brown or Black and Bone Brown phyllary colours appeared in F_1 and F_2 families except for three plants in one F_2 family and five in another with Prout's Brown phyllaries. These are unexplained results, more so that in a reciprocal cross of the former only Bone Brown plants were obtained. For floret colour, the cross D.D.P. × B.P. gave only D.D.P. in F_1, while five F_2 families also gave only D.D.P. but three segregated and in one of these the rare Purplish Lilac colour appeared in two plants. Crossing eradiata with semiradiata plants there was segregation in F_1 and every F_2 family, the F_2 families all from eradiata F_1 parents. The totals for the eight F_2 families were : radiata 26, semiradiata 10, eradiata 59. The parents had normalis disc florets, as had F_1 plants and most F_2 plants, but a few longiflora plants appeared in three F_2 families.

T.107.. T.2, plant 5 × S.P.48. 11 plants.

Pericline ovoid 11. Phyllaries Bone Brown 11 ; VL 2 : L 5 : S 3 : M 1. Florets Dull Dark Purple 11, but one with rays partially white ; radiata normalis 11.

T.104. S.P.15 × S.P.48. 24 plants.

Pericline ovoid 24. Phyllaries Bone Brown 6 : Prout's Brown 17 ; N 3 : VL 3 : L 3 : S 7 : M 5. Florets Dull Dark Purple 24 ; radiata 19 : semiradiata 3 ; normalis 22.

Plant 3 had phyllaries Bone Brown, L, florets radiata normalis.

Plant 10 had phyllaries Prout's Brown, S, florets radiata normalis.
Plant 13 had phyllaries Bone Brown, M, florets radiata normalis.
Plant 14 had phyllaries Prout's Brown, N, florets radiata normalis.

T.258. T.104, plant 10 selfed. 17 plants.
Pericline ovoid 17. Phyllaries Black 4 : Bone Brown 2 : Prout's Brown 11 ; VL 5 : L 5 : S 6 : M 1. Florets Dull Dark Purple 17 ; radiata normalis 17.

T.259. T.104, plant 10 × T.104, plant 3. 13 plants.
Pericline ovoid 13. Phyllaries Black 1 : Bone Brown 5 : Prout's Brown 7 ; N 1 : VL 5 : L 4 : S 3. Florets Dull Dark Purple 5 : Bishop's Purple 8 ; radiata 7 : eradiata 5 ; normalis 12.

T.271. T.104, plant 10 × T.104, plant 13. 6 plants.
Pericline ovoid 6. Phyllaries Black 4 : Prout's Brown 2 ; VL 2 : L 1 : S 3. Florets Dull Dark Purple 1 : Bishop's Purple 4 : Purplish Lilac 1 ; radiata normalis 6.

T.282. T.104, plant 10 × T.104, plant 14. 121 plants.
Pericline ovoid 121. Phyllaries Black 21 : Bone Brown 19 : Prout's Brown 81 ; N 4 : VL 27 : L 39 : S 21 (30 plants not scored for phyllaries). Florets Dull Dark Purple 108 : Purplish Lilac 13 ; radiata normalis 121.

Comments on the Crosses T.2·5 × S.P.48 and S.P.15 × S.P.48.

The former cross was not carried on beyond F_1 which bred true for ovoid pericline shape, Bone Brown phyllary colour, Dull Dark Purple floret colour, and radiata normalis floret characters. There was segregation for phyllary shape.

The latter cross bred true to ovoid pericline shape and normalis disc florets. There was segregation in all families for phyllary shape as was to be expected from a cross N × C. The F_1 from the cross for phyllary colour Bone Brown × Bone Brown gave Bone Brown 6 and Prout's Brown 17 and there was segregation in every F_2 family for Prout's Brown and Bone Brown or Black or both. F_1 florets were all Dull Dark Purple from the cross Marguerite Yellow × Bishop's Purple and some D.D.P. plants occurred in all F_2 families. In two F_2 families B.P. plants occurred and in two there were Purplish Lilac plants. It is remarkable that in a total of 157 F_2 plants none with M.Y. florets appeared. The F_1 was from radiata × semiradiata plants. F_2 families gave radiata individuals only, except for five eradiata plants in one family.

c. Involving Hybrids, that is so-called *C. jungens* and *C. pratensis.*

T.73. S.P.35. 1 selfed. 4 plants.
Pericline broadly ovoid 4. Phyllaries Bone Brown 4 ; S 1 : M 2 :

C 1. Florets Rood's Violet 1 : Bishop's Purple 3 ; radiata normalis 2 : radiata breviflora 1 : semiradiata breviflora 1.
Plant 1 had phyllaries S, florets Bishop's Purple, radiata breviflora.
Plant 3 had phyllaries C, florets Bishop's Purple, radiata normalis.
Plant 4 had phyllaries M, florets Rood's Violet, semiradiata breviflora.

T.239. T.73, plant 1 selfed. 1 plant.
Pericline broadly ovoid. Phyllaries Bone Brown ; M. Florets Bishop's Purple ; radiata breviflora.

T.225. T.73, plant 3 selfed. 86 plants.
Pericline broadly ovoid 86. Phyllaries Bone Brown 86 ; M 16 : VM 32 : C 38. Florets Bishop's Purple 86 ; radiata 86 ; normalis 55 : breviflora 31, some verging towards normalis.
Plant A had phyllaries VM, florets radiata normalis.
Plant B had phyllaries VM, florets radiata breviflora verging towards normalis.

T.479. T.225 A selfed. 22 plants.
Pericline broadly ovoid 22. Phyllaries Bone Brown 22 ; S 1 : M 3 : VM 6 : C 12. Florets colour Dull Dark Purple 4 : Bishop's Purple 18 ; radiata normalis 20.

T.515. T.225 B × T.225 A. 53 plants.
Pericline broadly ovoid 53. Phyllaries Bone Brown 50 ; S 4 : M 31 : VM 16. Florets Bishop's Purple 50 ; radiata 50 ; normalis 42 : intermediate between normalis and breviflora 7 : breviflora 1.

T.507. T.225 B × S.P.45·6. 59 plants.
Pericline broadly ovoid 59. Phyllaries Bone Brown 57 : Prout's Brown 2 ; VM 12 : C 47. Florets Bishop's Purple 59 : radiata 59 ; normalis 55 : intermediate between normalis and breviflora 3 : breviflora 1.

T.470. T.225 A × S.P.48. 32 plants.
Pericline broadly ovoid 32. Phyllaries Bone Brown 32 ; S 8 : M 19 : VM 5. Florets Bishop's Purple 30 ; radiata normalis 30.

T.226. T.73, plant 4 × T.73, plant 3. 7 plants.
Pericline broadly ovoid 7. Phyllaries Bone Brown 7 ; M 4 : C 3. Florets Rood's Violet 2 : Bishop's Purple 5 ; radiata 7 ; normalis 5 : breviflora 2.

T.230. T.73, plant 1 × T.73, plant 3. 63 plants.
Pericline broadly ovoid 63. Phyllaries Bone Brown 63 ; VL 1 : L 1 : S 11 : M 37 : VM 9 : C 4. Florets Dull Dark Purple 52 : Rood's Violet 11 ; radiata 62 : semiradiata 1 ; normalis 41 : breviflora 22.

Plant 1 had phyllaries M, florets Dull Dark Purple, radiata normalis.
Plant 3 had phyllaries M, florets Rood's Violet, radiata normalis.
Plant 14 had phyllaries M, florets Dull Dark Purple, radiata brevi-
flora.
Plant 32 had phyllaries C, florets Dull Dark Purple, radiata normalis.

T.512. T.230, plant 1 selfed. 39 plants.
Pericline broadly ovoid 39. Phyllaries Bone Brown 39 ; M 24 :
VM 14. Florets Dull Dark Purple 37 ; radiata 37 ; normalis 23 : inter-
mediate between normalis and breviflora 6 : longiflora 1 : breviflora 7.

T.513. T.230, plant 14 × T.230, plant 1. 44 plants.
Pericline broadly ovoid 44. Phyllaries Bone Brown 44 ; S 1 : M 28 :
VM 14 : C 1. Florets Dull Dark Purple 44 ; radiata normalis 27 :
intermediate between normalis and breviflora 12 : breviflora 5.

T.514. T.230, plant 32 × T.230, plant 3. 48 plants.
Pericline broadly ovoid 48. Phyllaries Bone Brown 48 ; M 25 :
VM 22 : C 1. Florets Dull Dark Purple 48 ; radiata 48 ; normalis 35 :
intermediate between normalis and breviflora 6 : breviflora 7.

Comments on the Selfing (and some Crossings) of S.P.35·1.

Stock Plant 35·1 was very definitely a natural hybrid between *C.
jacea* and *C. nigra*. It was important to know something of its breeding
behaviour in order to interpret the composition of what were
thought to be wild hybrid swarms. There was true breeding throughout for broadly ovoid periclines. All families segregated for phyllary
shape, except one with only one plant in it. Generally the scorings
agree closely with expectations based on the classes into which the
immediate parent or parents had been placed. For F_2 and F_3 families,
and for those which originated when offspring were crossed with *C.
jacea*, the hybrid indexes were high. Phyllary colour was Bone Brown
throughout, except for two plants with Prout's Brown phyllaries in
one F_2 family after crossing an F_3 plant with S.P.45·6. The parent
S.P.35·1 had D.D.P. florets, but in F_1 and F_2 families plants with B.P.
florets either appeared alone or were most numerous until (in T.230)
two F_2 plants were crossed together when, in F_3 families from T.230,
D.D.P. plants again appeared alone. Ray florets occurred alone in all
families, except for two casual semiradiata plants (one in F_1 and one in
an F_2 family). For disc florets, there was in most families interesting
segregation between normalis and breviflora together with some plants
showing intermediate structure of the disc florets.

T.85. S.P.35·1 × T.2, plant 1. 38 plants.
Pericline broadly ovoid 38. Phyllaries Bone Brown 38 ; N 16 :
VL 6 : L 10 : S 6. Florets Dull Dark Purple 38 ; radiata 35 : semiradiata 3 ; normalis 26 : breviflora 12. Traces of white in rays of two
plants.

Plant 11 had phyllaries S, florets radiata normalis.
Plant 12 had phyllaries N, florets radiata normalis.
Plant 26 had phyllaries L, florets radiata normalis.

T.232. T.85, plant 11 selfed. 69 plants.
Pericline broadly ovoid 69. Phyllaries Bone Brown 69 ; N 6 :
VL 10 : L 12 : S 28 : M 11 : VM 2. Florets Dull Dark Purple 61 ;
with some white or partially white rays 3 ; radiata 42 : semiradiata 19 ;
normalis 33 : breviflora 20 : normalis and breviflora in different heads 8.
Plant 47 had phyllaries M, florets radiata normalis.

T.555. T.232, plant 47 selfed. 17 plants.
Pericline broadly ovoid 17. Phyllaries Bone Brown 17 ; L 3 : S 5 :
M 8 : VM 1. Florets Dull Dark Purple 17 ; radiata 17 ; normalis 10 :
intermediate between normalis and breviflora 3 : breviflora 4.

T.238. T.85, plant 11 × T.85, plant 12. 33 plants.
Pericline ovoid 6 : broadly ovoid 27. Phyllaries Bone Brown 33 ;
N 3 : VL 7 : L 7 : S 12 : M 4. Florets Dull Dark Purple 30 ; radiata 30;
normalis 22 : breviflora 8.

T.237. T.85, plant 11 × T.85, plant 26. 38 plants.
Pericline broadly ovoid 38. Phyllaries Bone Brown 38 ; N 2 :
VL 2 : L 3 : S 11 : M 20. Florets Dull Dark Purple 38 ; radiata 38 ;
normalis 27 : breviflora 11.

T.81. S.P.35·1 × S.P.48. 34 plants.
Pericline ovoid 34. Phyllaries Bone Brown 30 : Prout's Brown 4 ;
L 1 : S 10 : M 20 : VM 1 : C 1. Florets Dull Dark Purple 34 ; radiata
normalis 34.
Plant 6 had phyllaries Bone Brown, M.
Plant 8 had phyllaries Bone Brown, VM.
Plant 11 had phyllaries Bone Brown, C.
Plant 33 had phyllaries Prout's Brown, M.
Plant 34 had phyllaries Prout's Brown, S.

T.442. T.81, plant 6 selfed. 11 plants.
Pericline ovoid 8 : broadly ovoid 3. Phyllaries Bone Brown 6 :
Prout's Brown 5 ; S 4 : M 4 : VM 3. Florets Bishop's Purple 11 ;
radiata normalis 11, of which 8 more or less female.

T.419. T.81, plant 8 selfed. 16 plants.
Pericline ovoid 15 : broadly ovoid 1. Phyllaries Bone Brown 16 ;
M 13 : VM 3. Florets Bishop's Purple 16 ; radiata 15 ; normalis but
partly female 15.

T.418. T.81, plant 34 selfed. 47 plants.
Pericline ovoid 47. Phyllaries Bone Brown 47 ; N 7 : VL 16 : L 23 :

M 1. Florets Bishop's Purple 47 ; radiata 37 : semiradiata 1 ; normalis but partly female 38. One plant had the capitula close together.

T.443. T.81, plant 6 × T.81, plant 8. 19 plants.
Pericline ovoid 19. Phyllaries Bone Brown 13 : Prout's Brown 6 ; S 1 : M 14 : VM 2. Florets Bishop's Purple 18 ; radiata normalis and more or less female 18.

T.422. T.81, plant 8 × T.81, plant 11. 71 plants.
Pericline ovoid 65 : broadly ovoid 6. Phyllaries Bone Brown 71 ; S 8 : M 59 : VM 2. Florets Rood's Violet 1 : Bishop's Purple 60 ; radiata normalis 61 of which 41 more or less female.

T.433. T.81, plant 11 × T.81, plant 8. 69 plants.
Pericline ovoid 61 : broadly ovoid 8. Phyllaries Bone Brown 58 : Prout's Brown 11 ; L 4 : S 21 : M 37 : VM 3. Florets Bishop's Purple 60 ; radiata 57 : semiradiata 2 : eradiata 1 ; longiflora 1 : normalis 59 of which 30 more or less female.

T.427. T.81, plant 8 × T.81, plant 33. 3 plants.
Pericline ovoid 1 : broadly ovoid 2. Phyllaries Bone Brown 2 : Prout's Brown 1 ; M 3. Florets Bishop's Purple 3 ; radiata normalis 3, of which two partly female.

T.431. T. 81, plant 8 × T.81, plant 34. 1 plant.
Pericline ovoid. Phyllaries Bone Brown ; S. Florets Bishop's Purple ; radiata normalis.

T.423. T.81, plant 11 × T.81, plant 34. 67 plants.
Pericline ovoid 60 : broadly ovoid 7. Phyllaries Bone Brown 60 : Prout's Brown 7 ; L 2 : S 34 : M 31. Florets Rood's Violet 2 : Bishop's Purple 54 (2 with white fleckings in ray florets) ; radiata 52 : semiradiata 2 ; normalis 52, of which 20 partly female : longiflora 3, one of which partly female : breviflora 1.

T.421. T.81, plant 34 × T.81, plant 8. 21 plants.
Pericline ovoid 18 : broadly ovoid 3. Phyllaries Bone Brown 19 : Prout's Brown 2 ; VL 3 : L 1 : S 6 : M 11. Florets Bishop's Purple 20 ; radiata normalis 20, of which 15 partly female.

T.435. T.81, plant 34 × T.81, plant 33. 15 plants.
Pericline ovoid 13 : broadly ovoid 2. Phyllaries Bone Brown 1 : Prout's Brown 14 ; VL 2 : L 3 : S 9 : M 1. Florets Bishop's Purple 10 ; radiata normalis and more or less female 10.

T.69. S.P.30 × S.P.35·1. 37 plants.
Pericline ovoid 12 : broadly ovoid 25. Phyllaries Bone Brown 33 : Russet 4 ; VL 6 : L 7 : S 18 : M 6. Florets — ; radiata normalis 12 :

semiradiata normalis 2 : radiata breviflora 3 : semiradiata breviflora 18.

Plant 5 had pericline ovoid, phyllaries Bone Brown, S, florets Rood's Violet, radiata breviflora.

Plants 13 and 29 had pericline ovoid, phyllaries Bone Brown, S, florets Rood's Violet, radiata normalis.

Plant 31 had pericline ovoid, phyllaries Bone Brown, M, florets Dull Dark Purple, semiradiata breviflora.

T.228.   T.69, plant 29 selfed.   8 plants.
Pericline ovoid 8.   Phyllaries Bone Brown 8 ; VL 1 : L 1 : S 2 : M 4. Florets Dull Dark Purple 1 : Rood's Violet 7 ; radiata 7 : semiradiata 1 ; normalis 7 : breviflora 1.

T.222.   T.69, plant 5 × T.69, plant 13.   67 plants.
Pericline elongate-ovoid 49 : ovoid 18.   Phyllaries Bone Brown 67 ; N 3 : VL 13 : L 7 : S 22 : M 21 : VM 1.   Florets Dull Dark Purple 20 : Rood's Violet 43 ; radiata 65 ; normalis 33 : breviflora 32.

T.210.   T.69, plant 31 × T.69, plant 13.   4 plants.
Pericline ovoid 4.   Phyllaries Bone Brown 4 ; N 1 : M 3.   Florets Dull Dark Purple 2 : Rood's Violet 1, radiata 3 ; normalis 2 : breviflora 1.

T.231.   T.69, plant 31 × T.69, plant 29.   5 plants.
Pericline ovoid 5.   Phyllaries Bone Brown 2 : Russet 3 ; L 1 : S 1 : M 3.   Florets Rood's Violet 5 ; radiata 5 ; normalis 1 : longiflora 2 : breviflora 2.
Plant 1 had phyllaries Bone Brown, S, florets radiata longiflora.
Plant 2 had phyllaries Bone Brown, L, florets radiata longiflora.
Plant 3 had phyllaries Russet, M, florets radiata normalis.

T.542.   T.231, plant 1 selfed.   1 plant.
Pericline ovoid.   Phyllaries Bone Brown ; S.   Florets Dull Dark Purple ; radiata normalis.

T.547.   T.231, plant 2 × T.231, plant 3.   2 plants.
Pericline ovoid 1 : broadly ovoid 1.   Phyllaries Russet 2 ; VL 2. Florets Rood's Violet 2 ; radiata longiflora 2 (one female).

T.552.   T.231, plant 3 selfed.   1 plant.
Pericline ovoid.   Phyllaries Russet ; L.   Florets Rood's Violet ; radiata normalis.

Comments on Crosses between S.P.35·1 and other Plants.

Three other plants besides S.P.35·1 are involved in the groups of crosses now to be considered.   T.2·1 was an offspring from crossing two *C. nemoralis* stock plants ; S.P.48 was typical *C. jacea* ; and

S.P.30 was *C. nigra* and a few genes of *C. jacea*. For pericline shape, the three F_1 families were all from parents one of which had pericline broadly ovoid and the other ovoid. The parents with ovoid perclines were not genetically equivalent for this character. With T.2·1 the F_1 plants had all broadly ovoid periclines and only one F_2 family segregated for ovoid and broadly ovoid, all the other F_2 plants having broadly ovoid periclines. With S.P.48 the F_1 had entirely ovoid periclines and F_2 families either had only ovoid periclines (three families) or segregated with larger numbers for ovoid than for broadly ovoid (excepting one very small family). With S.P.30 there was segregation in F_1 and one F_2 family also showed marked segregation, perhaps broadly ovoid 3 : ovoid 1. Other F_2 families were small. There was segregation for phyllary shape in all families except very small ones. The results agree in general with expectations. Particularly instructive are the results for F_1 families. With *C. nemoralis* N, VL, L, and S plants occurred ; with *C. jacea* L, S, M, VM, and C plants were scored ; with *C. nigra*, impure, there were VL, L, S, and M individuals. For phyllary colour, with T.2·1 there were only Bone Brown plants throughout. Introducing S.P.48 (which also had Bone Brown phyllaries) there was segregation for Bone Brown and Prout's Brown in F_1 and seven F_2 families while four F_2 families gave only Bone Brown offspring. S.P.30 had Russet coloured phyllaries and this colour appeared in some plants in F_1 and in three F_2 families. With T.2·1 there was true breeding for Dull Dark Purple (D.D.P.) in F_1 and all F_2 families, except that five plants had some ray florets with some white or flushed petals. With S.P.48 (with Bishop's Purple, B.P., florets), F_1 had D.D.P. florets but all F_2 plants had B.P. florets except three in which the florets were Rood's Violet (R.V.). In one F_2 family two plants with ray florets partially white were recorded. With S.P.30 (B.P.), the F_1 was D.D.P. and R.V., but there was some segregation in F_2 families for D.D.P. and R.V. All plants had rays or semirays, except one plant in an F_2 family. This may have been a mutation. With regard to disc florets the interest lies in the large number of plants showing either the breviflora character or structure intermediate between normalis and breviflora. It appears that in these groups of families the interspecific crossing resulted in upset of proper formation of stamens in a large number of the offspring, for all the four parents involved had normalis disc florets.

T.66. S.P.1 × S.P.33. 22 plants.
Pericline ovoid 22. Phyllaries Bone Brown 22 ; N 10 : VL 4 : L 1 : S 7. Florets Dull Dark Purple 22 ; radiata normalis 22.
Plant 1 had phyllaries N.
Plants 6 and 19 had phyllaries VL.
Plants 17 and 20 had phyllaries S.

T.352. T.66, plant 6 selfed. 6 plants.
Pericline ovoid 6. Phyllaries Black 1 : Bone Brown 5 ; VL 1: L 1 : S 3 : M 1. Florets Dull Dark Purple 6 ; radiata normalis 6.
10

T.355. T.66, plant 19 selfed. 26 plants.
Pericline elongate-ovoid 13 : ovoid 13. Phyllaries Bone Brown 20 :
Prout's Brown 6 ; VL 16 : L 8 : S 1 : M 1. Florets Dull Dark Purple
21 : Bishop's Purple 5 ; radiata normalis 26.

T.351. T.66, plant 20 selfed. 3 plants.
Pericline ovoid 3. Phyllaries Bone Brown 2 : Prout's Brown 1 ;
L 1 : M 2. Florets Dull Dark Purple 3 ; radiata 3 ; normalis 2 :
" quilled " 1.

T.364. T.66, plant 6 × T.66, plant 1. 38 plants.
Pericline elongate-ovoid 5 : ovoid 33. Phyllaries Bone Brown 38 ;
N 5 : VL 7 : L 14 : S 12. Florets Dull Dark Purple 34 : Bishop's
Purple 4 ; radiata 38 ; normalis 33 : longiflora 5.

T.366. T.66, plant 6 × T.66, plant 17. 63 plants.
Pericline ovoid 63. Phyllaries Bone Brown 57 : Prout's Brown 6 ;
N 3 : VL 15 : L 15 : S 20 : M 10. Florets Dull Dark Purple 60 : Mar-
guerite Yellow 3 ; radiata normalis 63.

T.358. T.66, plant 19 × T.66, plant 6. 36 plants.
Pericline elongate-ovoid 17 : ovoid 19. Phyllaries Bone Brown 26 :
Prout's Brown 10 ; N 4 : VL 10 : L 15 : S 6 : M 1. Florets Dull Dark
Purple 31 : Bishop's Purple 3 : Marguerite Yellow 1 ; radiata 35 ;
normalis 34 : longiflora 1.

T.363. T.66, plant 6 × T.66, plant 20. 23 plants.
Pericline elongate-ovoid 2 : ovoid 21. Phyllaries Black 1 : Bone
Brown 19 : Prout's Brown 3 ; N 1 : VL 3 : L 5 : S 10 : M 3. Florets
Dull Dark Purple 19 : Bishop's Purple 1 : Marguerite Yellow 1 ;
radiata normalis 21.

T.359. T.66, plant 20 × T.66, plant 6. 17 plants.
Pericline elongate-ovoid 16 : ovoid 1. Phyllaries Bone Brown 17 ;
N 1 : VL 6 : L 5 : S 3 : M 2. Florets Dull Dark Purple 17 ; radiata
normalis 17.

T.357. T.66, plant 19 × T.66, plant 1. 17 plants.
Pericline elongate-ovoid 13 : ovoid 4. Phyllaries Bone Brown 15 :
Prout's Brown 2 ; VL 13 : L 4. Florets Dull Dark Purple 15 : Bishop's
Purple 1 ; radiata 16 ; normalis 15 : longiflora 1.

T.84. S.P.27·3 × S.P.33. 73 plants.
Pericline ovoid 73. Phyllaries Black 1 : Bone Brown 72 ; N 66 :
VL 7. Florets Dull Dark Purple 72 ; semiradiata 1 : eradiata 71 ;
normalis 71 : curly longiflora 1.
Plants 2, 3, 26, and 32 had phyllaries Bone Brown, N, florets eradiata
normalis.

Plants 34 and 63 had phyllaries Bone Brown, VL, florets eradiata normalis.

T.297. T.84, plant 3 selfed. 8 plants.
Pericline ovoid 8. Phyllaries Bone Brown 8 ; N 8. Florets Dull Dark Purple 8 ; eradiata normalis 8.

T.294. T.84, plant 34 selfed. 80 plants.
Pericline ovoid 80. Phyllaries Bone Brown, 80 ; N 12 : VL 21 : L 6 : S 19 : M 19 : VM 2. Florets Dull Dark Purple 80 ; radiata 12 : semiradiata 6 : eradiata 62 ; normalis 58 : longiflora 22.

T.296. T.84, plant 63 selfed. 31 plants.
Pericline ovoid 31. Phyllaries Bone Brown 31 ; N 10 : VL 8 : L 6 : S 7. Florets Dull Dark Purple 27 ; radiata 3 : semiradiata 3 : eradiata 21 ; normalis 22 : longiflora 5.

T.316. T. 84, plant 2 × T.84, plant 34. 82 plants.
Pericline ovoid 82. Phyllaries Bone Brown 82. N 48 : VL 20 : L 5 : S 7 : M 2 : Florets Dull Dark Purple 60 ; radiata 15 : semiradiata 1 : eradiata 44 ; normalis 49 : longiflora 11.

T.319. T.84, plant 2 × T.84, plant 63. 66 plants.
Pericline ovoid 66. Phyllaries Black 2 : Bone Brown 64 ; N 48 : VL 10 : L 7 : S 1. Florets Dull Dark Purple 60 ; radiata 13 : semiradiata 7 : eradiata 40 ; normalis 47 : longiflora 13.

T.250. T.84, plant 32 × T.84, plant 26. 88 plants.
Pericline ovoid 88. Phyllaries Black 3 : Bone Brown 85 ; N 88. Florets Dull Dark Purple 82 ; semiradiata 1 : eradiata 81 ; normalis 76 : longiflora 6.

T.308. T.84, plant 34 × T.84, plant 63. 47 plants.
Pericline ovoid 47. Phyllaries Bone Brown 47 ; N 11 : VL 15 : L 9 : S 11 : M 1. Florets Dull Dark Purple 33 ; radiata 4 : semiradiata 4 : eradiata 25 ; normalis 25 : longiflora 8.

Comments on Two Groups of Families Involving S.P.33.

S.P.33 was used as pollen parent to produce with two other stock plants two F_1 and subsequent F_2 families. For pericline shape, each F_1 family was produced by crossing broadly ovoid with ovoid plants and gave only ovoid offspring, but the F_2 families gave different results. With S.P.1, six F_2 families segregated for ovoid and elongate-ovoid, an unexpected result ; with S.P.27·3 there were only plants with ovoid periclines in all families. Both F_1 families were from N × S plants for phyllary shape. There was segregation in these and all subsequent families except two. Of these, one was the result of selfing an extracted

N plant and the other of crossing together two extracted N plants.
Both families consisted only of N plants and thus confirmed the earlier
scorings. The hybrid indexes for two reciprocal families, T.363 and
T.359, VL × S and S × VL, were 249·9 and 194·1 respectively on
rather small numbers. Bone Brown × Prout's Brown and Black
× Prout's Brown were the phyllary colours in parents producing F_1
families. From the former, six F_2 segregating and two not segregating
families were obtained additional to one scored Black 1 and Bone Brown
5. From the latter there was no production in any family of plants with
Prout's Brown phyllaries though some of the families were relatively
large. The cross Marguerite Yellow × Dull Dark Purple gave only
D.D.P. in F_1. In five F_2 families plants of Bishop's Purple appeared,
and plants of M.Y. floret colour in three families. The summated F_2
figures were D.D.P.206, B.P.14, M.Y.5. The cross (T.84) D.D.P.
× D.D.P. gave throughout only plants with D.D.P. florets. S.P.1
× S.P.33 resulted only in radiata plants in F_1 and all F_2 families. With
S.P.27·3 as ovule parent the results were very different and there was
segreagtion in every family, except one small one. The original parents
were scored as eradiata and semiradiata respectively, and F_2 ratios
appeared approximating to 63 : 1 (eradiata : radiata and/or semiradiata). The parents had normalis disc florets but in at least some F_2
families in both groups longiflora plants appeared. One rare quilled
plant appeared in one F_2 family and a single curly longiflora plant in
one F_1 family. In several F_2 families from S.P.27·3 × S.P.33 ratios
approximated to normalis 3 : longiflora 1.

T.76. S.P.27·3 × S.P.49. 24 plants.
Pericline broadly ovoid 24. Phyllaries Black 4 : Bone Brown 20 ;
N 17 : VL 6. Florets Dull Dark Purple 23 ; eradiata 23 ; normalis 22 :
breviflora 1.
One would have expected a higher summation towards fimbriations,
considering that S.P.49 was M.
Plant 2 had phyllaries Bone Brown, VL, florets normalis.
Plants 4 and 24 had phyllaries Bone Brown, N, florets normalis.
Plant 9 had phyllaries Black, N, florets normalis.
Plants 12 and 15 had phyllaries Bone Brown, VL, florets normalis.

T.302. T.76 plant 2 selfed. 92 plants (not all fully scored).
Pericline broadly ovoid 92. Phyllaries Bone Brown 92 ; N 23 :
VL 10 : L 10 : S 18 : M 1. Florets Dull Dark Purple 69 ; eradiata 69 ;
normalis 68 : breviflora 1.

T.303. T.76 plant 9 selfed. 28 plants.
Pericline ovoid 28. Phyllaries Bone Brown 28 ; N 23 : VL 5.
Florets Dull Dark Purple 28 ; eradiata normalis 28.

T.301. T.76. plant 12 selfed. 48 plants.
Pericline ovoid 48. Phyllaries Bone Brown 48 ; N 6 : VL 11 : L 6 :
S 19 : M 5 : VM 1. Florets Dull Dark Purple 47 ; eradiata normalis 47.

T.320. T.76 plant 15 selfed. 28 plants.

Pericline ovoid 28. Phyllaries Bone Brown 28 ; N 5 : VL 5 : L 4 : S 11 : M 2. Florets Dull Dark Purple 27 ; eradiata normalis 27.

T.277. T.76, plant 24 selfed. 38 plants.

Pericline ovoid 17 : broadly ovoid 21. Phyllaries Bone Brown 38 ; N 15 : VL 8 : L 3 : S 11 : M 1. Florets Dark Dull Purple 31 ; eradiata 31 ; normalis 26 : breviflora 5.

T.311. T.76, plant 2 × T.76, plant 12. 81 plants.

Pericline —. Phyllaries Bone Brown 81 ; N 16 : VL 14 : L 13 : S 29 : M 4. Florets Dull Dark Purple 50 ; eradiata 50 ; normalis 49 : breviflora 1.

T.313. T.76, plant 9 × T.76, plant 12. 86 plants.

Pericline broadly ovoid 86. Phyllaries Black 4 : Bone Brown 82 ; N 47 : VL 15 : L 9 : S 10. Florets Dull Dark Purple 45 ; eradiata normalis 45.

T.312. T.76, plant 12 × T.76, plant 24. 90 plants.

Pericline broadly ovoid 90. Phyllaries Black 2 : Bone Brown 88 ; N 27 : VL 16 : L 14 : S 31 : M 2. Florets Dull Dark Purple 73 ; eradiata normalis 73.

T.322. T.76, plant 15 × T.76, plant 12. 83 plants.

Pericline broadly ovoid 83. Phyllaries Black 4 : Bone Brown 79 ; N 12 : VL 22 : L 7 : S 26 : M 3. Florets Dull Dark Purple 71 ; eradiata normalis 71.

T.82. S.P.45·1 × S.P.49. 18 plants.

Pericline elongate-ovoid 4 : ovoid 14. Phyllaries Bone Brown 14 : Prout's Brown 4 ; S 1 : M 5 : VM 10 : C 2. Florets Bishop's Purple 18 ; radiata 2 : semiradiata 9 : eradiata 3 ; normalis 10 : breviflora 4.

T.78. S.P.35·1 × S.P.49. 52 plants.

Pericline ovoid 4 : broadly ovoid 48. Phyllaries Bone Brown 48 ; VL 3 : L 3 : S 16 : M 30. Florets Dull Dark Purple 44 ; radiata 4 : semiradiata 21 : eradiata 19 ; normalis 30 : breviflora 14.

Plant 13 had pericline broadly ovoid, phyllaries M, florets radiata normalis.

Plant 17 had pericline ovoid, phyllaries VL, florets eradiata normalis.

Plant 20 had pericline broadly ovoid, phyllaries S, florets semiradiata breviflora.

Plants 24 and 41 had pericline broadly ovoid, phyllaries M, florets semiradiata normalis.

Plant 25 had pericline broadly ovoid, phyllaries S, florets eradiata normalis.

T.305. T.78, plant 13 selfed. 58 plants.
Pericline ovoid 58. Phyllaries Bone Brown 58 ; VL 4 : L 5 : S 17 :
M 22 : VM 9. Florets Dull Dark Purple 46 ; radiata 26 : semiradiata 6 :
eradiata 14 ; normalis 46.

T.276. T.78, plant 17 selfed. 56 plants.
Pericline ovoid 56. Phyllaries Bone Brown 56 ; VL 4 : L 15 : S 22 :
M 12 : VM 1. Florets Dull Dark Purple 51 ; radiata 8 : semiradiata 2 :
eradiata 41 ; normalis 43 : breviflora 8.

T.287. T.78, plant 25 selfed (1932). 89 plants.
Percline broadly ovoid 89. Phyllaries Bone Brown 89 ; VL 3 :
L 11 : S 45 : M 26 : VM 4. Florets Dull Dark Purple 68 : Rood's Violet
12 ; radiata 17 : semiradiata 1 : eradiata 62 ; normalis 10 : breviflora 70.

T.516. T.78, plant 25 selfed (1935). 42 plants.
Pericline broadly ovoid 42. Phyllaries Bone Brown 42 ; VL 2 :
L 15 : S 20 : M 5. Florets Dull Dark Purple 42 ; radiata 5 : semiradiata 1 : eradiata 31 ; normalis 27 : intermediate between normalis
and breviflora 9 : breviflora 1.

T.249. T.78, plant 13 × T.78, plant 24. 11 plants.
Pericline broadly ovoid 11. Phyllaries Bone Brown 11 ; S 1 : M 2 :
VM 7 : C 1. Florets Rood's Violet 10 ; radiata 7 : semiradiata 1 :
eradiata 2 ; normalis 5 : breviflora 5.

T.289. T.78, plant 13 × T.78, plant 25. 56 plants.
Pericline ovoid 56. Phyllaries Bone Brown 56 ; VL 5 : L 8 : S 14 :
M 26 : VM 1. Florets Dull Dark Purple 56 ; radiata 18 : semiradiata
8 : eradiata 21 ; normalis 34 : breviflora 13.

T.317. T.78, plant 17 × T.78, plant 41. 39 plants.
Pericline ovoid 39. Phyllaries Bone Brown 39 ; VL 3 : L 4 : S 16 :
M 12 : VM 2 : C 2. Florets Dull Dark Purple 39 ; radiata 4 : semi-
radiata 2 : eradiata 30 ; normalis 24 : breviflora 12.
Plant 11 had phyllaries S, florets eradiata breviflora.
Plant 25 had phyllaries S, florets radiata normalis.
Plant 38 had phyllaries S, florets eradiata normalis.

T.537. T.317, plant 25 selfed. 35 plants.
Pericline ovoid 35. Phyllaries Bone Brown 35 ; VL 5 : L 13 : S 16.
Florets Dull Dark Purple 35 ; radiata 7 : semiradiata 21 : eradiata 2 ;
normalis 2 : intermediate between normalis and breviflora 28.

T.557. T.317, plant 38 selfed. 5 plants.
Pericline : ovoid 4 ; broadly ovoid 1. Phyllaries Bone Brown 5 ; S 1 :
M 1 : VM 3. Florets Dull Dark Purple 2 ; eradiata normalis 2.
3 plants past flowering at scoring.

T.556. T.317, plant 11 × T.317, plant 25.   38 plants.
Pericline ovoid 38.   Phyllaries Bone Brown 38 ; L 13 : S 22 : M 3.
Florets Dull Dark Purple 32 ; semiradiata 8 : eradiata 24 ; normalis 9 :
intermediate between normalis and breviflora 9 : breviflora 14.

T.273. T.78, plant 20 × T.78, plant 17.   82 plants.
Pericline ovoid 82.   Phyllaries Bone Brown 82 ; VL 15 : L 14 : S 23 :
M 23 : VM 5 : C 2.   Florets Dull Dark Purple 70 : Rood's Violet 12 ;
radiata 5 : semiradiata 7 : eradiata 68 ; normalis 27 : breviflora 55.

T.283. T.78, plant 20 × T.78, plant 25 (1932).   49 plants.
Pericline elongate-ovoid 9 : broadly ovoid 40.   Phyllaries Bone
Brown 49 ; N 1 : VL 4 : L 6 : S 15 : M 21 : VM 2.   Florets Dull Dark
Purple 45 ;   radiata 4 : semiradiata 7 : eradiata 34 ;   normalis 23 :
breviflora 22.
Plant 4 had pericline elongate-ovoid, phyllaries VL, florets eradiata
breviflora.
Plant 5 had pericline broadly ovoid, phyllaries M, florets eradiata
normalis.

T.553. T.283, plant 5 selfed.   3 plants.
Pericline broadly ovoid 3.   Phyllaries Bone Brown 3 ; L 1 : S 1 : M 1.
Florets Dull Dark Purple 3 ; eradiata normalis 3.

T.554. T.283, plant 4 × T.283, plant 5.   3 plants.
Pericline broadly ovoid 3.   Phyllaries Bone Brown 3 ; N 1 : VL 2.
Florets Dull Dark Purple 3 ; eradiata 3 ; normalis 2 : intermediate
between normalis and breviflora 1.

T.510. T.78, plant 20 × T.78, plant 25 (1935).   57 plants.
Pericline elongate-ovoid 14 : broadly ovoid 43.   Phyllaries Bone
Brown 57 ; N 3 : VL 4 : L 8 : S 21 : M 19 : VM 1.   Florets Dull Dark
Purple 55 ;   radiata 11 : semiradiata 1 : eradiata 43 ;   normalis 31 :
intermediate between normalis and breviflora 9 : longiflora 4 : brevi-
flora 14.

T.292. T.78, plant 25 × T.78, plant 17.   67 plants.
Pericline ovoid 67.   Phyllaries Bone Brown 65 : Prout's Brown 2 ;
VL 2 : L 11 : S 46 : M 8.   Florets Dull Dark Purple 48 : Rood's Violet
17 ; radiata 7 : semiradiata 2 : eradiata 56 ; normalis 18 : breviflora
47.

T.315. T.78, plant 25 × T.78, plant 24.   56 plants.
Pericline broadly ovoid 56.   Phyllaries Bone Brown 56 ; VL 1 :
L 4 : S 17 : M 27 : VM 7.   Florets Dull Dark Purple 37 ; radiata 4 :
eradiata 33 ; normalis 29 : breviflora 8.

Comments on Crosses in which S.P.49 was Used.

S.P.49 was considered, especially on phyllary characters, to be a natural cross between *C. jacea* and *C. nigra*. It was crossed as pollen parent on to three other stock plants. The results for pericline shape suggest that fluctuations due to environmental conditions in the broad sense obliterate differences expressing different genotypes in some of the families. This would appear to be what happened for T.303, T.301, T.320, T.305, and T.289. Some families gave quite expected results, but scoring was exceptionally difficult in these families. For phyllary shape, there was segregation in every family. Most of the scorings gave results that agree with expectations. One aberrant result, that has been checked from preserved material, was in T.277 when a plant with N phyllaries segregated on selfing. Phyllary colour calls for little comment except for the appearance of two plants with phyllaries Prout's Brown in T.292. They may have been " shaded " individuals that were genotypically equivalent to Bone Brown plants. Dull Dark Purple floret colour dominated over Rood's Violet as did also Bishop's Purple. Relatively small numbers of plants with Rood's Violet florets segregated in F_2 families and from the F_1 produced by S.P.35·1 × S.P.49. The cross S.P.27·3 × S.P.49 gave only eradiata plants throughout. From crosses of radiata × eradiata there was segregation in F_1 and all, except very small, F_2 families. It is noteworthy that in most families of the latter groups (R × E) there appeared plants scored as semiradiata. The parents had all normalis disc florets. Plants with breviflora florets appeared in all three F_1 and in many F_2 families, especially those derived from S.P.35·1 × S.P.49. In two F_2 and three F_3 families there were plants with the disc florets intermediate between normalis and breviflora. Interspecific crossing again seems to lead to abnormalities in the formation of the androecium.

T.64. S.P.30 × S.P.36. 35 plants.
Pericline ovoid 35. Phyllaries Bone Brown 30 : Russet 5 ; N 16 : VL 11 : L 6 : S 2. Florets Dull Dark Purple 12 : Bishop's Purple 23 ; semiradiata normalis 7 : semiradiata breviflora 5 : eradiata normalis 9 : eradiata breviflora 13.

T.67. S.P.30 × S.P.1. 30 plants.
Pericline ovoid 30. Phyllaries Prout's Brown 30 ; N 24 : VL 6. Florets Dull Dark Purple 30 ; radiata 21 : semiradiata 9 ; normalis 17 : breviflora 13.
Plant 1 had phyllaries N, florets radiata normalis.
Plants 5, 6, and 30 had phyllaries N, florets semiradiata breviflora.
Plant 18 had phyllaries VL, florets semiradiata breviflora.

T.432. T.67, plant 5 × T.67, plant 1. 27 plants.
Pericline ovoid 25 : broadly ovoid 2. Phyllaries Bone Brown 17 : Prout's Brown 10 ; N 15 : VL 11. Florets Bishop's Purple 20 ;

radiata 16 : semiradiata 2 : eradiata 2 ; normalis 18 : longiflora 1 : breviflora 1.   Three normalis plants were female but not breviflora.

T.440.   T.67, plant 6 × T.67, plant 1.   10 plants.
Pericline ovoid 9 : broadly ovoid 1.   Phyllaries Bone Brown 9 :
Prout's Brown 1 ; N 3 : VL 7.   Florets Bishop's Purple 9 ; radiata 9 ;
normalis 8 : breviflora 1.   One normalis partly female.

T.437.   T.67, plant 18 × T.67, plant 1.   67 plants.
Pericline ovoid 67.   Phyllaries Bone Brown 53 : Prout's Brown 13 :
Russet 1 ;   N 45 : VL 18 : L 3.   Florets Rood's Violet 1 : Bishop's
Purple 62 : Marguerite Yellow 2 ; radiata 65 ; normalis 63 : breviflora 2.   13 normalis plants were more or less female.

T.434.   T.67, plant 30 × T.67, plant 1.   1 plant.
Pericline ovoid.   Phyllaries Prout's Brown ; N.   Florets Bishop's
Purple ; semiradiata ; normalis but female.

T.62.   S.P.30 × S.P.47.   80 plants.
Pericline elongate-ovoid 14 : ovoid 63 : broadly ovoid 3.   Phyllaries
Bone Brown 74 : Russet 6 ; N 8 : VL 30 : L 23 : S 13 : M 6.   Florets
Dull Dark Purple 80 ; radiata normalis 33 : semiradiata normalis 42 :
semiradiata breviflora 4 : eradiata breviflora 1.
Plant 12 had pericline ovoid, phyllaries Bone Brown, VL, florets
radiata normalis.
Plant 17 had pericline ovoid, phyllaries Bone Brown, S, florets
radiata normalis.
Plant 25 had pericline ovoid, phyllaries Russet, VL, florets semiradiata normalis.
Plant 30 had pericline ovoid, phyllaries Bone Brown, L, florets semiradiata normalis.
Plant 48 had pericline broadly ovoid, phyllaries Bone Brown, L,
florets radiata normalis.
Plant 65 had pericline elongate-ovoid, phyllaries Bone Brown, L,
florets semiradiata breviflora.

T.220.   T.62, plant 17 selfed.   1 plant.
Pericline ovoid.   Phyllaries Bone Brown ; VL.   Florets Dull Dark
Purple ; semiradiata breviflora.

T.213.   T.62, plant 25 selfed.   6 plants.
Pericline ovoid 1 : broadly ovoid 5.   Phyllaries Bone Brown 5 :
Prout's Brown 1 ; N 2 : VL 3 : S 1.   Florets Dull Dark Purple 6 ;
eradiata 6 ; normalis 4 : breviflora 2.

T.221.   T.62, plant 30 selfed.   2 plants.
Pericline ovoid 2.   Phyllaries Bone Brown 2 ; S 2.   Florets Dull
Dark Purple 2 ; radiata 1 : eradiata 1 ; normalis 2.

T.211.   T.62, plant 48 selfed.   10 plants.
Pericline ovoid 10.   Phyllaries Black 3 : Bone Brown 6 ;   N 2 :
VL 4 : L 1 : S 1 : M 1.   Florets Dull Dark Purple 9 ;   radiata 5 : semi-
radiata 4 ;   normalis 6 : breviflora 3.

T.215.   T.62, plant 25 × T.62, plant 12.   35 plants.
Pericline ovoid 35.   Phyllaries Bone Brown 35 ;   N 17 : VL 12 :
L 3 : S 3.   Florets Dull Dark Purple 35 ;   radiata 14 : semiradiata 13 :
eradiata 8 ;   normalis 30 : breviflora 5.

T.209.   T.62, plant 65 × T.62, plant 17.   3 plants.
Pericline elongate-ovoid 1 : ovoid 2.   Phyllaries Bone Brown 3 ;
N 2 : M 1.   Florets Dull Dark Purple 3 ;   radiata 3 ;   normalis 2 :
breviflora 1.

T.208.   T.62, plant 65 × T.62, plant 48.   1 plant.
Pericline ovoid.   Phyllaries Bone Brown ;   S.   Florets Dull Dark
Purple ;   radiata normalis.

Comments on Crosses Involving S.P.30.

S.P.30 was considered to be *C. nigra* with a few genes of *C. jacea* in
its genom.   It was crossed with S.P.36, which was thought to have a
similar taxonomic constitution, with S.P.1, and with S.P.47, a plant
from Jersey scored as *C. jacea* × *C. nigra*.   Crossing plants with
ovoid and broadly ovoid periclines respectively gave only ovoid plants
in F_1 and little segregation in F_2.   In the cross S.P.30 × S.P.47
(ovoid × ovoid) there was segregation into elongate-ovoid, ovoid
and broadly ovoid. F_2 families were mostly small.   The scorings for
phyllary shape follow expectations, allowing for some families being
very small.   The effect of bringing in more *C. jacea* genes with S.P.47
is obvious.   S.P.30 had Russet coloured phyllaries, the other parents
used had Bone Brown phyllaries.   Russet phyllaries appeared in some
plants in two F_1 families, but the gene combination or combinations
gave many plants with Prout's Brown phyllaries in the F_1 and F_2
families from the cross S.P.30 × S.P.1.   It would have been interesting
had some of these been carried on to F_3 families.   The cross S.P.30
× S.P.47, that is for floret colour Bishop's Purple × Rood's Violet,
gave only Dull Dark Purple in F_1 and F_2 families, the latter being mostly
small.   The Marguerite Yellow stock plants S.P.36 and S.P.1 gave
different results on being crossed as pollen parents with S.P.30.   The
former gave an F_1 of Dull Dark Purple 12 and Bishop's Purple 23, and
the latter an F_1 of Dull Dark Purple 30 only.   One F_2 family from the
latter segregated giving Rood's Violet 1, Bishop's Purple 62, and
Marguerite Yellow 2.   S.P.30 was semiradiata.   It is interesting that
eradiata plants occurred in not only F_1 families with eradiata pollen
parents but in one F_2 family (T.215) from semiradiata × radiata.
Semiradiata plants in this group are certainly not merely radiata plants
with the rays reduced by environmental conditions.   All plants used

as parents had normalis disc florets. Again, we have the phenomenon that crossing hybrids gives many plants with abnormal androecium, for many breviflora plants appeared, and in some F_2 families there were plants with disc florets intermediate between normalis and breviflora.

E. Involving Guernsey (Putative) Hybrids.

T.117. S.P.79·2 selfed. 11 plants.
Pericline broadly ovoid 11. Phyllaries Prout's Brown 10 ; S 4 : M 5. Florets Bishop's Purple 10 ; radiata 7 : semiradiata 3 ; normalis 3 : breviflora 7.
Plant 10 had phyllaries —, florets radiata breviflora.

T.413. T.117, plant 10 selfed. 3 plants.
Pericline ovoid 1 : broadly ovoid 2. Phyllaries Prout's Brown 3 ; L 1 : S 2. Florets Bishop's Purple 3 ; radiata normalis 3.

T.116. S.P.79·2 × S.P.79·1. 17 plants.
Pericline broadly ovoid 17. Phyllaries Prout's Brown 13 ; S 2 : M 6 : VM 3 : C 2. Florets Bishop's Purple 14 ; radiata 14 ; normalis 8 : breviflora 6.

T.143. S.P.79·2 × T.21, plant 5. 11 plants.
Pericline broadly ovoid 11. Phyllaries Prout's Brown 11 ; N 2 : VL 8 : L 1. Florets Bishop's Purple 11 ; radiata 2 : semiradiata 9 ; normalis 10 : breviflora 1.
Plant 1 had phyllaries L, florets semiradiata normalis.
Plants 4, 5, and 6 had phyllaries VL, florets semiradiata normalis.

T.436. T.143, plant 1 selfed. 20 plants.
Pericline ovoid 10 : broadly ovoid 8 : obloid 2. Phyllaries Bone Brown 4 : Prout's Brown 16 ; N 1 : VL 3 : L 5 : S 7 : M 3. Florets Bishop's Purple 11 ; radiata 4 : semiradiata 1 : eradiata 6 ; normalis 11, of which one was partly female.

T.411. T.143, plant 5 selfed. 4 plants.
Pericline ovoid 3 : obloid 1. Phyllaries Bone Brown 2 : Prout's Brown 2 : L 1 : S 2 : M 1. Florets Bishop's Purple 4 ; radaita 2 : eradiata 2 ; normalis 3 : intermediate between normalis and breviflora 1.

T.425. T.143, plant 6 selfed. 1 plant.
Pericline ovoid. Phyllaries Bone Brown ; N. Florets Bishop's Purple ; semiradiata normalis.

T.420. T.143, plant 1 × T.143, plant 4. 5 plants.
Pericline ovoid 3 : broadly ovoid 2. Phyllaries Bone Brown 5 ; N 3 : VL 1 : S 1. Florets Bishop's Purple 5 ; radiata 2 : semiradiata 1 : eradiata 1 ; normalis 3 : breviflora 1.

T.424. T.143, plant 4 × T.143, plant 1.   3 plants.
Pericline broadly ovoid 2.   Phyllaries Prout's Brown 3 ; VL 1 : L 1 :
S 1.   Florets Bishop's Purple 2 ;   semiradiata 2 ;   normalis 1 : brevi-
flora 1.

T.428. T.143, plant 5 × T.143, plant 1.   2 plants.
Pericline broadly ovoid 1 : obloid 1.   Phyllaries Prout's Brown 2 ;
S 1 : M 1.   Florets Bishop's Purple 2 ;   eradiata normalis 2.

T.438. T.143, plant 1 × T.143, plant 6.   2 plants.
Pericline broadly ovoid 2.   Phyllaries Prout's Brown 2 ;   L 1 : S 1.
Florets Bishop's Purple 2 ;   radiata 1 : semiradiata 1 ;   normalis 1 :
intermediate between normalis and breviflora 1.

T.146. S.P.79·2 × T.37, plant 7.   12 plants.
Pericline broadly ovoid 12.   Phyllaries Bone Brown 3 : Prout's
Brown 9.   VL 8 : L 4.   Florets Bishop's Purple 12 ; radiata 12 ; normalis
8 : longiflora 2 : breviflora 2.   Five normalis plants were female.
Plant 1 had phyllaries Bone Brown, VL, florets radiata normalis.
Plant 2 had phyllaries Bone Brown, L, florets radiata normalis.
Plants 3 and 12 had phyllaries Prout's Brown, VL, florets radiata
normalis.
Plant 4 had phyllaries Prout's Brown, L, florets radiata normalis.
Plant 6 had phyllaries Prout's Brown, VL, florets with radiata brevi-
flora.
Plant 7 had phyllaries Bone Brown, VL, florets radiata longiflora.
Plant 9 had phyllaries Prout's Brown, VL, florets radiata longiflora.

T.334. T.146, plant 2 selfed.   74 plants.
Pericline ovoid 3 : obloid 71.   Phyllaries Bone Brown 72 : Prout's
Brown 2 ;   N 1 : VL 8 : L 16 : S 31 : M 17 : VM 1.   Florets Bishop's
Purple 71 ;   radiata 71 ;   normalis 53 : longiflora (female) 1 : breviflora
16.   One breviflora verging to normalis.

T.328. T.146, plant 3 selfed.   8 plants.
Pericline ovoid 2 : obloid 6.   Phyllaries Bone Brown 8 ;   VL 4 : L 4.
Florets Bishop's Purple 8 ;   radiata 8 ; normalis 5 : breviflora 3.   One
normalis was partially female and one breviflora verged to normalis.

T.325. T.146, plant 7 selfed.   1 plant.
Pericline broadly ovoid.   Phyllaries Bone Brown ;   L.   Florets
Bishop's Purple ;   radiata longiflora.

T.335. T.146, plant 9 selfed.   57 plants.
Pericline ovoid 20 : obloid 37.   Phyllaries Bone Brown 43 :   Prout's
Brown 14 ;   N 1 : VL 17 : L 15 : S 20 : M 4.   Florets Bishop's Purple
57 ;   radiata 47 : semiradiata 2 : eradiata 1 ;   normalis 22 : longiflora 22 :
breviflora 6.   One breviflora verging to normalis.   Two longiflora
plants were female.

T.340. T.146, plant 1 × T.146, plant 9. 11 plants.
Pericline ovoid 3 : obloid 8. Phyllaries Bone Brown 9 : Prout's Brown 2 : VL 7 : L 3. Florets Bishop's Purple 11 ; radiata 11 ; normalis 5 : longiflora 3 : breviflora 3. One longiflora was female.

T.339. T.146, plant 1 × T.146, plant 12. 33 plants.
Pericline ovoid 7 : obloid 26. Phyllaries Bone Brown 31 : Prout's Brown 2 : N 2 : VL 5 : L 14 : S 11 : M 1. Florets Bishop's Purple 33 ; radiata 33 ; normalis 25 : longiflora 1 : breviflora 7. Three breviflora verging to normalis.

T.367. T.146, plant 2 × T.146, plant 6. 21 plants.
Pericline ovoid 2 : obloid 19. Phyllaries Bone Brown 21 ; N 2 : VL 5 : L 3 : S 7 : M 4. Florets Bishop's Purple 21 ; radiata 20 ; normalis 12 : longiflora 1 : breviflora 7. One longiflora was female. Two breviflora verged towards normalis.

T.346. T.146, plant 2 × T.146, plant 12. 50 plants.
Pericline ovoid 3 : obloid 47. Phyllaries Bone Brown 47 : Prout's Brown 3 ; VL 3 : L 7 : S 31 : M 9. Florets Bishop's Purple 49 ; radiata 49 ; normalis 36 : longiflora 3 : breviflora 10. One normalis was female.

T.331. T.146, plant 3 × T.146, plant 7. 10 plants.
Pericline ovoid 1 : obloid 9. Phyllaries Bone Brown 8 : Prout's Brown 2 ; VL 2 : L 4 : S 3 : M 1. Florets Bishop's Purple 10 ; radiata 10 ; normalis 9 : breviflora 1. One normalis was female.

T.330. T.146, plant 4 × T.146, plant 3. 14 plants.
Pericline broadly ovoid 14. Phyllaries Bone Brown 13 : Prout's Brown 1 ; VL 3 : L 4 : S 3 : M 4. Florets Bishop's Purple 14 ; radiata 14 ; normalis 9 : breviflora 5 (including 3 intermediates verging to normalis).
Plant 1 had phyllaries VL, florets radiata normalis.
Plant 6 had phyllaries S, florets radiata breviflora verging to normalis.
Plant 8 had phyllaries M, florets radiata normalis.
Plant 9 had phyllaries M, florets radiata normalis.

T.540. T.330, plant 1 selfed. 11 plants.
Pericline broadly ovoid 11. Phyllaries Bone Brown 7 : Prout's Brown 4 ; L 4 : S 6 : M 1. Florets Bishop's Purple 9 ; radiata 7 : semiradiata 2 ; normalis 8 : intermediate between normalis and breviflora 1.

T.531. T.330, plant 8 selfed. 10 plants.
Pericline broadly ovoid 10. Phyllaries Bone Brown 10. Florets Bishop's Purple 9 ; radiata 9 ; normalis 7 : intermediate between normalis and breviflora 2.

T.529. T.330, plant 9 selfed. 1 plant.
Pericline broadly ovoid. Phyllaries Prout's Brown ; M. Florets Bishop's Purple ; radiata normalis.

T.545. T.330, plant 1 × T.330, plant 8. 4 plants.
Pericline broadly ovoid 4. Phyllaries Bone Brown 4 ; VL 2 : S 2. Florets Bishop's Purple 4 ; radiata 4 ; normalis 3 : intermediate between normalis and breviflora 1.

T.560. T.330, plant 1 × T.330, plant 9. 65 plants.
Pericline ovoid 7 : broadly ovoid 58. Phyllaries Bone Brown 36 : Prout's Brown 29 ; N 1 : VL 4 : L 17 : S 29 : M 13 : VM 1. Florets Bishop's Purple 60 ; radiata 60 ; normalis 38 : intermediate between normalis and breviflora 13 : longiflora 9 (one longiflora was female).

T.533. T.330, plant 6 × T.330, plant 8. 3 plants.
Pericline broadly ovoid 3. Phyllaries Bone Brown 3 ; S 1 : M 1. Florets Bishop's Purple 3 ; radiata 3 ; normalis 2 : intermediate between normalis and breviflora 1.

T.534. T.330, plant 6 × T.330, plant 9. 54 plants.
Pericline broadly ovoid 54. Phyllaries Bone Brown 34 : Prout's Brown 18 ; VL 3 : L 6 : S 24 : M 18 : VM 3. Florets Bishop's Purple 52 ; radiata 52 ; normalis 29 : intermediate between normalis and breviflora 20 : longiflora 3.

T.324. T.146, plant 4 × T.146, plant 7. 10 plants.
Pericline broadly ovoid 10. Phyllaries Bone Brown 8 : Prout's Brown 2 ; VL 1 : L 3 : S 4 : M 2. Florets Bishop's Purple 10 ; radiata 10 ; normalis 9 : longiflora 1.

T.348. T.146, plant 4 × T.146, plant 9. 12 plants.
Pericline broadly ovoid 12. Phyllaries Bone Brown 8 : Prout's Brown 4 ; N 2 : VL 2 : S 3 : M 5. Florets Bishop's Purple 11 ; radiata 11 ; normalis 8 : longiflora 2 : breviflora 1. One longiflora and one normalis were female.

T.345. T.146, plant 12 × T.146, plant 9. 59 plants.
Pericline ovoid 14 : obloid 45. Phyllaries Bone Brown 48 : Prout's Brown 11 ; VL 6 : L 8 : S 31 : M 14. Florets Bishop's Purple 58 ; radiata 58 ; normalis 45 : longiflora 6 : breviflora 7. Four normalis had very little pollen. One breviflora verged to normalis.

Comments on Families Derived from, or in their Origin Involving, S.P.79·2.

S.P.79·2 originated from Guernsey and was tentatively accepted as *C. jacea* with a few genes of *C. nigra*. It was selfed, to produce very small F_1 and F_2 families, and crossed with T.21·5 (from S.P.25·5

$\times$ S.P.24·5, that is *C. nigra* $\times$ *C. nemoralis*) and with T.37·7 (from S.P.13·7 $\times$ S.P.24·5, that is *C. nemoralis*, with a few genes of *C. jacea* $\times$ *C. nemoralis*).

S.P.79·2 was typically broadly ovoid for pericline shape and on selfing bred true to this character. It is unique in our experiments that in twelve offspring families from crosses plants appeared with very broadly ovoid, or obloid, periclines. These included the broadest, and one may say the largest by bulk, of any periclines we have seen in the *C. nigra–C. jacea* series as used by us. The gene combinations, especially after crossing S.P.79·2 with T.37·7, favoured broad and bulky periclines. Since S.P.79·2 had phenotypic characters suggesting a hybrid origin, segregation of specific characters was to be expected. Of particular interest was the result of crossing it with a very similar stock plant of the same wild origin (S.P.79·1), when in a small family of thirteen plants three with phyllaries VM and two with phyllaries C appeared. It was very satisfactory to extract these plants of typical *C. jacea* characters from crossing two plants whose phyllaries were M. Crossing with N pollen parents (T.21·5 or T.37·7) naturally reduced the *C. jacea* characters in F_1 and F_2 families, but all except very small families showed segregation approximately as was to be expected from the characters of the immediate parents. Five additional VM plants were extracted in F_2 or F_3 families. S.P.79·2 had Prout's Brown phyllaries and bred true to this character. On crossing with pollen parents with Bone Brown phyllaries, Prout's Brown was dominant in T.143 and segregation in the ratio Prout's Brown 3 : Bone Brown 1 occurred in T.146. Except in one moderate sized and some small families, in F_2 families from T.146 there was segregation with Bone Brown plants in the majority. Floret colour was Bishop's Purple throughout the 32 families involved. With a total of 575 plants this is a very pleasing check on the accuracy of the crossing and selfing methods used. S.P.79·2 was a radiata plant, T.21·5 was eradiata, and T.37·7 was radiata. The introduction of the eradiata T.21·5 led to segregation of eradiata plants in F_2. Otherwise, apart from the appearance of a few plants with slightly shorter rays that had to be scored as semiradiata on our standards, there was only one aberrant offspring and that in an F_3 family (T.335). Plants with disc florets of the breviflora class and others intermediate between breviflora and normalis appeared in F_1, F_2, and F_3 families. This again agrees with the previously expressed view that interspecific crossing increases abnormal developments in the androecium. With T.21·5 no longiflora plants were produced in F_1 or any F_2 family. With T.37·7 (a longiflora plant) as pollen parent, longiflora plants occurred in F_1 and in ten F_2 and two F_3 families. Moreover, several longiflora plants were functionally female, a character usually associated with breviflora.

CHAPTER VII

GENETICS OF REPRODUCTIVE PARTS

PERICLINE SHAPE.

THERE are differences in pericline shape and size between one plant and another. Quite large wild populations are sometimes relatively uniform in these respects, while others are obviously not. Variation is, however, "continuous," taking the whole range of the plants studied, and any classes made must have artificial limits. The main difficulty, however, in attempting to analyze pericline shape is due to fluctuations on an individual plant and to environmental influences. To minimize the effect of such fluctuations and influences as far as possible we have scored for pericline characters only living capitula at full anthesis and have taken fair samples from individual plants. Periclines naturally become broader with the setting of cypselas but not longer, the ratio of length to breadth thus decreases with age from anthesis to fruit maturity. Generally, though not always, there is increase in size from elongate-ovoid or ovoid to broadly ovoid, while obloid periclines are largest of all. In plants growing under unfavourable conditions, such as in soil poor in nutrients, on a substratum too dry, with excessive competition with taller vegetation, or where there is cutting or grazing, the capitula are often reduced in size and tend to become narrower relative to diameter.

It is possible that some other scheme than that we adopted might serve better to reveal the genetics of pericline characters. Division into more than four classes, or calculation of volume, or diameter of the influorescence receptacle might possibly serve this purpose. Since a pericline is symmetrical relative to a longitudinal axis any transverse section at right angles to this axis gives a circle, but the diameter of this varies from base to apex of the axis of length continuing from the peduncle. In our definitions we have taken the greatest diameter and the length measured as a straight line from the tip of the peduncle to the end of the highest phyllary.

A considerable number of stock plants bred true to pericline shape as we have scored it on selfing. This was true for ovoid, broadly ovoid, and elongate-ovoid stock plants. The same is true for groups of families derived from certain crosses between stock plants scored into the same class, as, for example, those from S.P.1 × S.P.23 (BO × BO), S.P.13·7 × S.P.24·5) (O × O), and S.P.45·1 × S.P.16 (E × E). On the other hand, some series of families derived by crossing stock plants scored into different classes also bred true, at least to the F_2 generation, as, for example, S.P.27·3 × S.P.36 (BO × O) gave only O ; S.P.21 × S.P.26·1 (O × EO) gave only O ; and S.P.27·3 × S.P.33 (BO × O) gave only O.

In our experiments, elongate-ovoid periclines especially appeared when stock plants of the 45 series (S.P.45·1, S.P.45·2, etc.) were used. In T.527, T.519, and T.468, in which S.P.45·6 was used, the offspring were scored as ovoid but were slightly elongated and, in fact, inter-mediate between elongate-ovoid and ovoid.   Obloid periclines occurred, in bred families, only when stock plant 79·2 had been used as ovule parent in combination with one or another plant as pollen parent.

We can only postulate several genes in combination partially con-trolling pericline shape, in that their effects are masked at times by fluctuations due to differences in " environment " and difficulties in precise scoring.

Phyllary (Appendage) Shape.

In wild hybrid swarms, and in families from artificially made crosses, involving *C. jacea* and *C. nigra* or *C. nemoralis*, plants can be otained in which the appendages of the phyllaries range, in different individual plants, from pectinate through fimbriate to entire. The range is a wide one, and the variation, considered for all the plants we have analyzed, essentially a continuous one. Hence, our classes are arti-ficially spearated one from another and individuals placed in any one class, apart from the extreme classes, are not always exactly the same for phyllary (appendage) shape. That a few plants have been under-scored and a few overscored is probable. Nomenclaturally, we reckon plants scored as Very Much (VM) and as Complete (C) to belong to *C. jacea*, and those scored as None (N), or sometimes Very Little (VL), when a few of the pectinations are branched rather than fused, as *C. nigra* or *C. nemoralis*. The results of analyses and syntheses make it clear that the series of classes in the order N ⇌ VL ⇌ L ⇌ S ⇌ M ⇌ VM ⇌ C is a natural one in the sense that from left to right there is a piling up of genic effects from *C. nigra* or *C. nemoralis* to *C. jacea* and from right to left from *C. jacea* to *C. nigra* or *C. nemoralis*. In the British flora *C. nigra* and *C. nemoralis* are commoner and much more widely spread than is *C. jacea*. The field evidence is clearly in favour of the theory that, at least most often, where *C. jacea* occurs or from the evidence of hybridity has occurred, it has been introduced into populations of *C. nigra* or *C. nemoralis*. Whether this introduction be " natural " or " artificial " and whether the species be " native " or " alien " is discussed elsewhere. Hence it is generally most convenient to read the series from N to C rather than from C to N. This is particularly true in field studies on wild populations.

While the characters of the phyllary appendages give, with our present knowledge, the best characters for separating *C. jacea* from *C. nigra* and *C. nemoralis* and for recognizing and evaluating hybrid swarms between these taxa, this does not mean that there are no other

11

characters of taxonomic value. There are. It follows that plants scored N on phyllary shape may have some genes, concerned with other characters, of *C. jacea*. The converse may also be true and plants scored as VM or C for phyllary shape may have some genes of *C. nigra* or *C. nemoralis*.

From the large number of selfings and crossings described in this work the following generalizations regarding phyllary shape can be made :

1. Plants scored as N breed true, or at most throw a small proportion of plants scored as VL.

2. Plants scored as C when selfed or crossed together either breed true or segregate giving C, VM, and M.

3. Plants otherwise scored (VL, L, S, M, VM) segregate on selfing, usually very much as might be expected from their position in the series.

4. Crossings between plants scored into different classes segregate on the whole as might be expected from the position of the parents in the series.

Exceptions to generalizations 3 and 4 occur but most of them are in very small families and may thus have little or no numerical significance. In small families, too, even a few slight underscorings or overscorings may have undue influence on figures and the same is true if parents be on the " border line " of the artificial class boundaries. Allowing for these difficulties the figures obtained give a very clear outline picture of genetical behaviour that is completely in accord with field studies of hybrid swarms. Further details are given in the comments for groups of families derived from selfings and crossings and apparent aberrations in ratios are also considered in those comments. The device of the hybrid index can only be used effectively for large families. Indeed, it is doubtful if any of the bred families be large enough to give entirely satisfactory results, that is without allowing for a wide margin of " error," in the statistical sense, in the figure values obtained by calculating the hybrid index.

It is obvious that several pairs of genes are involved, probably at least three, in the differences in shape of phyllary appendages as between the stocks of *C. jacea* and *C. nigra* or *C. nemoralis* used in our experiments. The number may be considerably higher for there are certain characters, such as shape and size of appendage discs and length of pectinations, which we have not scored in detail. The phenotypic effects, as expressed in our scoring into the seven classes, would seem to be correlated with the piling up of genes in the direction of the genom most typical of *C. jacea* in the one direction or of *C. nigra* or *C. nemoralis* in the other. There is some evidence that these genes are not all exactly equivalent and some, or some combinations, behave more or less as recessives, at least their effects do not appear in the next immediate generation but in a later generation or generations.

Reciprocal crosses have given essentially similar results with no suggestions of maternal cytoplasmic effects.

PHYLLARIES—COLOUR OF DISC OF APPENDAGES.

We originally scored for phyllary colour, from living material only, into 36 classes. Distinctions were made between disc and margins (including pectinations or fimbriations). Generally, disc colour, especially at the centre, is deeper (that is, approximating more to black or deep brown than to white or straw colour) than that of the margins. After many experiments and careful consideration we reduced our classes to six based on disc colour only. The classes used here are designated : Black (Bl), Bone Brown (B), Prout's Brown (P), Russet (R), Tawny Olive (T), and Light Ochraceous-Buff (L.O.B.).

It is of importance to note that the darker colours, Black and Bone Brown, are associated with *C. nigra* or *C. nemoralis* and that the lighter colours, Russet, Prout's Brown, and Light Ochraceous-Buff are introduced on crossing with *C. jacea*. The only possible exception to this is in T.202, an F_2 from S.P.7 selfed. This stock plant was determined as *C. nemoralis*, but came from a population known to have been contaminated by *C. jacea*. This fact emerging from our scorings of bred families is in complete agreement with our field studies of wild populations. If plants with paler phyllaries, especially when, as often, there is a certain amount of associated gloss, occur in a population of knapweeds further investigation reveals other characters indicating hybridity.

Black and Bone Brown.—It is probable that these two classes, as we have scored plants into them, are not genetically distinct. The figures obtained give no approximation to regular or constant ratios and are often conflicting. Some factors modifying one colour may have caused the differences we recognized in the living plants. The differences were slight. Rain and air humidity sometimes altered depth of colour. Shading and possibly some substances in the soil solution may also be responsible for slight fluctuations. Another modifying factor is size of appendage disc. As between Black and Bone Brown, the larger the disc the more it is likely to be scored as Black. This is correlated with the fact, already mentioned, that the disc centre is nearly always darker in colour than the margins. Bone Brown is, at least sometimes, due to the combined action of genes that separately result in a paler colour, as in T.527, a family of 78 plants with Bone Brown phyllaries resulting from the cross Prout's Brown × Prout's Brown.

Prout's Brown.—This was the commonest phyllary colour in families derived from crosses between *C. jacea* and *C. nigra* or *C. nemoralis*. Plants with phyllaries Prout's Brown, on being selfed or crossed, sometimes bred true (as T.24, T.158, T.169, T.182, T.75, and T.298) but sometimes segregated (as T.275, T.243, T.519, T.468, T.378, T.379, T.381, T.432, and T.437). The relation between Prout's Brown and Bone Brown is not a simple one genetically and it is probable that plants scored as phenotypically the same do not all belong to the same genotype.

Russet.—This colour has been introduced into our bred families only through Stock Plant 34·1 (*C. jacea*, itself with phyllaries Prout's Brown) and Stock Plant 30 (a *C. jacea* × *C. nigra* hybrid, itself with Russet phyllaries). It was apparently recessive to Bone Brown and possibly also to Prout's Brown, though the numbers in the families in which it appears are mostly small.

Tawny Olive.—This phyllary colour characterized S.P.58·2. Only a very small family of six plants was raised by selfing this plant and all had Tawny Olive phyllaries.

Light-Ochraceous-Buff.—This phyllary colour appeared, in our experiments, only in F_2, F_3, and backcross families from the cross S.P.1 × S.P.48, that is, *C. nigra* (Bone Brown) × *C. jacea* (Bone Brown). L.O.B plants bred true to this character in 4 selfings and in 7 crossings. In one crossing (T.501) two L.O.B plants were crossed together and a resulting family of five plants gave B 3 : L.O.B 2. Plants with Bone Brown phyllary appendages selfed, crossed together, or crossed with Light Ochraceous-Buff plants gave only Bone Brown (or Bone Brown and Black) plants except in T.506, B × L.O.B, giving B 48 : L.O.B 8, T.500, L.O.B × B giving B 5 : L.O.B 7, T.550, a back cross, B × B, giving B 61 : P 7 : L.O.B 2, T.509, an F_2 crossed with S.P.45·6, that is L.O.B × P, giving B 21 : P 34, and T.224, an F_2, B selfed, giving B 65 : L.O.B 27. One may conclude that L.O.B is recessive to B, and there may be no more than one gene difference between them.

FLORET COLOUR.

The commonest floret colour of knapweeds of the *C. nigra* group in the British Isles is that matched with Ridgway's Color Standards, as Dull Dark Purple (D.D.P.). Typical *C. jacea* has, in two of our stock groups, florets of a paler colour that has been matched with Bishop's Purple (B.P.). More rarely plants occur with still paler florets whose colour has been matched with Argyle Purple (A.P.), or Purplish Lilac (P.L.), or Mallow Purple (M.P.). Very often when associated with the " breviflora " character the floret colour is brighter than Dull Dark Purple and has been scored as Rood's Violet (R.V.). The depth of colour is undoubtedly " determined " by inherited factor combinations, but it can also be modified to some extent by environmental conditions. Thus, capitula that have developed and opened in shade generally have florets of a paler colour than have capitula on the same plant that have been exposed during development and at anthesis to full sunlight. This interaction of genetical and environmental effects can cause some confusion in scoring. There is, however, another colour, occurring in the wild in small numbers of individuals in widely scattered populations in both radiata and eradiata variants, which we call Marguerite Yellow (M.Y.). In systematic accounts individuals showing it are often referred to as var. or forma *albiflora* or *alba*. The florets are not pure white but a very pale cream most nearly (though not exactly) matched with Ridgway's Marguerite Yellow. The genetical behaviour of Marguerite Yellow is here considered first. Parti-coloured capitula, in radaita variants in which the rays are white or white more or less flushed with purple, characterize some wild plants and the character has been introduced into crosses.

Marguerite Yellow (M.Y.).

The following facts emerge from the experiments :

1. Stock Plants 1, 15, 36, and 58·2 were Marguerite Yellow in floret colour and all bred true to this character on selfing.

2. S.P.1 × S.P.15 gave 29 M.Y. only.

3. S.P.1 × S.P.36 gave 73 D.D.P. only.   Comparison may be made with the genetics of floret colour we found for *C. scabiosa*, with complementary factors (Journ. Genetics, **34**, 485–95 : 1937).

4. No M.Y. plants appeared in any family unless one of the parents or grandparents had this character.

5. S.P.1 × S.P.23 (M.Y. × D.D.P.) gave 31 D.D.P. only.   The five F_2 families strongly suggest a 63 Dull Dark Purple : 1 Marguerite Yellow ratio.

6. S.P.1 × S.P.27·1 (M.Y. × D.D.P.) gave 39 D.D.P. only.   Three F_2 families showed results either approximating to or not inconsistent with a 63 : 1 ratio.   One F_2 family gave D.D.P. 12 : M.Y. 2.   A backcross, S.P.1 × F_2 gave D.D.P. 7 : B.P.31 : M.Y.7, a ratio of 5·43 coloured : 1 Marguerite Yellow.

7. In the F_2 and F_3 families derived from M.Y. × M.Y. giving D.D.P., *i.e.*, where there are apparently complementary factors involved, the ratios vary but suggest 15 D.D.P. : 1 M.Y. or 3 D.D.P. : 1 M.Y. in different families.

8. S.P.27·3 × S.P.36 or D.D.P. × M.Y. gave 54 D.D.P. only.   In F_2 there were ratios approximating to 63 : 1 and one of 15 : 1.

9. S.P.15 × S.P.5, *i.e.*, M.Y. × D.D.P. with some ray florets white or flushed, gave 10 D.D.P., of which 3 had partly white ray florets.

10. S.P.34·1 × S.P.36, *i.e.*, D.D.P. (*C. jacea*) × M.Y., gave 11 D.D.P. only.   In F_2 only one family segregated M.Y. in a ratio of 59 D.D.P. to 1 M.Y.   The remaining F_2 families were small.

11. S.P.34·1 × S.P.15, *i.e.*, D.D.P. (*C. jacea*) × M.Y., gave 39 B.P. Only one F_2 family gave a Marguerite Yellow flowered plant and that in the ratio D.D.P.32 : B.P.2 : M.Y.1.   None of the eight F_2 families contained more than 47 scorable plants, but it is interesting to note that plants with florets R.V., B.P., A.P., and the very rare Mallow Purple appeared within them, in addition to plants with florets D.D.P. and M.Y.

12. S.P.15 × S.P.45·1, *i.e.*, M.Y. × B.P. (*C. jacea*), gave B.P.26 only in F_1.   The five F_2 families were all small and only one M.Y. plant appeared in a total of 35 plants.

13. S.P.1 × S.P.48, *i.e.*, M.Y. × B.P. (*C. jacea*), gave 8 B.P. and (probably) 7 M.Y.   In one F_2 family there was a complicated segregation of B.P.65 : A.P.8 : P.L.15 : M.Y.4, or 22 coloured : 1 M.Y.   From this F_2 family were raised 15 F_3 families and 11 backcrosses with one or

other of the grandparents and 1 crossed with S.P.45·6 (B.P., *C. jacea*). The results are exceedingly interesting and significant. M.Y. plants selfed gave only M.Y. offspring. M.Y. × M.Y. gave either M.Y. only, or (in backcrosses with S.P.1) B.P. only (presumably complementary characters), or (another M.Y. plant backcrossed with S.P.1) B.P.56 : M.Y.3. Throughout the whole series no plants with florets of deep colour (D.D.P. or R.V.) appeared. When plants with P.L. (Purplish Lilac, the palest of the " purple " colours here considered) were used to produce F_3 families relatively high numbers of M.Y. plants appeared, in several families the ratios were or were approximately 1 : 1. Other F_3 families also gave relatively high proportions of M.Y. plants, but phenotypically similar backcrosses gave none or, with one exception, proportionately fewer M.Y. plants. The series confirms that a number of genes are concerned with floret colour, that some of these are complementary to production of one or other of the " purple " colours, that there are some cumulative effects, and that plants scored phenotypically into the same colour group are not always genotypically the same.

14. S.P.1 × S.P.33, *i.e.*, M.Y. × D.D.P., gave 22 D.D.P. in F_1. Only three families segregated M.Y. plants, two of them in ratios of 20 coloured to 1 M.Y. and the other in a ratio of 34 coloured to 1 M.Y. Mostly the families were small in numbers and the ratios may rather badly represent 15 : 1.

15. S.P.30 × S.P.36, *i.e.*, B.P. × M.Y., gave D.D.P.12 : B.P.23.

16. S.P.30 × S.P.1, *i.e.*, B.P. × M.Y., gave D.D.P. 30 in F_1. Crossings of F_1 plants resulted in four F_2 families of which only one gave M.Y. plants in the numbers of R.V.1 : B.P.62 : M.Y.2.

Rood's Violet (R.V.).

This is, compared with Dull Dark Purple, a rather bright colour. It is frequently, but not always, both in wild and bred plants, correlated with the *breviflora* female condition of the disc florets. It is probable that the Rood's Violet phenotype is due to one or other of two different gene associations. One is a modification of the gene combination that gives Dull Dark Purple, the same modified combination resulting in *breviflora* female disc florets. The other acts independently and finds a place in the " purple " series.

The following empirical facts may be noted and comments made :

1. S.P.7, S.P.10, and S.P.17, with R.V. florets, bred true on selfing to R.V. florets and their seven F_2 families also bred true to R.V. florets.

2. S.P.7 × S.P.17, *i.e.*, R.V. × R.V., gave only D.D.P. offspring. The F_2 families gave conflicting results : four gave only D.D.P. plants, one gave only R.V. plants, and one segregated D.D.P.2 : R.V.1.

3. S.P.8·1 (R.V.) selfed gave D.D.P.1 : R.V.3 : B.P.1.

4. S.P.8·1 × S.P.26·1, *i.e.*, R.V. × R.V., gave only R.V. in F_1, and F_2 families gave R.V. only or with a small proportion (1 : 13) of D.D.V. : R.V.

5. S.P.13·7 × S.P.13·3, *i.e.*, D.D.P. × R.V., gave only D.D.P. in F_1. The F_2 families were small and all gave D.D.P. with only one segregating D.D.P.3·7 : R.V.1.

6. S.P.25·2 × S.P.26·1, *i.e.*, D.D.P. × R.V., gave only D.D.P. and two F_2 families did likewise.

7. T.24·7 × T.37·3, *i.e.*, R.V. × B.P., gave only D.D.P.

8. S.P.21 × S.P.26·1, *i.e.*, D.D.P. × R.V., gave only R.V. as did one small F_2 family. Two derived R.V. plants crossed together gave a D.D.P.9 : R.V.2 ratio.

9. With the introduction of *C. jacea* into crosses and the frequent use of plants with paler floret colours (Bishop's Purple and Argyle Purple) there is much greater, but not absolute, association of Rood's Violet colour with *breviflora* female florets. This is well shown in T.243, T.242, T.522, T.222, T.249, and T.292.

10. Attention must be called to the interesting results of T.101 and T.103. The former was S.P.34·1 × T.2·5, *i.e.*, D.D.P. × D.D.P., and gave R.V.29 only, and 27 of these were *breviflora*, 1 was *normalis*, and 1 was intermediate between *normalis* and *breviflora* for disc florets. The latter was the reciprocal cross and gave D.D.P.77 only and the disc florets were all *normalis*. One F_2 from T.103 gave R.V.1 only and another gave D.D.P.14 only.

Bishop's Purple (B.P.).

This colour is generally associated with *C. jacea* or with crosses in which this was one of the parents. It has, however, appeared in a cross (T.541) between a M.Y. plant and a derived D.D.P. plant (an F_3 from M.Y. × D.D.P.). This cross gave D.D.P.7 : B.P.31 : M.Y.7.

The following empirical facts are noted and comments made for experiments involving *C. jacea* (or *C. jacea* hybrids) :

1. S.P.45·1 × S.P.45·2 and S.P.45·1 × S.P.45·3, all with florets B.P., gave only plants with florets B.P.

2. S.P.34·1 × S.P.15, *i.e.*, D.D.P. × M.Y., gave only 39 B.P. in F_1. In seven F_2 families, except two very small ones, there was segregation with appearance of B.P. plants, though the ratios were widely different one from another. One F_2 family bred true to the B.P. character.

3. S.P.15 × S.P.34·1, M.Y. × D.D.P., gave only B.P. in F_1.

4. S.P.2 × S.P.34·2, *i.e.*, D.D.P. × A.P., gave only B.P. in F_1.

5. S.P.34·2 × S.P.5, *i.e.*, A.P. × D.D.P. with white and flushed ray florets, gave only B.P. in F_1. The F_2 and F_3 families gave very varied results according to the immediate parent or parents used. Three F_3 families bred true to B.P. These had only B.P. plants as immediate parents. The results suggest the interaction of genes having a cumulative effect.

6. S.P.27·3 × S.P.45·2, *i.e.*, D.D.P. × B.P., gave only D.D.P., and nine F_2 families gave only D.D.P., except for one plant with R.V. florets.

7. S.P.15 × S.P.45·1, *i.e.*, M.Y. × B.P., gave only B.P. in F_1. Of F_2 families, one gave only B.P., three only A.P., and one segregated into B.P., A.P., and M.Y., but all the families were small.

8. S.P.45·1 × S.P.16, *i.e.*, B.P. × B.P. with rays white and flushed, gave only B.P., as did five F_2 families.

9. S.P.27·3 × S.P.48, *i.e.*, D.D.P. × B.P., gave only D.D.P. Five F_2 families gave only D.D.P. and three segregated.

10. S.P.35·1 was D.D.P. but on selfing gave R.V.1 and B.P.3. Later families, F_1 and F_2, mostly bred according to the character of the immediate parent or parents. Two plants of F_1, both B.P., crossed together, however, gave D.D.P.52 and R.V.11, and two F_3 families, from D.D.P. parents, gave only D.D.P.

11. S.P.35·1 × S.P.48, *i.e.*, D.D.P. × B.P., gave only D.D.P., but eleven F_2 families gave only B.P. apart from three R.V. plants.

12. S.P.30 × S.P.35·1, *i.e.*, B.P. × D.D.P., gave D.D.P. Three F_2 families segregated into D.D.P. and R.V. and another gave R.V.5 only.

13. S.P.45·1 × S.P.49, *i.e.*, B.P. × R.V., gave B.P. only.

14. S.P.30 × S.P.47, *i.e.*, B.P. × R.V., gave only D.D.P. and seven F_1 families, most of them small, gave only D.D.P.

15. The series of selfings, crossing, and backcrossings, to F_2 and F_3 generations involving S.P.79·1 and S.P.79·2, both B.P., yielded in 32 families only B.P. plants.

Argyle Purple (A.P.).

This colour is rare in the wild but is represented amongst our stock plants by S.P.34·2, which bred true to A.P. in a very small family. A small number of A.P. plants occurred in F_2 families from the cross S.P.34·1 × S.P.15, *i.e.*, D.D.P. × M.Y., and in larger numbers in F_2 families from the cross S.P.15 × S.P.45·1, *i.e.*, M.Y. × B.P. which in F_1 gave only B.P. A.P. also occurred in some F_2 and F_3 and backcross families from the cross S.P.1 × S.P.48, *i.e.*, M.Y. × B.P. The colour Argyle Purple is, in our experience, entirely limited to *C. jacea* and crosses involving this species.

Mallow Purple (M.P.).

This colour only appeared in the florets of one plant in an F_2 derived from S.P.34·1 × S.P.15, *i.e.*, D.D.P. × M.Y.

Purplish Lilac (P.L.).

This colour occurred only in F_2, F_3, and backcross families involving B.P. and (with one exception) M.Y. colours and the species *C. jacea*.

Dull Dark Purple (D.D.P.).

This, as previously remarked, is the usual colour of florets in plants of *C. nigra* s.s. It also occurs in *C. nemoralis*. The majority of *C. nigra* plants breed true to this character on selfing or on crossing with one another, or only throw plants with florets of the slightly brighter colour, Rood's Violet. Of course, if the Marguerite Yellow (M.Y.) variant, whether radiata or eradiata, be crossed with D.D.P. plants the results are different and are considered here under the heading Marguerite Yellow. Introduction of genes from *C. jacea* (or hybrids involving this) usually results in the appearance of plants with florets of paler colours (B.P., A.P., P.L.).

An unusually interesting variation is found occasionally in radiata plants in which some of the ray florets are white, white flecked, or white flushed purple. The character expression varies greatly, from all or many ray florets white to only one or two petals white in one or two capitula of the plant. In our experiments the gene or genes for the character occurred in S.P.5 and S.P.16. The character appeared in six groups of families involving one or other of these stock plants and in only one other family. With the varied degree of phenotypic expression it is hardly to be expected that clear cut ratios indicative of the number of genes involved would be obtained, but what may be 1 : 1, 3 : 1, 15 : 1, and 63 : 1 ratios are apparent in some of the figures given.

We have never seen plants of British knapweeds with ray florets purple coloured and the disc florets white or Marguerite Yellow.

RAY FLORETS.

Over the British Isles as a whole, plants of the *C. nigra* group without ray florets (*eradiata*) are much commoner than those with ray florets (*radiata*). Indeed in the north, east, and west, plants with ray florets are absent or rare, with very local exceptions so far as we have been able to ascertain. The reverse is true in parts of central south midland and southern vice-counties. The possibility that the *radiata* character has been introduced by hybridization with *C. jacea* is discussed elsewhere. The fact remains that most populations in this country with abundant plants showing the *radiata* character are, as shown by phyllary and other characters, hybrid swarms, complicates the genetical situation.

Difficulties of scoring are occasioned by the occurrence of plants with ray florets of different lengths, from 1·9 cm. to 4·3 cm. The lengths between these extremes form a continuous series and only arbitrary classes can be established—if this be worth while. In an attempt to study the genetical behaviour of the *radiata–eradiata* character group we have scored bred plants into three classes : *radiata*, with ray florets 2·5 cm. or more in length ; *semiradiata*, with ray florets less than 2·5 cm. in length ; *eradiata*, without ray florets.

In plants with *longiflora* capitula, *radiata* cannot always be distinguished from *eradiata* without difficulty and it is even more difficult to distinguish *semiradiata longiflora* from *eradiata longiflora*. In capitula with the *longiflora* character there is a tendency for the sex organs to be reduced in the outer florets and for these to become slightly zygomorphic. It is impossible not to have a doubt as to how some individuals should be scored and a few ratios may be confused by the phenotypes not giving a clear indication of genotypic constitution.

Ray and semiray florets are typically neuter but may show varied development of vestiges of style and stamens. In the most extreme development of ray florets all vestiges inside the corolla tube are absent.

The breeding results may be summarized as follows :

	Number of families giving—						
Origin.	R.	S.	RS.	RE.	RSE.	SE.	E.
R selfed . . .	56	1	10	2	3	—	—
R × R . . .	96	—	8	3	1	—	—
S selfed . . .	3	2	1	6	2	—	1
S × S . . .	1	2	3	1	2	—	1
R × S and S × R .	17	1	10	2	2	—	—
E selfed . . .	1	—	—	6	10	4	20
E × E . . .	1	—	1	12	8	1	29
E × R and R × E .	3	—	1	5	6	4	2
E × S and S × E .	—	—	—	6	9	3	4
Totals . .	178	6	34	43	43	12	57

R = radiata ; S = semiradiata ; E = eradiata.

The most significant fact from this table is that one or more families from everyone of the classes of selfings or crossings segregated for all three characters (*radiata, semiradiata,* and *eradiata*). The S selfed family giving E only was a small one (6 plants) as was the S × S family giving only E (2 plants). The family from E selfed giving only R had 7 plants and the family from E × E giving only R had 3 plants. Had these four families been considerably larger they might well have given RSE. Of the 373 families in the above table, 209 bred true to the character of the immediate parent or parents for the floret structure here considered.

The following Stock Plants bred true to R on selfing 1, 3, 4, 5, 15, 34·1, and 34·2, though five of them gave only small families. Stock Plants 7, 8·1 (?), 10, 13·6, 13·7, 27·1, 27·3, 36, and 58·2, on selfing bred true to E, though four gave only small families. Stock Plant 17 (S) on selfing segregated into R, S, and E and stock plants 35·1 (R) and 79·2 (R) into R and S. There is no family in which R appeared in which the parents or grandparents, or at least one of them, did not have this character. The same is true for E, with two exceptions : T.259, from R × R, gave R 7 : E 5 and T.433, from R × R, gave R 57 : S 2 : E 1. Each of these families had S.P.48 as paternal grandparent and this stock plant was S. There are one or two other suggestions in breeding results that S.P.48 is not completely homozygous for all the genes concerned with heteromorphic capitula.

Attention must be called to certain empirical facts :

1. S.P.27·3 × S.P.36, that is E × E, gave nine F_2 families all breeding true to E.

2. S.P.5 × S.P.3, that is, R × R, gave four F_2 families all breeding true to R.

3. The following crosses of R × R gave only R in F_1, F_2 F_3, and backcrosses : S.P.45·2 × T.2·2 (3 families), S.P.15 × S.P.45·1 (6 families), T.2·5 × S.P.45·1 (8 families), S.P.45·1 × S.P.16 (6 families), and S.P.1 × S.P.48 (29 families).

4. S.P.27·3 × S.P.49, that is, E × E, gave an F_1 and nine F_2 families with only E plants.

5. Reciprocal crosses gave similar, or within limits of size of families approximately similar, results : T.343 and T.361 ; T.1 and T.5 ; T.6 and T.2 ; T.3 and T.7 ; T.183 and T.173 ; T.383 and T.379 ; T.263 and T.278 ; T.431 and T.421 ; T.363 and T.359 ; and T.420 and T.424.

6. Slightly different results from reciprocal crosses were shown by T.110 (R 9 : S 2) and T.108 (R 30) and by T.422 (R 61) and T.433 (R 57 : S 2 : E 1).

The facts stated suggest strongly that genetical factors essentially control the appearance of rayed or unrayed capitula and that cytoplasmic factors are either not concerned or are rare or insignificant in their action. On the other hand, it is impossible to say how many genes are involved. Ratios of, or closely approximating to, 1 : 1, 3 : 1, 5 : 1, and 63 : 1 occur, but the majority of segregations do not give the ratios expected with one, two, or three pairs of independent genes.

As explained above, the division between R and S is an entirely artificial one. Had the division been made at, say 2·3 cm. or 3·0 cm. the figures for R and S would have been decidedly different in some families. Nevertheless, families from S selfed or S × S rarely breed true to S, and the few that do (four out of twenty-five) are very small indeed. In other words, most S plants are presumably in some degree heterozygotes for ray development.

Some R and some E plants are also heterozygous for ray development, either for the phenotypic extremes of radiata and eradiata or for degree of ray development. This is evidence for the existence, in some stocks, of genes, or gene combinations, that prevent the appearance of ray florets.

For all the families involved in our experiments we are forced to postulate a minimum of four pairs of genes together with one or more inhibitors.

DISC FLORETS.

Five kinds of disc florets have been named and scored : normalis (N), longiflora (L), breviflora (B), curly longiflora (C), and quilled (Q). The commonest, in the wild, is normalis, but in large populations some plants with longiflora and others with breviflora disc florets can usually be found. Curly longiflora is a rare and quilled a very rare condition. The least satisfactory class for definite scoring is breviflora since a continuous series from normalis to breviflora can be found in the wild and has been recorded in several groups of bred families. In the extreme form of breviflora the florets are not only shorter and smaller than normalis florets but they are functionally female only, with at most mere vestiges of stamens producing no pollen. In less extreme forms the stamens are more or less imperfectly developed and the anthers may or may not produce some viable pollen grains in some of the florets. No plants with capitula of neuter florets have appeared in bred families, but two such plants (S.P.67 and S.P.68) were found in a hybrid swarm at Wellington College, Berks.

Curly longiflora or quilled plants were not deliberately used in our general experiments. They appeared in very few families and, with one exception, in very small numbers. The quilled character only occurred in F_2 and F_3 families from the cross S.P.1 × S.P.27·1, both stock plants having normalis disc florets. Curly longiflora appeared in F_2 families of the following crosses : S.P.8·1 × S.P.26·1, i.e., L × L ; S.P.13·7 × S.P.13·3, i.e., N × N, but also giving numbers of longiflora plants ; and S.P.24·5 × S.P.13·7, i.e., N × N, but also giving numbers of longiflora plants. One curly longiflora also occurred in the F_1 from S.P.27·3 × S.P.33, i.e., N × N, from which many longiflora plants appeared in F_2 families. The only family in which more than two curly longiflora plants appeared was T.153. The history of this family was : T.41 : S.P.8·1 (longiflora) × S.P.26·1 (longiflora) gave longiflora 30 : curly longiflora 2. T.41, plant 1 × T.41, plant 2, gave normalis 8 : longiflora 33 : curly longiflora 14. T.41, plant 1, was curly longiflora and T.41, plant 2, was longiflora. Curly longiflora, from the few experiments in which it appeared, may be distinguished from longiflora by only one gene. Quilled is apparently a recessive to normalis, but is involved in too few experiments for more to be said regarding its genetical behaviour.

None of the stock plants used showed the breviflora character, nor did it appear in any family derived from the selfing of a stock plant, except from S.P.35·1 and S.P.79·2 selfed and these were of hybrid origin from the cross *C. jacea* × *C. nigra*. The breviflora character appeared in many families derived from various crosses but especially in those in which the two major species *C. jacea* and *C. nigra* were involved, either directly or by crossing segregates. Stock Plants 35·1 and 79·2, in various crosses, gave families with, in general, the greatest numbers of breviflora plants and plants intermediate between breviflora and normalis. S.P.30 (determined as *C. nigra* with a few genes of *C. jacea*, and probably a segregate from the cross *C. jacea* × *C. nigra*) also, in crosses, gave breviflora plants. There was usually an increase in the number of breviflora plants in F_2 and F_3 families when one, usually the ovule, parent was breviflora. Extreme breviflora plants were female and produced no good pollen. One selfing (T.239) of a breviflora plant gave one offspring only and that was breviflora. One selfing (T.413) of a plant " more or less breviflora " gave three normalis plants only. One crossing (T.229) of two breviflora plants gave normalis 11 : breviflora 65 : intermediate 1. One cross (T.367) was made with normalis as ovule and breviflora (not extreme) as pollen parent. This gave normalis 12 : longiflora 1 : breviflora 5 : intermediate 2. The one longiflora plant was female.

Twenty-three crosses of breviflora × normalis were made. All of the families so obtained were F_2 and F_3 families. The summated figures obtained were normalis 530 : longiflora 7 : breviflora 261 : intermediate between normalis and breviflora 75. These summated figures have, however, little significance since the ratios for individual families are so very different and the history of the various immediate parents also varied greatly. Four families gave approximately 1 : 1 ratios. Other ratios of normalis to breviflora approximated to 1 : 3, 5 : 1, 15 : 1, 8 : 1, 1 : 2, 2 : 1, 3 : 1.

The very occasional occurrence of single breviflora plants in groups of families where the vast majority of plants are normalis has to be recorded (e.g., T.477, T.485, T.161, T.185, T.457).

The genetical situation with regard to longiflora relative to normalis appears to be complicated. The only group of families breeding true to longiflora was that derived from S.P.21 × S.P.26·1, i.e., L × L. On the other hand, 14 groups of families had no plants with the longiflora character when the parent was or the parents were normalis. S.P.26·1, longiflora, was particularly powerful in producing longiflora offspring. Stock Plants 13·7, 17, and 33, though themselves normalis, gave numerous longiflora plants in later generations from various crosses in which they were used.

Most often normalis behaved as dominant to longiflora, but there were exceptions. The most noteworthy were T.30 and T.335. In T.30, S.P.24·5 × S.P.26·1, i.e., N × L, gave longiflora 39. In F_2, T.30, plant 1 selfed, gave normalis 1 : longiflora 20 and T.30, plant 2 × T.30, plant 3, gave normalis 1 : longiflora 4. T.335, T.146, plant 9 selfed, i.e., longiflora selfed, gave normalis 22 : longiflora 22 : breviflora 5 : intermediate between normalis and breviflora 1.

There are probably at least three gene differences between longiflora and normalis, and gene combinations prevent the phenotypic appearance otherwise expected.

In medium to large natural populations of British knapweeds of the *Centaurea nigra* group it is generally possible to find a few plants showing the " longiflora " character. These may or may not be rayed. It is necessary to examine the capitula closely to distinguish the zygomorphic rays from the more or less actinomorphic elongated " longiflora " disc florets when they occur together. The percentage occurrence of " longiflora " plants in wild populations varies greatly, but 1 to 2 per cent is common. The plants scored phenotypically as " semilongiflora " are possibly not all the same genotypically, but, in general, they appeared more or less intermediate between " longiflora " and " normalis." Five " semilongiflora " plants (A 3, B 7, C 11, D 18, D 20) were included amongst the stock plants used in the experiments considered immediately below. All the other stock plants used (15 in number) were longiflora in character. All the stock plants were eradiata (i.e., with no trace of rays).

Morphologically, the florets of longiflora capitula show some resemblance to ray florets though they occupy the position of disc florets. In our experience of both wild and bred plants, all capitula of a plant either show longiflora character or they do not, though the size of the florets may vary somewhat from plant to plant. Two modifications of the typical (commoner) longiflora character are "curly" and "quilled." In "curly" the relatively long strap-shaped corolla lobes are curled backwards. In "quilled" the corolla lobes are shorter and more or less erect ; in other words the florets are tubular for most of their length. The quilled plants of the present series do not show the character in an extreme condition.

Stock plants used in the experiments here under consideration were chosen from four wild populations in 1935 as follows :

A. Gloucestershire, near and on the north side of Stow-on-the-Wold.
B. Warwickshire, between Harwood's House and Halford.
C. Warwickshire, between Harbury and Ufton.
D. Warwickshire, Harbury Heath.

Every individual plant was given a number following the letter indicating the wild population from which it was selected.

The 1149 individuals of 34 families resulting from selfings and crossings have been analyzed for floret characters and the results are summarized under four group headings. All the offspring were eradiata except in group 2.

1. Selfings and crossings from eradiata longiflora parents and yielding only eradiata longiflora offspring.

Selfings.				Crossings.		
	Parent.	Offspring.			Parents.	Offspring.
T.562	D 17	4	.	T.577	D 15 × D 4	65
T.568	B 5	69	.	T.578	B 22 × C 12	48
T.569	B 4	46	.	T.579	D 17 × D 15	66
T.570	D 15	43	.	T.580	C 12 × B 5	57
T.574	C 10	3	.	T.587	B 5 × B 22	68
T.584	C 9	2	.	T.595	C 14 × D 15	37
T.593	C 14	1	.	T.596	C 10 × B 5	19
				T.597	A 21 × C 14	50
Totals		168	.	.		410

Grand total from 15 families : 578.

2. Families with some radiata plants.

From selfings.				From crossings.		
	Parent.	radiata.	eradiata.		Parents.	radiata.	eradiata.
T.561	D 16	5	5	.	T.564	D 16 × D 17	2	68
T.581	C 12	4	2	.	T.565	D 16 × B 8	28	46
T.582	A 21	1	35	.	T.594	A 2 × C 12	1	14
Totals		10	42	.			31	128

Grand totals from 6 families : 41 radiata : 170 eradiata. All plants were longiflora (none was curly or quilled). The parent B 8 was curly longiflora. All other parents were longiflora (none was curly or quilled).

3. Families from parents at least one of which is modified from eradiata longiflora.

Family.	Parent or parents.	longi- flora.	curly longi- flora.	quilled longi- flora.	semi- longi- flora	quilled semi- longi- flora.	nor- malis.
T.563	B 8	2	3	—	—	—	—
T.567	D 19	14	—	10	2	—	—
T.572	C 11	—	—	—	5	—	—
T.573	B 7	31	1	—	7	1	2
T.583	D 18	2	—	—	—	—	—
T.586	A 3	3	—	—	—	—	1
T.592	D 20	22	—	—	35	—	—
T.566	D 17 × B 8	—	42	—	—	—	—
T.575	D 19 × C 11	15	—	21	33	—	—
T.576	D 19 × D 15	53	—	—	15	—	—
T.590	A 3 × C 11	3	—	—	6	—	—
T.591	C 10 × B 7	15	—	—	—	—	—

Total families 12.   Total offspring 344.

The parents in the above table had the following of the characters scored :
A 3 semilongiflora.
B 7 semilongiflora, but near to normalis.
B 8 full curly longiflora.
C 10 full longiflora.
C 11 semilongiflora, but near to normalis.
D 15 full longiflora.
D 17 full longiflora.
D 18 semilongiflora.
D 19 longiflora somewhat quilled.
D 20 semilongiflora.

4. Longiflora plant selfed giving a segregated offspring.
T.571. B 22 selfed gave : 8 eradiata ; 7 longiflora : 1 quilled longiflora ; 3 of the plants had hermaphrodite and 5 female flowers.

For the majority of the plants scoring presented no difficulties, the characters shown by them being clear-cut. There were, however, exceptions : D 19 had florets " somewhat quilled " ; C 11 and B 7 had semilongiflora florets which were near to normalis ; in T.575 there were intermediates between the groups and scoring was somewhat arbitrary ; the same was true for T.576.
Selfings often gave small or relatively small families. Selfings of A 21, B 4, B 5, B 7, D 15, and D 20, however, gave fair sized to relatively

large families. Crossings generally gave large families, though the cross A 3 × C 11 was an exception. A 3 and C 11 gave very small families on selfing.

More than half the offspring (578 out of 1141) were in families yielding only eradiata longiflora offspring. C 12 was the only stock plant, involved in these, that as a parent in another crossing was one parent of a family producing (one) radiata offspring and which on selfing gave (four) radiata offspring. In the production of radiata plants the stock plants C 12 and D 16 are the most interesting of the parents used. They were eradiata full longiflora in characters. It is clear that they contained recessive genes for radiata though whether the radiata character sometimes produced in their offspring is genetically equivalent to the character shown in radiata normalis plants, so common in many wild populations in southern (not south-western) and south midland counties of England, remains uncertain. Only 3 normalis plants appeared among the 1141 offspring of the above experiments and these were all eradiata.

The semilongiflora plants among the offspring mostly had at least one semilongiflora parent. Exceptions are the 2 semilongiflora plants in T.567 and the 15 in T.576, from families with D 19 as one (or only) parent and this may well have been heterozygous for genes concerned with the semilongiflora character. The genes for the quilled character also mainly come from D 19 which was itself " somewhat quilled." The curly longiflora character came (with one exception) from B 8 which was well marked curly longiflora. In T.566 curly longiflora was clearly dominant over non-curly longiflora.

CYPSELAS.

The fruits of knapweeds are derived from inferior one-ovuled ovaries. The hard pericarp is free from the thin testa and does not open or split at maturity, that is on being shed and before germination. The convenient term cypselas is given to such fruits, characteristic of the family *Compositae*.

The following is a general description of cypselas in *C. nigra* and *C. nemoralis*. Compressed obovoid-ellipsoid or narrowly obovoid-ellipsoid, 3 to 4 mm. long and 1·25 to 2 mm. at the greatest breadth, the extreme base obtuse or acute, with an oblique laterally placed hilum (area of attachment to the capitulum receptacle) near the base, pubescent all over or with few scattered hairs, surface colour Grayish Olive, Light Grayish Olive, Smoke Gray, Pale Smoke Gray, or Benzo Brown (Ridgway, Color Standards, Plate XLVI), pappus present (papposa) but may be poorly developed (vestigial) or, in a few plants determined on phyllary characters as *C. nemoralis*, absent (epapposa).

Cypselas of *C. jacea* are compressed obovoid-ellipsoid, 3 to 3·5 mm. long and 1·25 to 1·75 mm. at greatest breadth, the extreme base acute, with an oblique laterally placed hilum near the base, pubescent all over or with few scattered hairs, surface colour Purple-Drab (Ridgway, Plate XLV), Pale Smoke Gray, or Benzo Brown, pappus absent.

There is considerable fluctuation in some of these characters, as pubescence, colour, and degree of pappus development, even in cypselas from the same capitulum. The presence (and if present the degree of development of) or absence of the pappus is the most interesting character of the cypselas from our immediate point of view. It is considered of taxonomic importance by some authors. Our material of *C. jacea* has cypselas devoid of pappus. The statements (by Butcher and Strudwick, 'Further Illustrations of British Plants,' 216–17 : 1930, and by Clapham, Tutin, and Warburg, 'Flora of the British Isles,' 1107–08 : 1952) that *C. nigra* (or *C. obscura* or *C. nigra* subsp. *nigra*) has pappus absent or O and that *C. nemoralis* (or *C. nigra* subsp. *nemoralis*) has pappus present or of short bristles, are not confirmed by our observations and experiments. Generally speaking a pappus is present in British specimens of *C. nigra* and of *C. nemoralis*, though the degree of development of the bristles varies. The pappus is absent in *C. jacea* and in some individuals that in most characters agree with *C. nemoralis* and come from areas with hybrid populations. The absence of a pappus, or its very great reduction, suggests that the plants have genes of *C. jacea* in their genom.

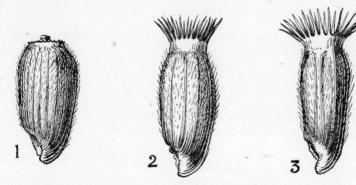

Fig. 3.—*Cypselas.* 1. *C. jacea.* 2. *C. nemoralis.* 3. *C. nigra.*

The following are the scorings for pappus character of Stock Plants we have used :

1. Pappus present and relatively well developed : S.Ps. : 10, 58·2.
2. Pappus present but relatively well developed to vestigial in different cypselas from the same plant : S.Ps. : 7, 27·1.
3. Pappus present but vestigial : S.Ps. : 1, 6.
4. Pappus present but relatively well developed to none in different cypselas from the same plant : S.Ps. : 35·2, 38·3.
5. Pappus vestigial to none in different cypselas from the same plant ; S.Ps. : 5, 8·2, 13·6, 13·7, 15, 17, 23, 25·2, 27·3, 36, 47.

12

6. Pappus none :   S.Ps. : 3, 4, 8·1, 13·3, 16, 21, 26·1, 30, 33, 34·1, 34·2, 35·1, 45·1 to 45·4, 48, 49, 79·1, 79·2.

The scorings for a number of bred families (picked at random) will indicate the kinds of segregation obtained for pappus characters. P = pappus present and relatively well developed ;   V = pappus present but vestigial ;   N = pappus absent.

T.2 S.P.5 × S.P.3.   V to N 3 : N 2.

T.13. S.P.1 × S.P.23.   P to N 1 : V to N 7 : N 22.

T.72. S.P.27·3 selfed.   P 13 : P to V 25 : V 26 : V to N 15.

T.243. T.113·5 selfed, *i.e.*, F_2 from S.P.34·2 × S.P.5.   V 4 : V to N 11 : N 28.

T.261. T.13·8 selfed, *i.e.*, F_2 from S.P.1 × S.P.23.   V to N 2 : N117.

T.273. T.78·20 selfed, *i.e.*, F_2 from S.P.35·1 × S.P.49.   P to N 4 : V to N 14 : N 54.

T.483. T.224·58 selfed, from T.68·15 selfed, *i.e.*, an F_3 from S.P.1 × S.P.48.   P to N 5 : V to N 18 : N 36.

The following comments may be made :

1. Stock plant 10 had the best developed pappus of any of the plants with which we have experimented. The bristles constituting the pappus were 1 to 2 mm. long.

2. T.13 was essentially a family without pappus, except for one plant. The 7 plants scored as V to N had only a few very short bristles on a few of the cypselas, most of which were without pappus. T.261 also was a family almost clear of all bristles.

3. T.72, T.243, T.273, and T.483 obviously showed segregations. In T.72, the cypselas were dark coloured and some on every plant had a pappus and six plants had exceptionally well developed pappus. In T.483, five plants showed cypselas with every intermediate development of pappus from the full development found in any of our plants to none at all.

A few scorings of pappus characters from wild plants may be given. They are, of course, additional to those for our stock plants :

V.C. 1.   *C. nigra.*   Sennen Green.   P (very well developed).

V.C. 2.   *C. nigra.*   Callington.   V to N in one head.

V.C. 8.   *C. nemoralis.*   Salisbury Plain.   N.

V.C.17.   *C. nigra.*   Thetford to Old Malden.   P.

V.C.17.   *C. nemoralis.*   Colley Hill.   V.

V.C.17.   *C. nemoralis.*   Reigate.   P to V.

V.C.17.   *C. jacea* × *C. nemoralis.*   Old Malden.   V to N.

V.C.22.   *C. jacea* × *C. nemoralis.*   Bradfield.   V to N.

V.C.22.   *C. jacea* × *C. nigra.*   Bradfield.   N.

V.C.23.   *C. nemoralis.*   Woodstock.   N.

V.C.23.   *C. jacea* × *C. nemoralis.*   Woodstock. N.

V.C.23.   *C. jacea* × *C. nigra.*   Stonesfield.   P.

V.C.23.   *C. jacea* × *C. nigra.*   Stonesfield.   V to N.

V.C.28.   *C. nigra.*   Appleton.   P to V.

V.C.46.   *C. nigra.*   Near Aberystwyth.   P to V.

V.C.46.   *C. nigra.*   Near Aberystwyth.   P.

V.C.46. *C. nigra.* Near Aberystwyth. V to N.
V.C.67. *C. nigra.* Newton Hall. V.
V.C.85. *C. nigra.* St. Andrews. P to N.
V.C.87. *C. nigra.* Callender. P to V.
V.C.88. *C. nigra.* Lock Tay side. P to N.
V.C.96. *C. nigra.* Castle Urquhart. V to N.

CHAPTER VIII

COMPATIBILITY AND INCOMPATIBILITY

In the section of this work dealing with vegetative multiplication and sexual reproduction facts were given that clearly showed that self sterility, and with certain parents cross sterility, was due to incompatibility of pollen and stigma-style. Most often self-incompatibility was complete to almost complete, but there were exceptions to which attention is drawn below. Cross fertility or cross sterility varied with the parents used. The occurrence of self-incompatibility partly determined the practical methods we used in our breeding work with *Centaurea*, but the general scheme of the experiments was planned for other purposes than the study of compatibility and incompatibility in the genus. For example, had the genetics of incompatibility been a main aim of our work more criss-cross crossing and reciprocal crossing utilizing every individual of one or more families would have been carried out and microscopic methods for determination of compatibility or incompatibility would have been devised and used. In incompatible pollinations of *Centaurea* the pollen grains do not send pollen tubes into the stigma and generally the pollen does not germinate at all. We have a great many figures of the number of cypselas produced and plants raised from 235 self and 312 cross pollinations and it was to be expected that a consideration of these would throw light on the genetics of incompatibility in knapweeds.

Before analysing our figures one must note some difficulties. In *Centaurea*, incompatibility does not always result in complete sterility. There are many different sizes (numbers of plants) in the families raised by selfing and by crossing. There is "many a slip 'twixt the cup and the lip " or between pollination and a resulting mature offspring. We have no evidence of parthenocarpy as applied to *Centaurea* cypselas beyond the fact that a varying number of cypselas in different families often fail to germinate. It is, therefore, sometimes difficult to decide whether incompatibility and its degree is judged better by a number of apparently good cypselas, of germinated cypselas, or of plants raised. We can, for nearly every family, give figures for capitula pollinated, apparently good cypselas per capitulum obtained, and number of plants raised. Below 50 plants raised the same figure at least approximates to the number of cypselas satifactorily germinated. Above 50 not all seedlings were grown on. There were, of course, in some families, some deaths between seedling and mature stages, but generally these were few. After carefully allowing for all known factors we have defined as fertile (F) pollinations giving 10 or more mature plants per capitulum, as sterile (S) pollinations giving 3 or fewer mature plants per capitulum, and as semi-fertile (sf) pollinations giving 4 to 9 mature plants per capitulum pollinated under control. Reference to the number of apparently good cypselas has, however, been constantly made as a partial check on the use of these chosen figures and adjustments or special comments have sometimes to be made.

The risk of loss of potentially " good " cypselas by galling or larvae cannot be entirely ignored but was reduced to a minimum by having the plants in the insect-proof breeding house for pollination and cypsela setting. Gall-fly parasitizing occurs before the capitula open and some heads used may have been galled, with consequent reduction of numbers of " good " cypselas. Examination of large numbers of mature capitula showed that this was, at most, a very insignificant cause of sterility in the breeding house.

Conditions in the breeding house were, unavoidably, artificial in several respects. The plants were mostly grown in 9 to 12 inch pots and usually had been potted up in the spring. There was some restriction of root growth. Ventilation in the house was reduced by ventilators having to be covered with fine gauze. We have no evidence that such conditions restricted cypsela output but we had no time to carry out control experiments on a large scale to investigate this point.

Again, selfing and crossing under control were, of course, limited to pollination by one kind of pollen only, both per floret and per capitulum. Whether pollen mixture would in any way influence pollen germination or pollen tube growth or fertilization we do not know. Mixed pollination is certainly the rule in the wild, unless the plants be unusually isolated. The same is true in the breeding ground unless the plants be artificially protected from insect visitors.

We have now to analyze a selection of our figures. Selfings and crossings that gave no offspring are not given in the chapter summarizing the results of scorings of families but we have here to record both negative and positive results.

1. Selfings that gave no offspring.

Selfing number.	Stock plant number.	Capitula used.	Apparently " good " cypelas produced.	Species or hybrid.
T. 9 .	2	. 20	. 0	. C. nemoralis.
T. 27 .	26·1	. 8	. 1	. C. nigra (with a few genes of C. jacea).
T. 31 .	24·5	. 1	. 0	. C. nemoralis.
T. 46 .	15	. 2	. 0	. C. nemoralis (with a few genes of C. jacea).
T. 54 .	6	. 5	. 0	. C. nemoralis.
T. 58 .	21	. 3	. 0	. C. nemoralis (with a few genes of C. jacea).
T. 61 .	38·3	. 20	. 8	. C. nemoralis
T. 63 .	47	. 4	. 0	. C. jacea × C. nigra.
T. 70 .	45·1	. 8	. 2	. C. jacea.
T. 83 .	45·2	. 15	. 0	. C. jacea.
T.604 .	1013	. 31	. 4	. C. nemoralis.

2. Stock plant crossings that gave no offspring.

Cross number.	Stock plants used.	Capitula. used.	Apparently " good " cypselas produced.	Species used.
T. 48 .	13·6 × 13·3 .	3	. 0	. (*C. nemoralis* × *C. jacea*) × *C. nemoralis.*
T.114 .	34·1 × 5	. 1	. 0	. *C. jacea* × *C. nemoralis.*

3. Backcross giving no offspring.

Cross number.	Cross attempted.	Capitula used.	Apparently " good " cypselas produced.	Backcross.
T.106 .	T.2·5 × S.P.5	2	. 3	. (S.P.5 × S.P.3) × S.P.5. No offspring raised.

S.P.3 and S.P.5 were both *C. nemoralis.*

4. F$_1$ produced offspring but F$_2$ sterile or nearly so.

Cross or selfing number.	Cross or selfing.	Capitula used.	Apparently " good " cypselas produced.	Number of offspring raised.
T. 22 .	S.P.10 selfed .	19	. 203	. 45
T.149 .	T.22·2 × T.22·8 .	1	. 0	. 0
T.142 .	T.22·2 selfed .	5	. 0	. 0
T. 99 .	S.P.15 × S.P.34·1 .	3	. 95	. 61
T.461 .	T.99·24 selfed .	29	. 0	. 0
T.463 .	T.99·26 selfed .	21	. 0	. 0
T.462 .	T.99·5 selfed .	24	. 0	. 0
T.460 .	T.99·48 selfed .	18	. 0	. 0
T.459 .	T.99·5 × T.99·26 .	7	. 0	. 0
T. 64 .	S.P.30 × S.P.36 .	2	. 43	. 35
T.254 .	T.64·15 selfed .	12	. 1	. 0
T.257 .	T.64·20 × T.64·18 .	4	. 3	. 0
T.105 .	S.P.15 × S.P.5 .	3	. 76	. 10
T.405 .	T.105·5 × T.105·8 .	7	. 124	. 0
T.403 .	T.105·5 selfed .	48	. 0	. 0
T.404 .	T.105·8 selfed .	39	. 5	. 0
T.116 .	S.P.79·2 × S.P.79·1 .	2	. 36	. 17
T.426 .	T.116·7 × T.116·3 .	3	. 2	. 0
T.416 .	T.116·3 × T.116·14 .	7	. 2	. 0
T.415 .	T.116·8 selfed .	5	. 0	. 0
T.414 .	T.116·7 selfed .	17	. 0	. 0
T.409 .	T.116·3 selfed .	15	. 0	. 0
T.410 .	T.116·12 selfed .	9	. 0	. 0
T.412 .	T.116·8 × T.116·11 .	6	. 1	. 0
T. 87 .	S.P.45·2 × T.2·2 .	3	. 42	. 12
T.398 .	T.87·4 selfed .	60	. 29	. 7
T.401 .	T.87·10 selfed .	32	. 19	. 5
T.400 .	T.87·7 selfed .	20	. 1	. 0
T.399 .	T.87·5 selfed .	24	. 7	. 0

Cross or selfing number.	Cross or selfing.	Capitula used.	Apparently " good " cypselas produced.	Number of offspring raised.
T.396	T.87·10 × T.87·8	7	9	0
T.395	T.87·5 × T.87·7	6	1	0
T.394	T.87·4 × T.87·10	6	6	0
T.393	T.87·4 × T.87·7	7	3	0
T.397	T.87·10 × T.87·5	6	6	0
T.392	T.87·4 × T.87·5	7	2	0

5. F_1 produced offspring, F_2 from selfings sterile or nearly so, from crossing sibs fertile.

Cross or selfing number.	Cross or selfing.	Capitula used.	Apparently " good " cypselas produced.	Number of offspring raised.
T. 41	S.P.8·1 × S.P.26·1	4	56	32
T.125	T.41·3 selfed	22	3	3
T.197	T.41·4 selfed	3	0	0
T.128	T.41·1 selfed	10	4	1
T.153	T.41·1 × T.41·2	4	73	55

6. Inequalities in sterility in F_2.

Cross or selfing number	Cross or selfing.	Capitula used.	Apparently " good " cypselas produced.	Number of offspring raised.
T.100	S.P.34·1 × S.P.36	2	15	11
T.274	T.100·3 selfed	16	17	14
T.275	T.100·6 selfed	11	22	13
T.298	T.100·6 × T.100·8	6	136	66
T.310	T.100·7 × T.100·11	5	0	0
T.299	T.100·8 × T.100·7	6	0	0
T.290	T.100·3 × T.100·8	5	1	0
T.288	T.100·3 × T.100·7	5	2	0
T.286	T.100·8 selfed	22	2	0
T.285	T.100·7 selfed	18	3	0

7. F_1 and F_2 produced offspring, marked sterility in F_3.

Cross or selfing number.	Cross or selfing.	Capitula used.	Apparently " good " cypselas produced.	Number of offspring raised.
T. 69	S.P.30 × S.P.35·1	2	68	37
T.231	T.69·31 × T.69·29	5	5	5
T.542	T. 231·1 selfed	28	1	1
T.547	T.231·2 × T.231·3	8	4	2
T.552	T.231·3 selfed	12	2	1
T.559	T.231·2 selfed	6	4	0
T. 14	S.P.1 × S.P.27·1	2	51	39
T.326	T.14·39 selfed	14	222	81
T.528	T.326·64 selfed	22	10	9
T.538	T.326·16 × T.236·64	7	11	8
T.549	T.326·73 selfed	10	0	0
T.530	T.326·16 selfed	19	0	0
T.329	T.14·39 × T.14·30	9	335	85
T.532	T. 329·28 selfed	42	57	3

8. High numbers of plants raised from selfings.

Selfing number.	Selfing.	Capitula used.	Apparently " good " cypselas produced.	Number of offspring raised.
T. 22	S.P.10 selfed	19	203	45
T. 72	S.P.27·3 selfed	18	145	81
T.198	T.42·1 selfed	34	285	93
T.214	T.65·2 selfed	11	456	70
T.224	T.68·15 selfed	5	152	93
T.225	T.73·3 selfed	23	303	85
T.241	T.80·2 selfed	32	94	75
T.243	T.113·5 selfed	16	186	52
T.255	T.13·27 selfed	36	279	88
T.261	T.13·8 selfed	44	844	120
T.280	T.13·29 selfed	20	114	64
T.294	T.84·34 selfed	35	395	80
T.302	T.76·2 selfed	19	271	92
T.326	T.14·39 selfed	14	222	81
T.335	T.146·9 selfed	14	120	57
T.305	T.78·13 selfed	10	89	58
T.276	T.78·17 selfed	27	899	56
T.287	T.78·25 selfed	19	240	89
T.516	T.78·25 selfed	21	78	42

9. Reciprocals (examples).

Cross number.	Cross or selfing.	Capitula used.	Apparently " good " cypselas produced.	Number of offspring raised.
T. 24	S.P.17 selfed	23	53	36
T.158	T.24·7 × T.24·3	3	71	47
T.157	T.24·3 × T.24·7	3	4	0
T. 66	S.P.1 × S.P.33	5	69	33
T.358	T.66·19 × T.66·6	7	370	36
T.365	T.66·6 × T.66·19	5	3	0
T. 84	S.P.27·3 × S.P.33	3	179	73
T.308	T.84·34 × T.84·63	6	90	47
T.323	T.84·63 × T.84·34	6	5	0
T. 1	S.P.2 × S.P.3	1	10	10
T. 5	S.P.3 × S.P.2	2	103	61
T. 2	S.P.5 × S.P.3	1	71	63
T. 6	S.P.3 × S.P.5	1	40	33
T. 3	S.P.4 × S.P.5	2	140	65
T. 7	S.P.5 × S.P.4	2	140	85
T. 37	S.P.13·7 × S.P.24·5	1	43	33
T. 42	S.P.24·5 × S.P.13·7	1	22	16
T. 98	S.P.34·1 × S.P.15	3	122	39
T. 99	S.P.15 × S.P.34·1	3	95	61

Selfing number.	Selfing.	Capitula used.	Apparently " good " cypselas produced.	Number of offspring raised.
T.431	T.81·8 × T.81·34	5	4	1
T.421	T.81·34 × T.81·8	6	31	21
T.489	S.P.1 × T.224·58	6	6	2
T.483	T.224·58 × S.P.1	10	298	59

The above are examples of the 20 pairs of reciprocal crosses made (apart from one which was rejected because of damage by slugs). The total results can be summated as follows :

A. Reciprocals fertile 8.

B. Reciprocals sterile 1.

C. Reciprocals semi-fertile 1.

D. One fertile, one sterile 4.

E. One fertile, one semi-fertile 2.

F. One semi-fertile, one sterile 4.

The four reciprocal pairs in group D are extremes and clearly show that some reciprocals can give very different results for the character pair compatibility and incompatibility.

A selection of series of crossings and selfings will illustrate the results obtained. The three columns of figures give the number of capitula, the "good" cypselas obtained, and the number of plants raised respectively. In every series, the first cross is an F_1 the others are F_2 crossings or selfings except where square brackets are used. In the diagrams a continuous line indicates fertility, a broken line indicates semi-fertility, and a line of dots indicates sterility. The arrow to any line gives the direction of the cross, from the ovule to the pollen parent. The letters F, sf, S, in round brackets after a parent, refer to its fertility, semi-fertility, or sterility on selfing. Not every parent was selfed.

SERIES A.

T. 98.	S.P.34·1 × S.P.15	3	122	39
T.389.	T.98·18 selfed	40	6	4
T406.	T.98·29 selfed	12	1	0
T.390.	T.98·31 selfed	13	7	4
T.391.	T.98·37 selfed	18	1	0
T.407.	T.98·19 × T.98·29	6	130	45
T.385.	T.98·19 × T.98·31	8	171	39
T.384.	T.98·19 × T.98·37	2	231	49
T.387.	T.98·31 × T.98·29	5	1	0
T.388.	T.98·31 × T.98·37	5	142	38
T.402.	T.98·37 × T.98·29	5	140	22
T.386.	T.98·37 × T.98·31	8	188	20

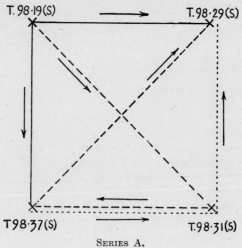

SERIES A.

SERIES B.

T. 84.	S.P.27·3 × S.P.33	.	.	.	3	.	179	.	73
T.304.	T.84·2 selfed	.	.	.	37	.	8	.	0
T.297.	T.84·3 selfed	.	.	.	23	.	13	.	8
T.300.	T.84·6 selfed	.	.	.	21	.	5	.	0
T.393.	T.84·8 selfed	.	.	.	7	.	3	.	0
T.294.	T.84·34 selfed	.	.	.	35	.	395	.	80
T.296.	T.84·63 selfed	.	.	.	33	.	42	.	31
T.316.	T.84·2 × T. 84·34	.	.	.	6	.	322	.	82
T.319.	T.84·2 × T.84·63	.	.	.	5	.	247	.	66
T.314.	T.84·6 × T.84·23	.	.	.	5	.	3	.	0
T.309.	T.84·8 × T.84·6	.	.	.	6	.	4	.	0
T.250.	T.84·32 × T.84·26	.	.	.	11	.	220	.	88
T.308.	T.84·34 × T.84·63	.	.	.	6	.	90	.	47

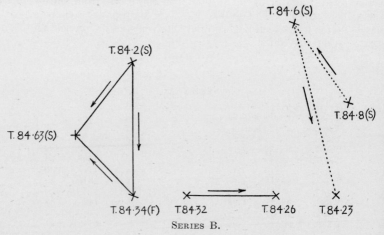

SERIES B.

SERIES C.

T. 77.	S.P.27·3 × S.P.45·2	. .	2 .	125 .	23
T.368.	T.77·1 selfed	. . . .	49 .	12 .	4
T.372.	T.77·2 selfed	. . . .	17 .	3 .	0
T.369.	T.77·6 selfed	. . . .	43 .	2 .	0
T.371.	T.77·11 selfed	. . .	37 .	3 .	0
T.370.	T.77·22 selfed	. . .	42 .	1 .	0
T.380.	T.77·1 × T.77·2	. . .	5 .	194 .	20
T.377.	T.77·1 × T.77·6	. . .	6 .	180 .	28
T.378.	T.77·1 × T.77·11	. . .	6 .	197 .	86
T.374.	T.77·2 × T.77·1	. . .	6 .	135 .	14
T.383.	T.77·2 × T.77·6	. . .	6 .	77 .	10
T.379.	T.77·6 × T.77·2	. . .	3 .	143 .	54
T.381.	T.77·6 × T.77·11	. . .	6 .	293 .	58
T.382.	T.77·11 × T.77·2	. . .	6 .	1 .	0
T.373.	T.77·22 × T.77·2	. . .	6 .	2 .	0
T.375.	T.77·22 × T.77·6	. . .	6 .	0 .	0
T.376.	T.77·22 × T.77·11	. . .	9 .	29 .	16

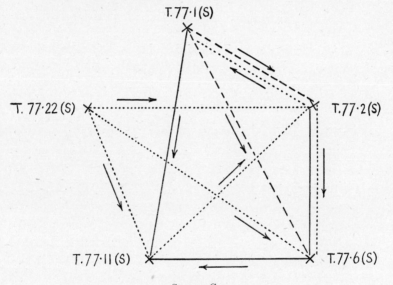

SERIES C.

SERIES D.

T.104.	S.P.15 × S.P.48	. .	3 .	62 .	24
T.260.	T.104·3 selfed	. .	23 .	4 .	0
T.258.	T.104·10 selfed	. .	26 .	23 .	17
T.307.	T.104·11 selfed	. .	19 .	1 .	0
T.268.	T.104·13 selfed	. .	26 .	0 .	0
T.269.	T.104·14 selfed	. .	35 .	2 .	0
T.259.	T.104·10 × T.104·3	. .	9 .	14 .	13
T.271.	T.104·10 × T.104·13	. .	7 .	10 .	6
T.282.	T.104·10 × T.104·14	. .	7 .	316 .	121
T.321.	T.104·11 × T.104·23	. .	5 .	1 .	0
T.284.	T.104·13 × T.104·8	. .	7 .	1 .	0

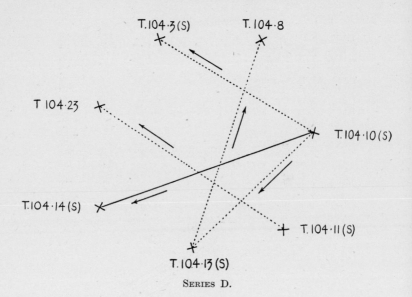

SERIES D.

SERIES E.

T. 2.	S.P.5 × S.P.3	.	.	.	1	.	71	.	63
T. 89.	T.2·1 selfed .	.	.	.	16	.	5	.	0
T. 90.	T.2·2 selfed .	.	.	.	19	.	12	.	0
T. 88.	T.2·3 selfed .	.	.	.	14	.	2	.	1
T. 92.	T.2·4 selfed .	.	.	.	26	.	11	.	7
T. 91.	T.2·5 selfed .	.	.	.	6	.	2	.	0
T. 94.	T.2·1 × T.2·2	.	.	.	3	.	0	.	0
T. 96.	T.2·3 × T.2·2	.	.	.	2	.	16	.	7
T. 93.	T.2·3 × T.2·4	.	.	.	2	.	25	.	17
[T.101.	S.P.34·1 × T.2·5	.	.	.	2	.	42	.	29]
[T.103.	T.2·5 × S.P.34·1	.	.	.	2	.	177	.	77]
[T.106.	T.2·8 × S.P.5	.	.	.	2	.	3	.	0]
[T.107.	T.2·5 × S.P.48	.	.	.	1	.	16	.	11]
[T.111.	T.2·5 × S.P.45·1	.	.	.	2	.	131	.	87]
[T.112.	T.2·5 × S.P.34·2	.	.	.	1	.	58	.	5]

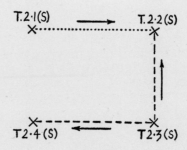

SERIES E.

SERIES F.

T. 24.	S.P.17 selfed	.	.	.	.	23	.	53	.	36
T.187.	T.24·1 selfed	.	.	.	.	16	.	11	.	4
T.188.	T.24·3 selfed	.	.	.	.	11	.	0	.	0
T.189.	T.24·7 selfed	.	.	.	.	5	.	13	.	3
T.186.	T.24·1 × T.24·3	.	.	.	.	3	.	1	.	0
T.171.	T.24·3 × T.24·4	.	.	.	.	3	.	1	.	1
T.158.	T.24·7 × T.24·3	.	.	.	.	3	.	71	.	47
T.169.	T.24·7 × T.24·4	.	.	.	.	3	.	48	.	31
[T.161.	T.24·7 × T.37·3	.	.	.	.	3	.	57	.	16]

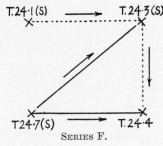

SERIES F.

SERIES G.

T. 74.	S.P.27·3 × S.P.36	.	.	.	2	.	14	.	54
T.356.	T.74·1 selfed	.	.	.	28	.	11	.	6
T.337.	T.74·6 selfed	.	.	.	29	.	69	.	17
T.338.	T.74·15 selfed	.	.	17	.	44	.	16
T.336.	T.74·22 selfed	.	.	10	.	3	.	0
T.360.	T.74·1 × T.74·15	.	.	3	.	141	.	52
T.361.	T.74·1 × T.74·16	.	.	3	.	155	.	19
T.362.	T.74·1 × T.74·17	.	.	6	.	3	.	0
T.342.	T.74·15 × T.74·16	.	.	5	.	166	.	66
T.341.	T.74·15 × T.74·22	.	.	5	.	232	.	65
T.343.	T.74·16 × T.74·1	.	.	6	.	274	.	56
T.344.	T.74·16 × T.74·22	.	.	6	.	341	.	80

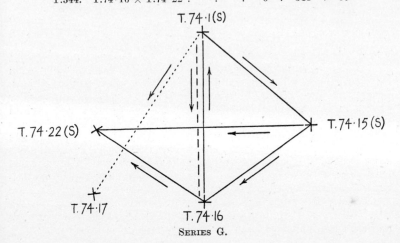

SERIES G.

SERIES H.

T. 37.	S.P.13·7 × S.P.24·5	. .	1	. 43	. 33
T.193.	T.37·1 selfed .	. . .	18	. 3	. 3
T.194.	T.37·2 selfed .	. . .	16	. 136	. 29
T.195.	T.37·3 selfed .	. . .	4	. 47	. 34
T.196.	T.37·7 selfed .	. . .	10	. 7	. 5
T.177.	T.37·1 × T.37·2	. . .	2	. 0	. 0
T.173.	T.37·1 × T.37·3	. . .	3	. 13	. 8
T.172.	T.37·1 × T.37·6	. . .	2	. 0	. 0
T.164.	T.37·2 × T.37·3	. . .	3	. 24	. 18
T.163.	T.37·2 × T.37·5	. . .	3	. 22	. 2
T.183.	T.37·3 × T.37·1	. . .	2	. 35	. 23
T.162.	T.37·3 × T.37·5	. . .	—	. —	. 0
T.175.	T.37·3 × T.37·7	. . .	3	. 103	. 41
[T.165.	T.37·2 × T.24·4	. . .	3	. 44	. 29]
[T.180.	T.37·3 × T.56·1	. . .	1	. 21	. 14]
[T.166.	T.37·7 × T.30·4	. . .	3	. 5	. 5]

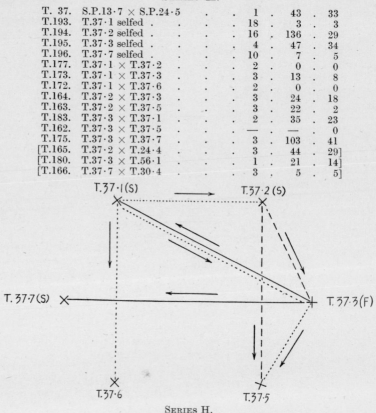

SERIES H.

DISCUSSION.

It is obvious from the large numbers of experiments that pollination by " own " pollen is either quite ineffective or, with few exceptions, results in low output of viable seed. Such self-incompatibility obviously favours cross fertilization and the formation of hybrid swarms since there are no specific sterility barriers between the species of the *Jacea* section dealt with in this work. It is also shown that there are cross-incompatibilities and cross-compatibilities between different stocks within the species and within the hybrid swarms. The empirical facts suggest that the genetical basis of compatibility and incompatibility is a complicated one in the group of species with which we are concerned. The following data have to be borne in mind :

1. More or less sterility on selfing is the general rule, but there are marked exceptions and some few selfings have given full fertility.

2. Sterility is sometimes much more marked in F_2 than in F_1 or in F_3 than in F_1 or F_2.

3. Reciprocals may give essentially similar or more or less different results.

4. The plants with which we are concerned are tetraploids ($x = 11$, $2n = 44$).

The incompatibility system in our knapweeds is oppositional, in that there is inhibition of like genotypes, with some exceptions. Bateman (' Heredity ' **6**, 285–310 : 1952) considers the distinction between complementary and oppositional ways of determining self-incompatibility to be basic. In the *Centaurea jacea-nigra* series incompatibility is also multipolar in contrast to the di- or tripolar system of *Primula*, *Lythrum*, etc., and it is also homomorphic. We have, however, the complication that the plants are tetraploids. Incompatibility in tetraploids has been worked out, with special reference to *Verbascum*, by Lawrence (' Genetica,' **12**, 269–96 : 1930). We have also to note that *Centaurea* is a genus of *Compositae* and that there has been described for two genera (*Parthenium* and *Crepis*) of that family a special kind of self-incompatibility (Gerstel, ' Genetics,' **35**, 482–506 : 1950 and Hughes and Babcock, "Genetics,' **35**, 570–588 : 1950). It is postulated for *Crepis* that pollen behaviour is sporophytically or diploid determined, that some alleles in the diploid pollen show dominance, and that reciprocal differences are due to dominance not to homozygosity of one parent. In addition, " other genes are believed to be able to exert some modifying effects, especially when associated with the *S* alleles of weaker potency."

We must now comment on the eight series of selfings and crossings of which the results are set out in some detail above.

Series A.—The original cross was fertile. Four F_1 plants were self-sterile. Crossed together these gave different results. The reciprocal crossings of T.98·31 and T.98·37 are shown as giving different results on the basis of our arbitrary class limits. This may, here, be misleading and both crosses may be F or, at least, sf. It would appear that the results can be interpreted on the basis of tetraploidy, that is of an allelic series spread through four chromosomes. Tentatively, the following would seem to fit, though other schemes are also possible : T.98·19, $S_1 S_2 Z_1 Z_2$; T.98·29, $S_3 S_4 Z_3 Z_4$; T.98·31, $S_3 S_4 Z_3 Z_4$; T.98·37, $S_3 S_5 Z_4 Z_5$.

Series B.—This series originated with a very fertile first cross. Selfings of F_1 plants were S with one exception (T.84·34) which was, at least relatively, fertile. The crossings of F_1 plants unfortunately form isolated groups, but it is interesting that T.84·2, as ovule parent, is fertile with T.84·34 and T.84·63 and T.84·34 with T.84·63.

Series C.—This full series includes two sets of reciprocal crossings. The original cross was F but the five selfings of F_1 plants were all S. Again, a scheme based on tetraploidy would appear to fit, such as : T.77·1, $S_1 S_2 Z_1 Z_2$; T.77·2, $S_1 S_4 Z_2 Z_3$; T.77·6, $S_1 S_3 Z_1 Z_3$; T.77·11, $S_1 S_4 Z_2 Z_3$; T.77·22, $S_1 S_2 Z_3 Z_4$.

Series D.—The first cross was probably F, but the selfings and all but one of the crossings of F_1 plants were S. No reciprocal crossings were made. One concludes that, apart from T.104·14, the F_1 plants used had similar alleles of the SZ group unless there has been sporophytic determination with dominance on the side of the pollen parent.

Series E.—The original cross was highly F, while all selfings made of F_1 plants were S. The main interest of the complete series is the "recovery" of fertility on outcrossing with other stock plants than the parents and the failure of obtaining offspring from one backcross.

Series F.—This instructive series was started with the selfing of Stock Plant 17. Technically the selfing was S since only 36 plants were raised from 23 selfed capitula. Three selfings and two crossing of F_1 plants were S but two crossings were F. T.24.7 was the ovule parent for each of these latter crossings. If S.P.17 were a heterozygote tetraploid ($S_1 S_2 Z_3 Z_4$) it would on selfing be sterile but its offspring would segregate for S and Z alleles (gametes $S_1 Z_3$, $S_1 Z_4$, $S_2 Z_3$, $S_2 Z_4$) and the offspring would be a mixture of cross-compatibles and cross-incompatibles.

Series G.—This series contrasts, in having many fertile crosses, with series D. The first cross was F as were also five crossings of F_1 plants. It is doubtful if the apparent difference between the reciprocal crossing of T.74·1 and T.74·16 has much significance. One judges that F_1 plants with a variety of alleles were selected for crossing since only the cross T.74·1 × T.74·17 was sterile. Many combinations are possible. An example would be : T.74·1, $S_1 S_2 Z_1 Z_2$; T.74·15, $S_3 S_4 Z_3 Z_4$; T.74·16, $S_5 S_6 Z_5 Z_6$; T.74·17, $S_1 S_2 Z_1 Z_2$; T.74·22, $S_1 S_2 Z_1 Z_2$.

Series H.—The first cross was F and selfings of F_1 plants were technically S or sf though T.195 is probably better termed F than sf. Reciprocals from crossing T.37·1 and T.37·3 gave different results. Various allelic combinations can be postulated, as, for example: T.37·1, $S_1 S_4 Z_2 Z_3$; T.37·2, $S_1 S_2 Z_3 Z_4$; T.37·3, $S_1 S_3 Z_1 Z_3$; T.37·5, $S_1 S_3 Z_1 Z_3$; T.37·6, $S_1 S_4 Z_2 Z_3$; T.37·7, $S_2 S_4 Z_2 Z_4$.

General conclusion.—While sporophytic determination of compatibility on the side of pollen is not excluded the results of our analysis suggests that gametophytic determination with tetraploidy explains fairly satisfactorily the results so far obtained, apart from the occasional occurrence of self-fertile plants. It is difficult to account for these last unless there be one or more genes for fertility as recorded for various other genera (*e.g.*, *Nicotiana*, *Antirrhinum*, *Petunia*). In some respects the conditions found in our knapweeds recall those described by Stout for *Cichorium* (see *Journ. Genetics*, **7**, 71–103 : 1918).

CHAPTER IX

EXPERIMENTS INVOLVING *CENTAUREA SCABIOSA* AND *C. ASPERA*

Centaurea scabiosa *L. in Relation to other Knapweeds.*

THE greater knapweed, *Centaurea scabiosa* L., has, like *C. nigra* s.l., a wide range in the British Isles. According to Druce, ' The Comital Flora of the British Isles,' 175 (1932), it occurs in 84 vice-counties in Great Britain, 22 in Ireland, and in the Channel Islands. It is rare or absent in parts of the extreme north and west. We have grown a number of variants of the species and have used them in crosses and attempted crosses, but we have not made such an extensive or intensive study of this species as we have of species of section *Eujacea*. There is considerable variation in both vegetative and floral characters in *C. scabiosa* as it occurs in the British Isles. Variable characters include those of leaf-shape, especially degree and nature of the lobing or cutting of the lamina, degree of spine development in the phyllaries and the colour of these, shape and length of ray florets, and colour of florets. So far, our own researches lead us to the conclusion that these varia-tions are intraspecific and due to mutations (in so far as they are genetically distinct) and not to hybridization. An account of varia-tions in *C. scabiosa* is given by C. E. Britton in ' Rep. Bot. Exch. Club, 1922,' 767–73 (1923).

In Britain, *C. scabiosa* occurs especially in dry pastures, on grassy cliffs, banks, and road verges, especially on calcareous soils. In many localities it grows in the same communities as plants of *C. nigra* or *C. nemoralis* and sometimes with hybrid swarms between these and *C. jacea*, as on Oxfordshire oolites or Wiltshire chalk. Quite frequently it can be found " cheek by jowl " with these species, certainly within easy pollinating distance. We have however, never seen any plants we could accept as hybrids between *C. scabiosa* and *C. nigra*, *C. nemoralis*, or *C. jacea*, either in the wild or in herbaria, nor have we found them in our cultivated stocks or families. Moreover, deliberate attempts to make such crosses have failed, as the following examples show :

T.38. S.P.13·7 (*C. nemoralis* with a few genes of *C. jacea*) × *C. scabiosa* (8).

T.50. S.P.2 (*C. nemoralis* radiata) × *C. scabiosa* (8).

T.16. S.P.1 (*C. nigra* radiata) × *C. scabiosa* (11).

T.17. *C. scabiosa* (11) × S.P.1 (*C. nigra* radiata).

T.15. *C. scabiosa* (11) × S.P.29·1 (*C. jacea* × *C. nemoralis*).

13

T.28. *C. scabiosa* (1) × S.P.24·5 (*C. nemoralis radiata*).
T.23. *C. scabiosa* (3) × S.P.24·5 (*C. nemoralis radiata*).

None of the above crosses yielded any viable seeds. No plants have been raised by us showing characters or character combinations suggesting a mixture of genes from *C. scabiosa* and *C. nigra*, *C. nemoralis*, or *C. jacea*. These results are in agreement both with the usually accepted taxonomy and with the cytology. Thus Hayek (in ' Denk-schr. Akad. Wiss. Wien,' **72**, 585 : 1901) has the following scheme of classification :

   IV. Subgenus *Cyanus* Cass.
      II. Section *Acrocentron* Cass.
        (c) Collinae—*C. collina* L.
        (e) Sopholomae—*C. scabiosa* L.
   V. Subgenus *Jacea* Cass.
      III. Section *Eujacea* Hayek.
        C. jacea L.
      IV. Section *Lepteranthus* DC.
        C. nemoralis Jord., *C. nigra* L.

We have obtained very small F_1 and F_2 families from the cross *C. scabiosa* × *C. collina*. These were described by us in *Journ. Genetics*, **34**, 487–95 (1937), together with the results of making crosses between various stocks of *C. scabiosa*. There was a high degree of, but not complete, sterility between *C. scabiosa* and *C. collina*.

It will suffice here to note that cytological examination showed that stock plants used by us had the following $2n$ chromosome numbers : *C. scabiosa* 20, *C. collina* 60, *C. jacea* 44, *C. nigra* 44, and *C. nemoralis* 44.

The observations and the experimental results we have obtained make us suspicious of records of hybrids between *C. scabiosa* and *C. nigra*, *C. nemoralis*, or *C. jacea*. C. E. Britton (*l. c.* 772) gives to a supposed hybrid between *C. scabiosa* and *C. nemoralis* the name × *C. cantiana*, from W. Kent, on the hills near Luddesdown. In ' British Plant List,' ed. 2, 64 (1928) Druce has *C. nemoralis* × *scabiosa* = *brittonii* Dr., but no further account or specimen of this has been traced in the Druce Herbarium at Oxford or elsewhere. We have several times seen hive bees alighting on and nectar sucking from florets of *C. nigra* and *C. scabiosa* successively and reciprocally.

C. scabiosa × *C. aspera.*

A cross was made between *C. scabiosa* S.P.16 and *C. aspera*. The ovule parent was collected near Woodstock, Oxfordshire, on field path to Shipton, 12.viii.31 and the pollen parent at Vazon Bay, Guernsey, 1936.

C. scabiosa (other stock plants than S.P.16) has $2n = 20$ and *C. aspera* (according to Clapham, Tutin, and Warburg, ' Flora of the British Isles,' 1108 : 1952) has $2n = 22$. Nine cross-pollinated capitula yielded 16 cypselas and from these three offspring were raised.

C. scabiosa S.P.16 agreed with the description published of *C.*

scabiosa S.P.8 in *Journ. Gen.*, **34**, 488 (1937) except for colour of florets and sex of disc florets. The florets were pinkish white and the disc florets were breviflora female.

C. aspera differs from *C. scabiosa* S.P.8 especially in the less pinnatifid (rather coarsely dentate) leaves, smaller capitula, and in having 3 to 5 spines at the apex of the phyllaries.

The F_1 plants had the following characters : Perennial herbs (one plant is still alive after 15 years). Stems up to 5·2 dm. tall, moderately branched with the main stem suberect, branches elongated and horizontally spreading with a tendency to bend toward the ends, final branches ending in solitary capitula, with shallow longitudinal furrows, branches in lower and middle parts with numerous rather stiff spreading hairs, in upper part the hairs are shorter and stiffer, below the capitula there are some arachnoid hairs. Cauline leaves deeply toothed to deeply pinnatilobed but none pinnatifid, teeth or lobes oblong to linear-oblong, apiculate, lower shortly petiolate, upper sessile, with a dense indumentum on both surfaces of rather short and fairly stiff hairs. Pericline ovoid 1·5 cm. long, 1·1 cm. diameter. Phyllaries becoming longer the higher they are on the spiral, with stiffly pectinate margins, the uppermost and terminal pectinations subspinous, lowest lanceolate to ovate-lanceolate, middle elongate-ovate, upper narrowly oblong with an obovate appendage, uppermost narrowly oblong with an oblong appendage, lower part Elm Green (Ridgway, ' Color Standards,' Pl. XVII), appendage and margins Clove Brown (Ridgway, Pl. XL), spinous pectinations Buckthorn Brown (Ridgway, Pl. XV). Ray and disc florets Liseran Purple (Ridgway, Pl. XXVI) ; ray florets 3·1 cm. long, disc florets 2 cm. long. The florets are female in that though anthers are developed they produce no good pollen. This condition is similar to that in the *C. scabiosa* ovule parent. No cypselas were set in any of the three plants.

C. jacea *and* C. nigra *pollinated by* C. aspera.

Attempts were made to cross *C. aspera* on to *C. jacea* and *C. nigra* but no cypselas were obtained :

T.600, *C. jacea* (T.507·18) × *C. aspera*, 17 capitula, no cypselas.

T.598, *C. nigra* (S.P.1) × *C. aspera*, 15 capitula, no cypselas.

T.605, *C. nigra* breviflora × *C. aspera*, 4 capitula, no cypselas.

CHAPTER X

CONCLUSIONS

EXPERIMENTS have shown that individuals of *C. nigra, C. nemoralis*, and *C. jacea*, occurring in Britain and agreeing in what are regarded as essential taxonomic characters with type specimens, are inter-fertile, apart from incompatibilities which cut across taxonomic boundaries. The taxa as such are not defined by genetical barriers of sterility. Judging from the samples examined, they have the same chromosome number of $2n = 44$. It has been convenient for analysis of wild populations to retain the three names for taxa that can, most often, be recognized in the field by phenotypic characters. It is obvious, however, from our experiments and field studies that, in Britain, there is a complicated pattern of behaviour sometimes resulting in no definite pigeon-hole scheme of clear-cut taxa but to groupings with blurred boundaries. Nevertheless, a general working taxonomic scheme has proved possible and under this many kinds of morphological and physiological data can both be utilized and them-selves be conveniently classified. Of course, any character or group of characters can be given pre-eminence, or entirely isolated, and made the basis of a special classification. Such classifications have useful but limited functions. There are good *a priori* reasons for constructing many of them. We have done this from time to time in our own attempts at analysis and synthesis within the British knap-weeds. To say that this is all that can be done is, however, a policy of despair and, we contend, against the facts. Actually, in the British knapweeds, it is surprising how the special classifications have helped to provide a clearer picture of the existing position and hence a basis for a general classification.

The following are theoretical possibilities for a nomenclatural scheme of the British knapweeds of the *Eujacea* section:

1. One species, with three main paramorphs, presumably best to be treated as sub-species. Cytogenetical data provide the strongest argument for this. The consequent nomenclatural system would be cumbersome for the field studies and in publication. The preferable basic nomenclature would be *Centaurea jacea* subsp. *jacea, C. jacea* subsp. *nigra, C. jacea* subsp. *nemoralis*.

2. Two species, *C. jacea* and *C. nigra* with *C. nemoralis* made a subspecies of the latter. This is the plan followed by Clapham, Tutin, and Warburg 'Flora of the British Isles' Cambridge, 1952). The reasons for this classification are not given. Presumably it is based

on the fact that in phyllary shape *C. nemoralis* and *C. nigra* resemble one another more than either do *C. jacea*. In other characters such as habit and leaf shape, this resemblance does not hold. It is, however, possible that phylogenetically *C. nemoralis* and *C. nigra* are closer than either is to *C. jacea*.

3. Three species, *C. jacea, C. nigra,* and *C. nemoralis*. This is fairly simple and, allowing for hybridization and the occurrence of intermediates of unproved origin in some areas, works well in practice for all purposes for which we have tested it.

4. Many more species based solely on phenotypic characters. This results either in a very great multiplication of names, one might say a multiplication " with no end to it," or in confusion of plants with a more or less wide range of characters in the same species of which there will still be a considerable number.

We can only say that on the basis of intensive and extensive experience we find that the third course is most satisfactory. It enables us to describe populations with a minimum of repetition, to trace the effects of hybridization, to map range and distribution most simply and clearly, and to record many facts of variation on a comparative basis. Moreover, it gives us the most concise way of tracing and recording correlation of morphological and physiological characters.

There are three taxonomic matters all interrelated, which need detailed consideration, if we accept three basic taxa within the knapweeds. These are : the diagnostic characters separating the accepted species ; the breakdown of these diagnoses as a result of hybridization ; variation of characters within the species.

In Chapter III, we give the reasons for using the names *C. jacea, C. nemoralis,* and *C. nigra* for the three species we find it most convenient to accept. The essential gross phenotypical characters by which these names can be given to individual plants are :

C. jacea.—Stems usually well branched with slender branches, not swollen below the capitulum. Capitulum medium in size. Phyllaries with appendages entire or slightly dentate-fimbriate or dentate-laciniate, shining, membranaceous or scarious with broad pale margins, concave, fully covering the pericline. Radiate. Florets often Argyle Purple or Bishop's Purple. Cypselas without pappus.

C. nemoralis.—Stems much branched with slender branches. Leaves relatively narrow. Capitula medium to small in size. Phyllaries with appendages pectinate, with Black or Bone Brown discs, not shining, flat or at least not markedly concave, often not fully covering the pericline. Eradiate. Florets Dull Dark Purple or Rood's Violet. Cypselas pappose.

C. nigra.—Stems more or less branched with rather stout branches often swollen below the capitula. Leaves relatively broad. Capitula medium to large in size. Phyllaries with appendages pectinate, Black or Bone Brown, not shining, flat, fully covering the pericline. Eradiate. Florets Dull Dark Purple or Rood's Violet. Cypselas pappose.

The diagnoses are stated dogmatically. They do not take into account the effects of hybridization or of even a weak "flow of genes," or of paramorphic variation, or of modifications or fluctuations correlated with extreme habitat conditions. All of these are the concern of the taxonomist and are considered later since they are, at least largely, responsible for the "blurred" delimitations between the species found in some individuals and some populations.

We have shown that fertile crosses between the three species are the rule, though certain individuals may be cross-incompatible and most of them are self-incompatible. This general occurrence of self-incompatibility, together with efficient entomophily, favours hybridization. Both in the wild and in the breeding ground we have observed pollinating insects visiting successively capitula, at anthesis, of plants of different taxa, even of different species of Centaurea. The results of analysis and synthesis under full control in the breeding ground agree exactly with independent analyses of many wild populations. If two or more of the three species meet there is crossing, segregation, back-crossing, and every degree of inter-crossing within the limits of compatibility. The flowering heads are so attractive to pollinators, especially bees, that cross-pollination is probably never a limiting factor given a minimum number of plants in a population. Half-a-dozen plants must usually be sufficient for full seed setting.

It seems most probable from a study of ranges of knapweeds in the British Isles and of their ecological distribution that all three species owe much of their successful dispersal to man's influence, direct and indirect. Centaurea nigra has the widest range and the greatest ecological tolerance. C. nemoralis is widely distributed in the central south and south midlands of England but becomes progressively less common as latitude increases. Casual occurrences are frequently recorded and, since collectors tend to preserve specimens of the unusual, the material in a herbarium may give a wrong impression since it is far from being a random sample. C. jacea has a scattered and casual distribution and the evidence is strongly in favour of its being intermittently introduced from the continent with agricultural seeds, feeding grain, fodder, and the like. Large pure populations of C. jacea have, so far as we know, not been recorded for the British Isles.

We have thus to picture populations of C. nigra established on heaths and grassy downs in the south of England and on cliffs and grassy banks near the sea, on road verges, and sometimes in pastures and along field paths throughout the British Isles and C. nemoralis occurring particularly in the south of England, in similar habitats but usually those with calcareous soils. Into such populations C. jacea has been from time to time introduced and "introgressive hybridization" has then resulted. Since, as our genetical experiments have shown, a considerable number of different genes are involved in interspecific hybridization one would expect the individuals in a "hybrid swarm" to be very diversified. This is what we have found in various wild populations some of which have been shown by experiment to be " hybrid swarms " and others have been reasonably judged to be such by close analogy with experimental results. In some populations it is literally true that no two individuals were alike in the sum total of phenotypic characters known by experiment to be correlated with different genoms. To give names to all possible character combinations, or even to the very numerous ones we have found in the wild, would serve no useful purpose. All of them are in greater or less degrees heterozygotes and consequently the genom and the phenom are temporary. Out-crossing, imposed by self-incompatibility, reduces the chances of homozygosity greatly and apomixis by seeds is not recorded in our experiments. Furthermore, vegetative multiplication is restricted and relatively slow, at least there are no vegetative disseminules in any way corresponding in structure or behaviour to the normal method of reproduction, multiplication, and dispersal by seeds encased in cypselas. As a result we do not find that uniform local populations characterized by one or a few peculiarities are readily established and maintained.

Contamination of populations of *C. nigra* or *C. nemoralis* may have been heavy and/or recent, as at Wellington College or near Woodstock. At the other extreme it may have been light and many generations ago. We then find only slight traces in morphological or physiological characters to indicate what may now be termed " gene-flow." In British knapweed populations this is the distribution of a few genes of *C. jacea* through populations essentially of *C. nigra* or *C. nemoralis*. The knapweeds on Epsom Downs and near Headley in Surrey illustrate this condition.

Our genetical experiments have shown that the shape of the phyllaries is a sure and easily scorable criterion of hybridization within a population and of the present degree of contamination. There are, however, other " spot characters " which, occurring in a British knapweed population, at least lead one to look for other signs of interspecific mixing. We can indeed list the characters proving or suggesting hybridization or " gene flow " in a population mainly of either *C. nemoralis* or *C. nigra* or both :

1. Phyllaries with appendages intermediate in shape between the pectinate ones of *C. nemoralis* or *C. nigra* and the entire to shallow toothed or very slightly laciniate fimbriate ones of *C. jacea*.

2. Phyllaries with appendages of paler colour than Bone Brown.

3. Phyllaries with a shiny surface.

4. Phyllaries with appendages very narrow and long drawn out.

5. Primary flowering, in the south of England, at its maximum in July.

6. Florets paler than Dull Dark Purple.

7. Ray florets present (radiata).

8. Cypselas with imperfect and variable development of pappus.

We suggest that specific names should not be used to designate plants of hybrid origin in British knapweeds but that these should be recognized for what they are by the combined use of the names of the known or putative parents and precised by reference to phyllary structure according to the scheme we have proved to be extremely practical. Thus, instead of referring to a plant as *Centaurea jungens* (which name as used by British botanists has covered a number of hybrids of different characters and gene content) we would prefer to say it is, for example, *Centaurea jacea* × *C. nigra* and has phyllaries S.

Since hybrid swarms and gene flow, or in more general terms various degrees of introgressive hybridization, are common in parts of England among the knapweeds, it is most important that taxonomists interested in the group should acquire the habit of studying populations instead of collecting one specimen here and another there. Two general methods should be used in the field for such population study. First, that of adequate random sampling, following the known rules for accumulating data for biometrical analysis. Second, the rapid survey of the whole population or of as large a part of it as is possible, to detect any " abnormal " plants that may be missed by random sampling. Random sampling provides material for a fair overall picture of the constitution of a population. Independent selection of aberrant individuals, that can often be " spotted " quickly by an experienced investigator glancing over very large populations, allows a suitable range of stock plants to be accumulated for genetical and other experiments. It has to be remembered that the " normal " can often only be adequately investigated by comparison with the " abnormal." Both generalizations and exceptions have importance in synthetic taxonomy.

Intraspecific variations in the British knapweeds may be fewer than we originally thought. We tend now more to the view that genetically based variation in certain characters (such as phyllary colour, presence or absence of rays and degree of pappus development) is due to new gene combinations caused by hybridization rather than to gene mutation not associated with interspecific crossing. Characters that are probably gene mutational within the species are : some habits, such as dwarfness, when genetically differentiated and not imposed solely by habitat conditions, some leaf shapes, especially degree of lobing, Marguerite Yellow floret colour, white or white flecked ray florets, and longiflora and breviflora disc florets at least in part. However, with regard to longiflora and breviflora characters, we have to note two sets of facts : that plants showing these characters occur spasmodically in many (probably most) populations of, say, a thousand or more plants ; that there is some evidence of their greater frequency in wild populations that are either hybrid swarms or show a good deal of " gene flow " from one species to another. The breviflora character is often associated with femaleness (male sterility) of the disc florets and these are often of a brighter colour than are hermaphrodite florets (Rood's Violet as contrasted with Dull Dark Purple). That hybridization between species can lead to modification in the reproductive system and increased gynodioecism in knapweeds is a reasonable hypothesis. In some wild populations and in some bred families there is continuous grading between normalis hermaphrodite and breviflora female disc florets. This enables reciprocal crosses to be made occasionally and from such it is clear that the character breviflora associated with a greater or less degree of male sterility is not, or is not entirely, controlled by cytoplasmic genes.

The British knapweeds are not highly plastic. On the five soils of the transplant experiments of the British Ecological Society at Potterne there were no marked differences in structure or habit recorded in ramets of one clone of *Centaurea nigra* after thirteen years. Ramets of the same clone transplanted to the Herbarium Experimental Ground at Kew, however, developed a modified ascending habit of the stems. There is no doubt that stem heights can be considerably modified by certain environmental conditions, such as soil dryness, exposure, cutting, and grazing. There are ecotypes as well as ecads distinguishable by stem heights.

Some facts of interest arise from a comparison of the results we have obtained with knapweeds and those from experiments and observations we have made with species of some other genera and in particular *Silene*, *Ranunculus*, *Saxifraga*, *Anthyllis*, and *Geum*. The outstanding feature of British knapweed populations is the fairly frequent occurrence of hybrid swarms in the south. There is, indeed, sometimes such extensive introgressive hybridization that one can reasonably refer to local amalgamation of species. In this respect, behaviour is similar to that found for *Geum rivale* and *Geum urbanum*. In contrast, *Silene vulgaris* (*S. cucubalus*) and *S. maritima* are relatively isolated species, but the isolation is ecological not cytogenetical. Owing to differences in structure and behaviour they rarely meet and still more rarely have interpenetrating distributions. Their geographical ranges overlap but do not coincide. Natural hybrids occur but are rare, compared with hybrids of *Centaurea* in the southern half of England. Large wild hybrid swarms of *Silene* have not been found and even moderate gene flow has not been traced beyond very restricted areas. On the other hand, gene mutations, not associated with interspecific hybridization, are relatively common in the British bladder campions and involve all aerial organs, whether vegetative or reproductive. There is strong, even if circumstantial, evidence that *Silene maritima* is a native of the British flora in the full sense of the term " native." In this it contrasts with the knapweeds whose range and distribution in the British Isles is largely dependent on made-man or man-modified habitats even if they be in part, natural immigrants. The failure to obtain hybrids between *Ranunculus acris* and *R bulbosus* may be compared with the genetic independence of *Centaurea nigra* or *C. nemoralis* and *C. scabiosa*.

Gynodioecism or some other form of separation of " sex-organs " is probably of very wide occurrence in the angiosperms and it is probable that population analysis will reveal its occurrence in most " hermaphrodite " species. Gynodioecism is, of course, well known in *Labiatae* and in some other families, where it can almost be said " to be the rule."

It is common in most of the large populations of *Silene vulgaris* and *S. maritima* we have analyzed. We found it in *Saxifraga granulata*, while male, female, hermaphrodite, and sometimes neuter plants are recorded in our publications on *Ranunuclus acris* and *R. ficaria*. We give details in this work of the fairly frequent occurrence of gynodioecism in wild populations and bred families of knapweeds.

The reason why local more or less homozygous populations of knapweeds are not likely to become established have been given. Ecotypes are not necessarily homozygous since they result only from selection by a given environment in favour of characters suiting plants to that environment. Characters not selected (for or against) by a given set of environmental factors can be present or absent in any proportion in the homozygous or the heterozygous condition in the ecotype population of a given habitat. Can we distinguish ecotypes in the British knapweeds? Three are suggested as having some standing : first, the extreme *C. nemoralis* populations on chalk and some oolitic limestones in the southern half of England. These are often " contaminated " by *C. jacea*, but allowing for this the physical and chemical conditions of the substratum have largely favoured the narrow leaved, very slender branched, late flowering plants of *C. nemoralis*. One can place such plants as *C. nemoralis* " ultra-nemoralis " in the sense that they show those characters of *C. nemoralis* that contrast with the characters of *C. nigra* in a more extreme development than in typical *C. nemoralis*. The word " typical " is here used to mean agreeing in diagnosed characters with Jordan's type.

A second possible ecotype is represented by the plants growing on Kings' Sedgemoor, in Oxey and Pixey Meads, and in Cherwell water meadows near Oxford. This ecotype, if such it be, is placed by us in *C. nigra* with mixture of some genes from *C. jacea*. It phenotypically comes nearer to *C. nemoralis* than does typical *C. nigra* (typical, i.e., as compared with the Linnean type). However, the characters separating it from *C. nigra* of other habitats appear to be partly contributed by *C. jacea* genes and partly by habitat favouritism. Plants of this grouping are relatively early or intermediate flowering, most often radiata, mostly few headed, and with brightly coloured florets that retain their colour well on drying. The earlier flowering is a *C. nigra* character for southern England, but has also selective value for the marshy-mead habitat since the vegetation is cut for " hay " and the earlier flowering allows seed setting before the harvest. The radiata character may be a gift from *C. jacea*.

A third partial ecotype, possibly a climatically controlled ecotypic cline, is found within *C. nigra* in relation to flowering period. In the southern and south midland counties there are early flowering plants with the morphological characters of *C. nigra*. These plants are particularly noticeable where they occur as local pockets within populations of *C. nemoralis*, as on Epsom Downs, or on different but juxtaposed geological outcrops, as near Oxford. However, as one proceeds north, and to a certain extent to the extreme west, flowering of *C. nigra* plants is seasonally retarded in the British Isles. It has not been possible to conduct a sufficient number of transplant experiments to disentangle all the different genotypes for flowering periods from the direct effects of environment. We know there are earlier and later flowering " races " but there is an interesting field here for detailed investigation by combined extensive field observations and transplant and genetical experiments. " *Centaurea nigra* " was for many years listed as a plant for the phenological observations conducted by the Royal Meteorological Society. In 1936, in response to a request circulated to contributors, specimens of the plants recorded for first flowering were sent to Kew. The result was a " mixed bag " of 135 specimens of which 95 were probably used for records from 49 vice-counties. In addition to *Centaurea nigra*, plants of *C. nemoralis*, hybrids between *C. jacea* and *C. nigra* and *C. nemoralis*, and ten of *C. scabiosa* were received, all having been equally recorded as " black knapweed." That different taxa were being scored makes one doubt the face value of the phenological records for the country as a whole when these records were summarized under the one name of " black knapweed." If the functions of plants are to be used to measure climate or weather the " instruments " should be standardized, that is, ramets of a clone should be used.

The analysis of populations of British knapweeds, so far as we have been able to carry it out up to the present, is far from complete. The results can, however, be stated with considerable confidence in the form of a generalization. The marked reticulation of characters found from individual to individual and from population to population is due primarily to hybridization and secondarily to recurrent mutation. Limitations to reticulation are imposed by the selective action of environments in which climatic, edaphic, and biotic factors are all involved.

The wider interest of our studies are twofold. We have stated problems, within the knapweeds, requiring further investigation and we hope that others will be stimulated by our pioneer researches to undertake their solution. It is probable that the results we have obtained with *Centaurea*, in comparison with those obtained for *Silene* and other genera, can, with due precautions, be used as analogies for the taxonomic treatment of other groups that cannot, at present, be so intensively studied. Recent work for ' The Flora of Tropical East Africa ' has shown clearly that there are groups in which classification on the basis of gross morphology alone can only be of limited value. For example, in *Clematis, Clematopsis,* and *Jasminum* it is obvious that population analysis, cytogenetical investigation, and cultural experiments are essential for a sound evaluation of characters, for an understanding of their reticulation, and then for the construction of a more generally useful systematic arrangement. The herbarium taxonomist is again and again limited, in actual practice, by the absence of facts that cannot be obtained from the material at his disposal. Progress is, however, being made towards the ideal of improved taxonomy by the methods we have both advocated and used. If our work with the British knapweeds, by illustrating the numerous interesting possibilities of synthetic taxonomy, leads to researches along corresponding, but improved, lines by our younger colleagues we shall be satisfied.

A SHORT GLOSSARY

(of unusual terms or terms which we use in a precise, limited, or some special way)

apomixis : reproduction without fertilization.

arachnoid : like a spider's web.

capitulum : the inflorescence unit ; a head of florets surrounded by bracts or phyllaries.

cauline : borne on the stem.

chromosome : a structural unit of a nucleus as seen at nuclear division.

climax : in ecology, the relatively final stage reached by vegetation within given climatic conditions.

clone : the sum total of individuals (ramets) derived from one by vegetative propagation or other form of apomixis.

compatibility : that, for genetic reasons, named pollen germinates on and pollen tubes grow down to effect fertilization in a named gynoecium.

cypsela : a one-seeded fruit formed from an inferior ovary.

diploid : with two sets of chromosomes in the nuclei.

ecad : a plant or population showing modification of structure or behaviour due to direct action of the environment without change of genetic control.

ecotype : a plant or population showing variation which, within a species, has led to selection by the habitat.

entomophily : pollination by insect agents.

fimbriations : the irregular cuttings or teeth of appendages of the bracts or phyllaries.

forb : a herb other than a grass.

gene : the ultimate unit of inheritance as determined by breeding experiments and (sometimes) by cytological research.

genetic : connected with genes.

genotype : the sum total of genes (of an individual or a taxon).

gynodioecism : the condition, within a species, of some individuals producing only hermaphrodite and others only female flowers.

heterozygous : having some genes different in one set of chromosomes from those in another set or other sets.

hexaploid : having six sets of chromosomes.

homozygous : having equivalent genes in two or more sets of chromosomes.

hybrid (in the broad sense) : an organism produced by fusion of unlike gametes.

hypocotyl : the seedling axis immediately below the cotyledons.

incompatibility : that, for genetic reasons, named pollen does not germinate on or pollen tubes do not grow down to effect fertilization in a named gynoecium.

indumentum : a covering of hairs or bristles.

metaphase : the stage of nuclear division in which the chromosomes lie in a plane half-way between the poles of the spindle.

mutation : a genetic or chromosomal change and its result.

obloid : a three-dimensional shape, in the " ovoid " series, in which the diameter is greater than the length.

pappus : hairs or bristles on the ridge at the top of a cypsela, often considered as representing a calyx.

paramorph : an intraspecific variant.

pectinations : the fine, often regular and hair-like or comb-like, marginal divisions of appendages of the bracts or phyllaries.

pericarp : (of cypselas) the combined ripened ovary wall and floret receptacle.

pericline : the sum total of bracts or phyllaries surrounding the head of florets.

phenotype : the sum total of characters (of an individual or a taxon).

phyllaries : the bracts surrounding the head of florets.

phylogeny : the origin and development of phyla (or taxa and hence, better, taxogeny).

radicle : the young root of an embryo or seedling.

ramet : a physiologically independent individual of a clone.

ruderal : a plant growing in waste places or in habitats much modified by man.

score (to) : observing, measuring, etc., and recording characters.

segregation : the separation of genes (and hence of characters) in the production of and in hybrids.

synthetic taxonomy : the process and result of using as many characters and data as possible in classification.

taxogeny : the origin and development of taxa.

tetraploid : having four sets of chromosomes.

tiller : a lateral shoot outgrowth arising at or near ground level.

top hamper : shoots, stems, leaves, etc., of the preceding season.

GENERAL INDEX.

aborted capitula, 38
Aglais urticae L., 45
Alderney, 80
amalgamation, 4
Amathes sexstrigata Haw., 46
Anglesey, 73
Angus, 77
annual reproductive capacity, 32, 41
Anthophora bimaculata Panz., 46
Anthyllis, 187
Antirrhinum, 178.
Antrim, 79
Apanteles sicarius, 35
Aphantopus hyperanthus L., 45
Apis mellifera L., 46
apomicts, 3, 30
appendage shape, 147
Argyll, 77

Babington, 16, 18
Banff, 77
basal leaves, 28
Bateman, 177
Bedford, 69
Berks, 62
birds, 36
black fly, 36
Bombus agrorum Fabr., 46
Bombus humilis Illiger, 46
Bombus lapidarius L., 46
Bombus lucorum L., 46
Bombus ruderarius Müll., 46
Bombus soröensis Fabr., 46
Bombus subterraneus L., 46
Bombus sylvarum L., 46
Bombus terrestris L., 46
Brachypterus glaber Steph., 47
Bracon sp., 35
Bradfield, 6
Brecon, 72
breeding experiments, 83 *seq.*
Britton, C. E., 4, 19, 20, 21, 179
Bucentes geniculata Deg., 47
Bucks, 67
Butcher & Strudwick, 15

Calliphora erythroecephala Meig., 47
Calocoris norvegicus Gmel., 47
Cambridge, 68
Cardigan, 72
Carmarthen, 72
Carnarvon, 73

cattle, 36
Centaurea aspera Willd., 179–81
Centaurea babingtonii Lacaita, 15
Centaurea collina L., 49, 180
Centaurea decipiens Thuillier, 17, 18
Centaurea drucei C. E. Britton, 19
Centaurea jacea L., 13, etc.
Centaurea jacea L. forma *humilis* Schrank, 27
Centaurea jacea L. subsp. *jungens* (Gugl.), 20
Centaurea moncktonii C. E. Britton, 20
Centaurea nemophila Jordan, 20
Centaurea nemoralis Jordan, 14, 19, etc.
Centaurea nemoralis Jordan var. *debeauxii* (Gren. et Godr.) C. E. Britton, 20
Centaurea nemoralis Jordan var. *microptilon* C. E. Britton, 21
Centaurea nemoralis Jordan var. *minima* C. E. Britton, 26
Centaurea nigra L., 13, etc.
Centaurea nigrescens Willd., 16, 18
Centaurea obscura Jordan, 15
Centaurea pratensis Thuillier, 20
Centaurea scabiosa L., 49, 56, 151, 179–81
Centaurea subjacea Hayek, 20
Centaurea surrejana C. E. Britton, 19
Centaurea viretorum Jordan, 20
chalk downs, 5
characters, 8
characters of interspecific hybridity, 7 *seq.*
Chrysogaster metallina Fabr., 47
Cichorium, 178
Cladium mariscus, 68
Clapham, Tutin, & Warburg, 15
Clematis, 189
Clematopsis, 189
cloning, 31
Cnemodon vitripennis Meig., 47
Coenonympha pamphilus L., 45
Coleoptera, 45, 47
Colias croceus Fourc., 45
colour of florets, 150
colour of phyllaries, 149
compatibility, 166 *seq.*
competition, 30
continuous variation, 9
controlled experiments, 7

14

INDEX TO SELFINGS AND CROSSINGS.

Figures in roman give pages to the scorings in Chapter VI, Genetical Experiments. Figures in *italics* give page references in other chapters than Chapter VI.

PLATE II.

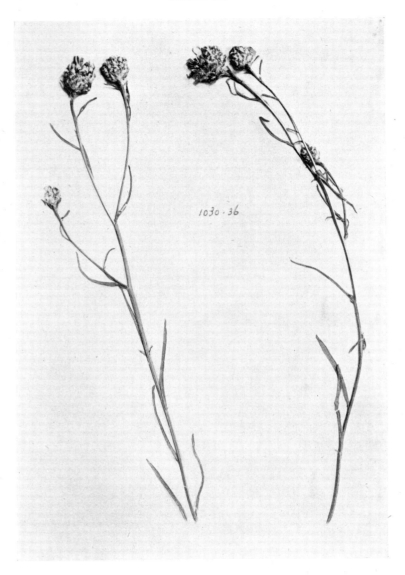

Centaurea jacea L.
Type specimen in the Linnean Herbarium of the Linnean Society, London.

PLATE III.

Centaurea nemoralis Jordan.
Type specimen in the Herbarium, Royal Botanic Gardens, Kew.

PLATE IV.

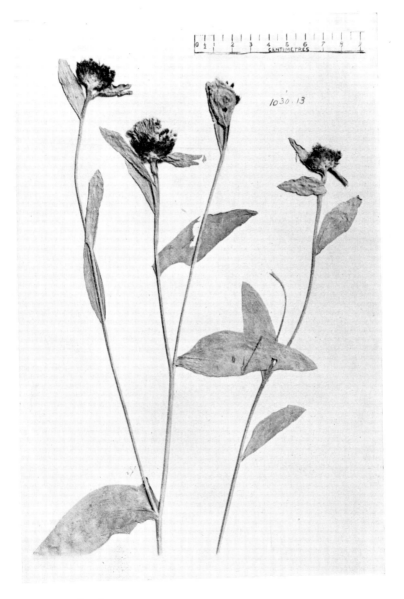

Centaurea nigra L.
Type specimen in the Linnean Herbarium of the Linnean Society, London.

PLATE V.

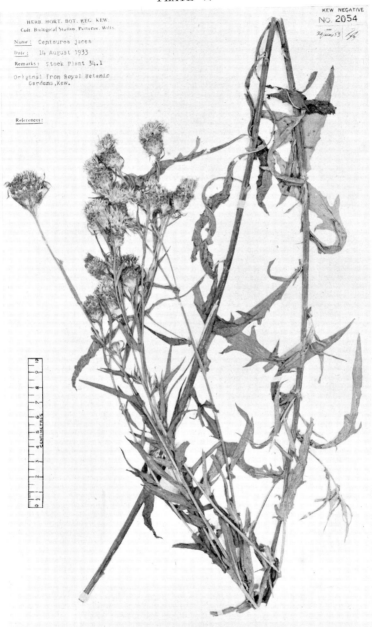

HERB. HORT. BOT. REG. KEW
Cult. Biological Station, Potterne, Wilts.

Name : Centaurea jacea

Date : 14 August 1933

Remarks : Stock Plant 34.1

Original from Royal Botanic
Gardens, Kew.

References :

Centaurea jacea L.
Stock Plant 34·1. Originally in cultivation in the Royal Botanic Gardens, Kew.

PLATE VI.

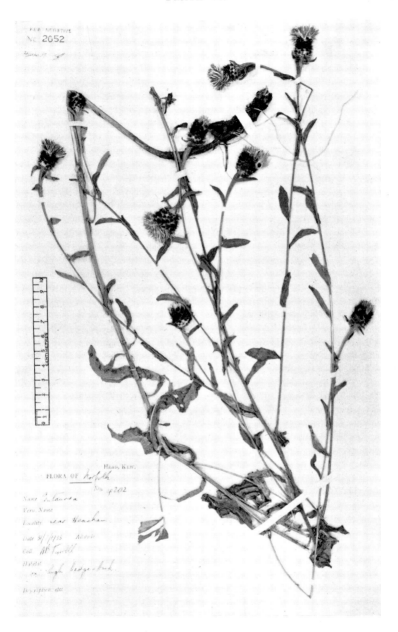

Centaurea nemoralis Jordan.
Wild material from near Heacham, Norfolk.

PLATE VII.

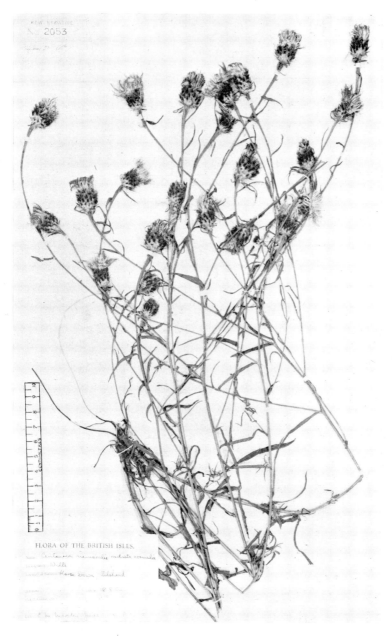

Centaurea nemoralis Jordan, narrow leaved variant.
Wild material from near Tilshead, Wilts.

PLATE VIII.

Centaurea nigra L.
Wild material from Crowborough, E. Sussex.

PLATE IX.

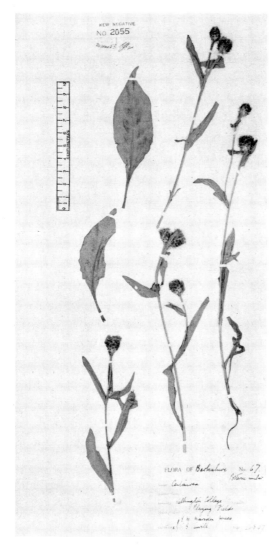

Centaurea jacea L. × *C. nigra* L.
Wild material from Wellington College, playing fields.   Neuter florets.

PLATE X.

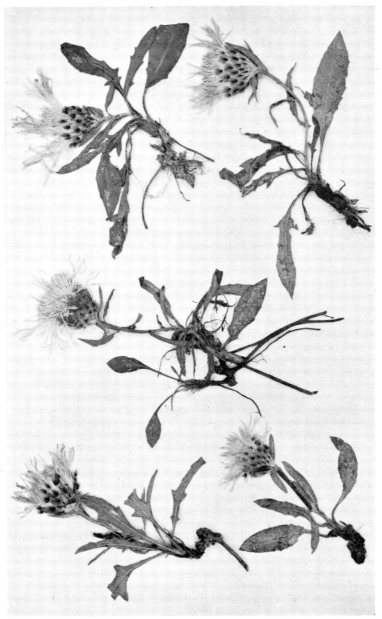

Centaurea nemoralis Jordan.   Wild material of dwarf plants with ray florets from Walker's Hill, Wilts.

PLATE XI.

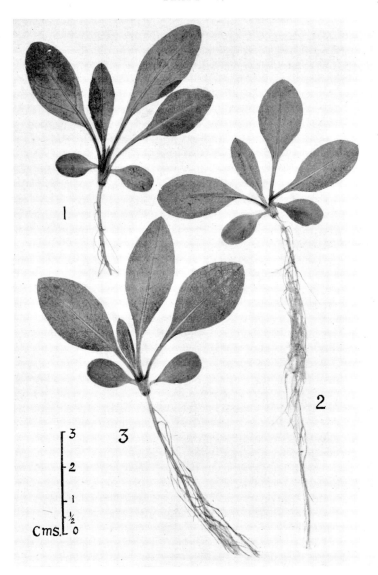

Seedlings : Cypselas sown 4 April, 1953.   Seedlings collected 27 May, 1953.
1. *Centaurea jacea*.   2. *C. nemoralis*.   3. *C. nigra*.

PLATE XII.

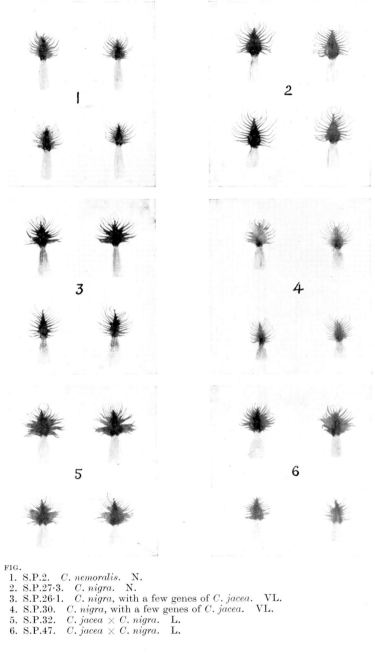

FIG.
1. S.P.2. *C. nemoralis.* N.
2. S.P.27·3. *C. nigra.* N.
3. S.P.26·1. *C. nigra*, with a few genes of *C. jacea.* VL.
4. S.P.30. *C. nigra*, with a few genes of *C. jacea.* VL.
5. S.P.32. *C. jacea* × *C. nigra.* L.
6. S.P.47. *C. jacea* × *C. nigra.* L.

PLATE XIII.

FIG.
1. S.P.29.   *C. jacea* × *C. nigra*.   S.
2. S.P.35·2.   *C. jacea* × *C. nigra*.   S.
3. S.P.35·1.   *C. jacea* × *C. nigra*.   M.
4. S.P.49.   *C. jacea* × *C. nigra*.   M.
5. S.P.34·1.   *C. jacea*.   VM.
6. S.P.45·1.   *C. jacea*.   C.

PLATE XIV.

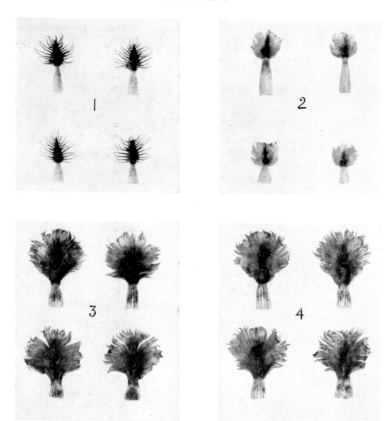

FIG.
1. S.P.5. *C. nemoralis.* N.
2. S.P.34·2. *C. jacea.* VM.
3. S.P.79·1. *C. jacea* with some genes of *C. nigra.* M.
4. S.P.79·2. *C. jacea* with some genes of *C. nigra.* M.

PLATE XV.

FIG.
1. S.P.13·7.   *C. nemoralis* with a few genes of *C. jacea*.   VL.
2. S.P.24·5.   *C. nemoralis*.   N.
3. S.P.79·2.   *C. jacea* with some genes of *C. nigra*.   M.
4. T.37, plant 7, N (S.P. 13·7 × S.P. 24·5).
5. T.146, plant 11, VL (S.P.79·2 × T.37, plant 7)
6. T.146, plant 2, L (S.P.79·2 × T.37, plant 7).

PLATES XV.—XVI.

Parents   S.P.13·7 (VL) × S.P.24·5.   (N).

F_1 T.37 gave N 33.

Parents   S.P.79·2 (M) × T.37, plant 7.   (N).

F_1 T.146 gave VL 8 : L4.

          T.334 = T.146, plant 2 selfed.

F_2 T.334 gave N 1 : VL 8 : L 16 : S 31 : M 17 : VM 1.

PLATE XVI.

FIGS.
1–6. T.334 (T.146, plant 2 selfed). 1. N ; 2. VL ; 3. L ; 4. S ; 5. M : 6. VM.

PLATE XVII.

Parents   S.P.30 (VL) $\times$ S.P.47 (L).

F$_1$ T.62 gave N 8 : VL 30 : L 23 : S 13 : M 6.

PLATE XVII.

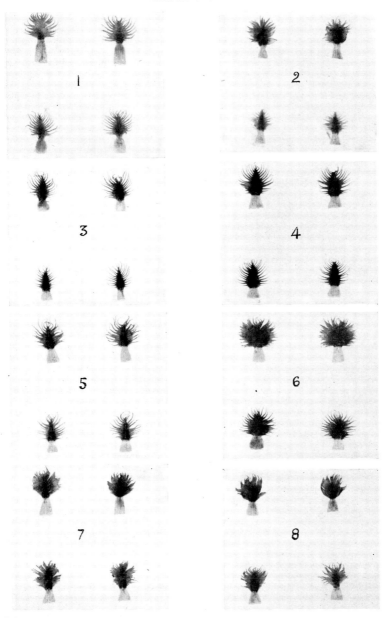

FIG.
1. S.P.30. *C. nigra* with a few genes of *C. jacea*. VL.
2. S.P.47. *C. jacea* × *C. nigra*. L.
3–8. T.62 (S.P.30 × S.P.47). 3. N ; 4. VL ; 5. L ; 6. S ; 7. M ; 8. M.

PLATES XVIII.—XIX.

Parents   S.P.27·3 (N) $\times$ S.P.33 (S).

F_1 T.84 gave N 66 : VL 7.

F_2 T.294 gave N 12 : VL 21 : L 6 : S 19 : M 19 : VM 2.

PLATE XVIII.

FIG.
1. S.P.27·3.   *C. nigra.* N.
2. S.P.33.   *C. jacea* × *C. nemoralis.*   S.
3. T.84, plant 47 (S.P.27·3 × S.P.33).   N.
4. T.84, plant 34 (S.P.27·3 × S.P.33).   VL.

17

PLATE XIX.

FIGS. 1–6. T.294 (T.84, plant 34 selfed). 1. N ; 2. VL ; 3. L ; 4. S ; 5. M ; 6. VM.

PLATE XX.

Parent   S.P.35·1 (M) selfed.

F_1 T.73 gave S 1 : M 2 : C 1.

PLATE XX.

FIG.
1. S.P.35·1. *C. jacea* × *C. nigra*. M.
2–5. T.73 (S.P.35·1 selfed).   2. S ;   3. M ;   4. M ;   5. C.

Parents   S.P.35·1 (M) $\times$ S.P.49 (M).

F_1 T.78 gave VL 3 : L 3 : S 16 : M 30.

F_2 T.273 gave VL 15 : L 14 : S 23 : M 23 : VM 5 : C 2.

PLATE XXI.

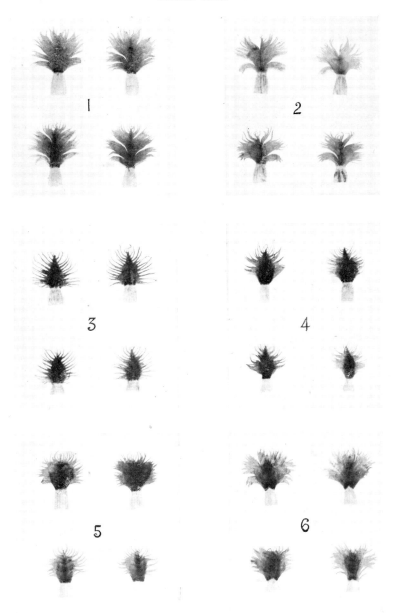

FIG.
1. S.P.35·1 (*C. jacea* × *C. nigra*. M.)
2. S.P.49 (*C. jacea* × *C. nigra*. M).
3–6. T.78 (S.P.35·1 × S.P.49).   3. VL ; 4. L ; 5. S ; 6. M.

PLATE XXII.

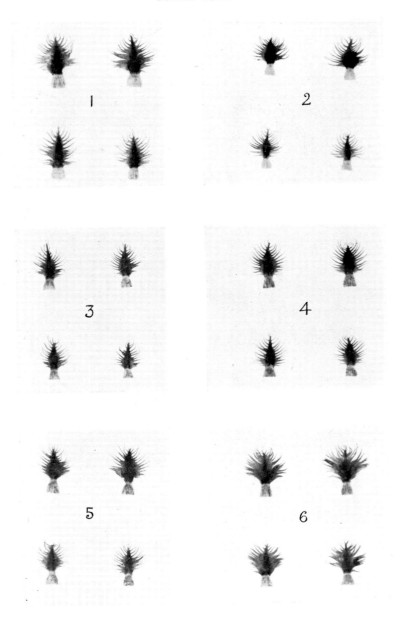

FIG.
1. T.78 plant 20.   S.
2. T.78 plant 17.   VL.
3–6. T.327   (T.78, plant 20 × T.78, plant 17).   3. VL ; 4. VL ; 5. L ; 6. S.

PLATE XXIII.

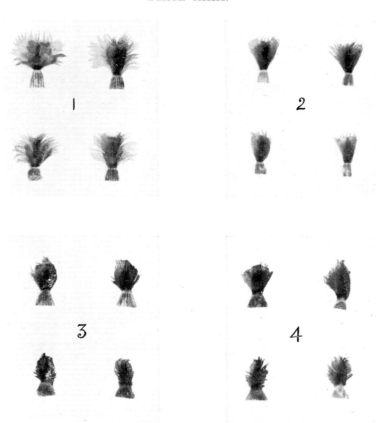

FIGS.
1–4. T.273 (T.78, plant 20 × T.78, plant 17).   1. M ; 2. VM ; 3. C ; 4. C.

PLATE XXIV.

Parents   S.P.79·2 (M) × S.P.79·1 (M).

F₁   T.116 gave S 2 : M 6 : VM 3 : C 2.

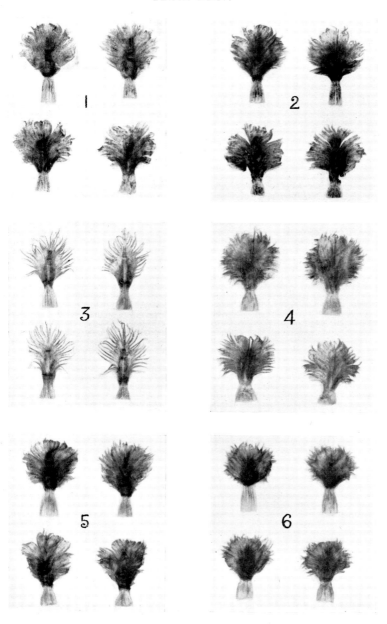

PLATE XXIV.

FIG.
1. S.P.79·2 (*C. jacea* with some genes of *C. nigra*. M).
2. S.P.79·1 (*C. jacea* with some genes of *C. nigra*. M).
3–6. T.116 (S.P.79·2 × S.P.79·1). 3. S ; 4. M ; 5. VM ; 6. C.

PLATE XXV.

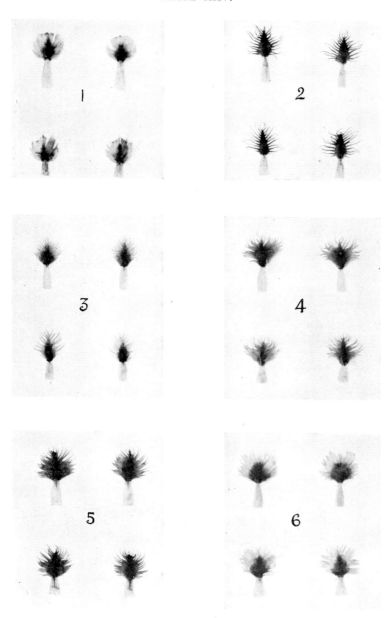

FIG.
1. S.P.34·2 (*C. jacea.* VM).
2. S.P.5 (*C. nemoralis.* N).
3–6. T.113 (S.P.34·2 × S.P.5). 3. L ; 4. S ; 5. S ; 6. M

PLATE XXVI.

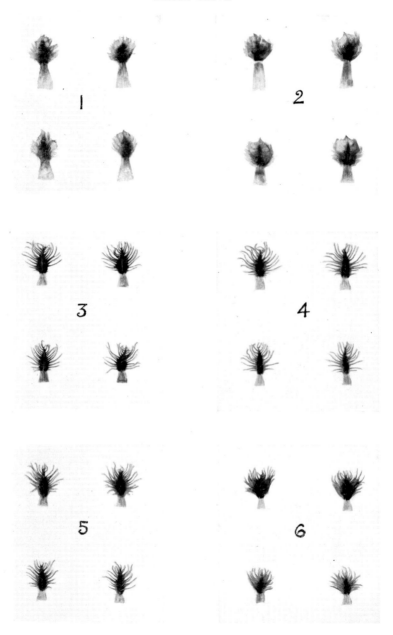

FIGS.
1–3. T.113 (S.P.34·2 × S.P.5). 1. VM ; 2. C.
3–6. T.243 (T.113, plant 5, S, selfed). 3. N ; 4. VL ; 5. L ; 6. S.

PLATE XXVII.

FIGS.
1-3. T.243 (T.113, plant 5, S, selfed). 1. M; 2. VM; 3. C.
4. T.98, plant 31 (S.P.34·1, *C. jacea*, VM × S.P.15, *C. nemoralis*, with a few genes of *C. jacea*, VL). Abnormal phyllaries.
   T.99, plant 27 (S.P.15 × S.P 34·1). Abnormal phyllaries.